Applicable Mathematics

and

Mathematical Methods

Volume 1

Second Edition

A Pearson Custom Publication

Applicable Mathematics
and
Mathematical Methods
Volume 1
Second Edition

Dr Derek W. Arthur

PEARSON
Custom
Publishing

Pearson Education Limited
Edinburgh Gate
Harlow
Essex CM20 2JE

And associated companies throughout the world

Visit us on the World Wide Web at:
www.pearsoned.co.uk

First published 2006

This Custom Book Edition © University of Edinburgh 2007

ISBN 10   1 84658 445 0
ISBN 13   978 1 84658 445 9

Printed and bound in Great Britain by Antony Rowe

Introduction

The content of this textbook is closely based on the lectures that have been delivered in the two courses *Applicable Mathematics 1* and *Mathematical Methods 1* at the *University of Edinburgh*, from 2001. These courses are taught in parallel, in alternate lectures. Although the two parts in this book are largely independent, there are points of contact between them.

A possible timetable is set out in the table on page vii.

How the text is structured

Most of the text, printed in this font size, is aimed at presenting a coherent 'storyline' as succinctly as possible, backed up by a generous selection of examples. Each of these is numbered and presented with a full solution, terminated by a ■ character.

Three other elements are woven throughout the text.

Frame X.xx   *Key formula*

These boxes contain the most important and heavily used of the formulae in the text. They are individually numbered to aid cross-reference and are presented in this way so they are easily found.

The remaining two are asides from the main story, but often contain useful ideas. They are presented in this way to avoid interrupting the flow of the main story.

Notation

Notation is the lifeblood of mathematics since, without it, communication between users of mathematics would be difficult and prone to misunderstanding. Although modern notation is very powerful, there are two problems students should be aware of.

Mathematics is a wide-ranging discipline and there are relatively few common symbols to use. This means that some notations need to be used for more than one idea and care is needed to interpret each use according to the context. These 'notes' will try to help in this.

Modern mathematics has reached a good understanding of what makes a successful notation, but in many cases old and dangerous notations persist, because of widespread use. A simple example is the sine function, which was notated hundreds of years ago as $\sin x$, but really should be written as $\sin(x)$; indeed that is essential for computer programming. The earlier notation, however, is deeply engrained in the literature. This book could restrict itself to use $\sin(x)$ throughout, but that may leave the reader in difficulties when encountering the older notation.

Think about it like this

There are often parallels between mathematical results or methods, and ideas encountered in elementary science, or even everyday life. Some of these can help students get a better grasp of the mathematics or help in memorising a key result. Also, some mathematical methods occur, identically structured, in different contexts. Links of these kinds are mentioned in 'asides', as here.

How to use this book

Try to read through the pages devoted to each lecture, as shown in the table on page vii, *before* attending the lecture. Make a note of parts that you find difficult so that you can concentrate on those when they are covered. If you still have problems with them, this record will help when you seek further assistance. The text has generous margins to allow students to add notes or comments.

The worked examples show how the material can be put into practice. There are exercises for you to try on your own, many of which are similar in style to the examples. They are generally located at the end of the section in which the relevant material has been introduced. There are further exercises at the end of each chapter. The majority of these are examination questions set in previous sessions.

Much of the content of *Mathematical Methods 1* is what is traditionally known as *calculus*. At first sight this appears to be merely a way to manipulate symbols, but in reality it underpins most modelling in mathematical applications, especially in physical science and engineering. It is therefore of great benefit to a student in those disciplines to achieve a grasp of the objectives of calculus and the way it can be implemented in real applications. The "Think about it like this" items strive to help you understand the fundamentals of calculus, while the latter parts of the book contain an enhanced number of examples of its application.

A valuable resource in any textbook is the **index**. The index in this volume has been constructed with an emphasis on the description of a method or the definition of a term. Thus, if you look under *partial fractions*, you will find the two main appearances: the construction of these in the first part and their use as an integration tool in the second. Minor references, which are likely to be a distraction, are generally not given. There are exceptions, where earlier references provide a reason for the inclusion of the item later in the text.

Finally, it was noted above that there is a shortage of symbols available to notate the wide range of concepts in mathematics. One consequence is a heavy use of the letters of the Greek alphabet. This is not restricted to mathematicians, since scientists and engineers also use such letters in standard notations, e.g., ρ for *density* and λ for *wavelength*. The main text gives the name for each used, normally at the time of its first occurrence. The full list of letters – upper and lower cases – is provided on page vii.

D.W.A.
May 2006

Contents

Applicable Mathematics

Contents   v

Mathematical Methods

Outline Lecture Programme

The table below gives a possible way in which the text in this book could be distributed across a timetable consisting of 40 lectures of 50 minutes each. Each part would occupy 20 lectures, as shown in the table.

Lecture	AM1 Sections	MM1 Sections
1	1.1–1.4	1.1–1.3
2	1.5–1.7	1.4–1.5
3	1.8–1.10	1.6–1.6
4	1.11–1.14	2.1–2.2
5	2.1–2.4	2.3–2.4
6	2.5–2.7	3.1–3.2
7	3.1–3.2	3.3–3.4
8	3.3–3.4	3.5–4.2
9	4.1–4.4	4.3–4.4
10	4.5–4.7	4.5–4.6
11	4.8–4.10	5.1–5.4
12	4.11–4.12	5.5–5.6
13	5.1–5.2	5.7–5.8
14	5.3–5.4	6.1–6.2
15	5.5–5.7	6.3–6.4
16	5.8–5.10	6.4–7.1
17	6.1–6.2	7.2–7.2
18	6.3–6.5	7.3–7.4
19	6.6–6.8	8.1–8.2
20	6.9–6.11	8.3–8.4

The Greek Alphabet

Upper	Lower	Name	Upper	Lower	Name
A	α	alpha	N	ν	nu
B	β	beta	Ξ	ξ	xi
Γ	γ	gamma	O	o	omicron
Δ	δ	delta	Π	π	pi
E	ϵ	epsilon	R	ρ	rho
Z	ζ	zeta	Σ	σ	sigma
H	η	eta	T	τ	tau
Θ	θ	theta	Υ	υ	upsilon
I	ι	iota	Φ	ϕ	phi
K	κ	kappa	X	χ	chi
Λ	λ	lambda	Ψ	ψ	psi
M	μ	mu	Ω	ω	omega

Notes

APPLICABLE

MATHEMATICS

1

1 BASIC ALGEBRA

This first chapter covers various 'manipulations' using elementary algebra, as well as the concepts of **equations**, **identities** and **inequalities**. Some terminologies, and their associated notations, are introduced.

1.1 Numbers and Symbols

There are five basic sets of numbers that feature in practical mathematics. Four are defined here; the fifth, *complex numbers*, is covered separately (Chapter 6).

$$\mathbb{N} = \{1, 2, 3, \ldots\}$$ **natural** numbers

$$\mathbb{Z} = \{\pm 1, \pm 2, \pm 3, \ldots\}$$ **integers**

$$\mathbb{Q} = \{\tfrac{p}{q} \; : \; p \text{ in } \mathbb{Z}, \; q \text{ in } \mathbb{N}\}$$ **rational** numbers (fractions)

$$\mathbb{R} = \text{set of lengths on a 'number' line}$$ **real** numbers

Notation

> There is general agreement about which letters to use here, but not every author uses this style of printing. You may encounter other typefaces such as $\mathcal{N}$, N, **N** and $\mathfrak{n}$.

The notation $\{\cdots\}$ represents a **set**, consisting of an unstructured collection of **elements**. Sometimes sets can be described by listing the elements, as for $\mathbb{N}$. It is, perhaps, more common to use the method for $\mathbb{Q}$. Here the colon ':' is read as *such that*.

It is impossible to define $\mathbb{R}$ easily using either method. Fortunately, it contains the numbers with which we are most familiar: measures we could obtain using a (hypothetical) exact tape measure.

In addition to numbers, algebra makes great use of **symbols**. These may be abstract entities in their own right although, in practical mathematics, they often represent numbers or physical 'variables'. There are some standard conventions – set out below – which roughly divide the alphabet into three. Note that some **greek letters** are used to augment the more usual roman ones, often reflecting their corresponding roman versions.

constants: a, b, c, α [*alpha*], β [*beta*], $\ldots$

variables: x, y, z, t, τ [*tau*], $\ldots$

counters (indexes): i, j, k, l, m, n, r

There are also some special conventions, e.g., θ [*theta*] and ϕ [*phi*] are commonly used for **angles**, f and g for **functions**. *Time*, or quantities behaving like time, may be abbreviated by t (or τ). Other physical quantities may be similarly represented, e.g., v for velocity and E for electric field.

It is best to avoid upper case letters for general purposes, since they often have special uses, e.g., for angles and matrices.

Numbers and symbols are used to construct **terms**, which in turn combine, usually linked by $+$ or $-$, to form **expressions**. A number or symbol in a term, multiplying the rest, is a **factor**. A factor that is a number is often called the **coefficient** of the rest of the term.

Example 1.1   The expression $1 + x + \frac{1}{2}x^2 + \frac{1}{6}x^3$ contains 4 terms, e.g., 1 and x. The number $\frac{1}{2}$ is the coefficient for x^2. The term $\frac{1}{6}x^3$ contains three factors of x.   ■

1.2   Arithmetical Operations

Simple expressions contain **(binary) operators** to indicate arithmetic:

$$+, \quad -, \quad \times, \quad \div \text{ (or } /), \quad \text{powering (sometimes written } \hat{\ }).$$

These are defined for operations involving *two* quantities; when more than two are involved the outcome can be ambiguous.

Example 1.2   What does $9 - 4 + 1$ mean?

$$\begin{array}{lll} - \text{ first :} & 9 - 4 = 5, & 5 + 1 = 6; \\ + \text{ first :} & 4 + 1 = 5, & 9 - 5 = 4. \end{array}$$

■

To resolve this we must either enforce an order, e.g., by using brackets, or construct rules that dictate the order. The second solution is preferred, with bracketing being used to overrule it when necessary.

There is an elaborate set of these **rules of precedence**, covering special functions such as sin, cos and log; the following are the basic ones.

Frame 1.1   Rules of precedence

(1) first do powers
(2) then do $\times$, $\div$
(3) then do $+$, $-$
in (2) & (3), work from left to right

If these rules clash with the intended order, brackets can be used to force an alternative: *expressions within brackets must be evaluated before any involvement with expressions outside.*

Example 1.3   Return to Example 1.2.

The rules of precedence force the $-$ first (on the left), then the $+$ (on the right):

$$9 - 4 + 1 = 5 + 1 = 6.$$

If the alternative order is required then brackets are necessary:

$$9 - (4 + 1) = 9 - 5 = 4.$$

This calculation is consistent with using a basic rule of algebra – a minus sign outside a bracket changes the signs of *all* terms inside – followed by the rules of precedence:

$$9 - (4 + 1) = 9 - 4 - 1 = 5 - 1 = 4.$$

∎

Think about it like this

Brackets can be inserted even when they are redundant, but care is always needed in removing them in case they are not redundant. The simplest situation, one that often trips up students in calculations, is the rule mentioned above: $a - (b + c) = a - b - c$. Always be on your guard when a minus sign appears in front of a bracket.

Example 1.4 $4 \times 2^3 - 12 \div 6 \times 2$

Perform 2^3 first; then $\times$ in the first term and $\div$ in the second; then $\times$; then $-$:

$$4 \times 8 - 12 \div 6 \times 2 = 32 - 2 \times 2 = 32 - 4 = 28.$$

This agrees with the output from a *modern* calculator, if the keys are pressed in the left to right order in the expression, as it is originally presented. ∎

Example 1.5 $ab + cd = (ab) + (cd)$

This may seem obvious but old calculators use operators in the order in which they find them and so would deliver $(ab + c)d$, which is different. ∎

Notation

One complication that must be borne in mind is that regular mathematical notation sometimes uses other devices that have a bracketing effect and even in some cases, invisible brackets! It is an unfortunate fact that some notational ideas became common currency centuries ago, before mathematicians tidied things up. The outcome is that some of the oldest and most common notations conflict with the mainstream.

When we write $\frac{a}{b+c}$, the denominator has brackets implied by the division line; when written as $a/(b + c)$ the brackets are compulsory, since $a/b + c = \frac{a}{b} + c$, by rules (2) and (3) above. A further case is the square root symbol: in $\sqrt{a + b}$ the line is again a bracket and an alternative is $\sqrt{(a + b)}$.

Examples of invisible brackets are given by 'powering' and subscripts. It is generally accepted that text written on a higher or lower level is treated as if in brackets. Thus, x_{2+1} stands for x_3, not $x_2 + 1$. Likewise, the possibly ambiguous quantity 2^{3^4} stands for 2^{81} and not 8^4, since the 3^4 is 'bracketed'; we shall see another explanation for this later.

Repeated division using a 'division rule (line)', such as $\frac{\frac{a}{b}}{c}$ should be avoided, since there is no left to right order to resolve the ambiguity, although one might pick up a clue from the lengths of the division rules. It is somewhat safer to write $a/b/c$, provided you remember that this is $(a/b)/c$, working from left to right. In some circumstances it can be helpful to use a mixture, e.g., $\frac{4}{2/3} = 4 \times {}^3/_2 = 6$.

Deciding on the order in which to evaluate expressions is called **parsing**.

Ex 1.1 Insert brackets, then evaluate: $2 \times 3 - 6/4 - 3^2$.

1.3   Equations and Identities

When two expressions are linked by '=', a new and useful idea is introduced, one that allows us to state that something is **true** and hence to use mathematics to model 'real' situations. Equality is only part of a collection of such links, including $<$ and $>$ to which we shall return in §1.11.

There are two possible scenarios when an equality is indicated.

Case 1 The equality forces two quantities to be equal, thereby constraining the possible values that can be taken by any variables involved. This is called an **equation** (or sometimes a *formula* – see §1.8).

Example 1.6   The following are equations:

$2x = 10$ $\qquad\qquad$ $x = 5$, only

$x^2 = 289$ $\qquad\quad$ $x = 17$ or $x = -17$

$x^2 + y^2 = 0$ $\qquad$ $x = 0$ and $y = 0$, only

∎

Case 2 The equality implied by the expression is *always* true, no matter what values any variables take. This is called an **identity**. Strictly speaking, it has a separate notation, '$\equiv$' pronounced *equivalent to*, but this is usually reserved for cases where there may be ambiguity or where the fact it is an identity is to be stressed.

Example 1.7   The following are identities:

$$\frac{x}{\sqrt{x}} = \sqrt{x}$$

$$\frac{1}{a} + \frac{1}{b} = \frac{a+b}{ab}$$

$$\sin^2 x + \cos^2 x = 1$$

$$(a+b)^2 \equiv a^2 + 2ab + b^2 \qquad\qquad (1.1)$$

$$u^2 - v^2 \equiv (u-v)(u+v) \qquad\qquad (1.2)$$

∎

A principal aim of algebra is to *solve equations*, i.e., to find all or some of the values of the variables involved. One technique is to use identities to turn terms in the original expression into equivalent terms, so that any solution still remains valid, but the new form is simpler to solve.

Example 1.8   Solve $(x+y)^2 - (x-y)^2 = 0$.

This is an equation since, for example, $x = y = 1$ makes the left-hand side 4, not 0. There are two ways in which to use identities from Example 1.7.

Method 1   Use (1.1) twice, with $a = x$, $b = y$; $a = x$, $b = -y$:

$$(x^2 + 2xy + y^2) - (x^2 - 2xy + y^2) = 0,$$

then remove the brackets to obtain

$$x^2 + 2xy + y^2 - x^2 + 2xy - y^2 = 0,$$

which simplifies to $4xy = 0$, with the clear solution: $x = 0$ *or* $y = 0$.

Method 2   Use (1.2), with $u = x + y, \; v = x - y$:

$$[x + y - (x - y)]\,[x + y + (x - y)] = 0,$$

which simplifies to $(2x)(2y) = 0$ and the solution is completed as in the previous method.

■

1.4   Factorisation

There are numerous laws of algebra that, just like identities, allow us to simplify or expand expressions. They are mostly 'obvious', such as $x(y+z) = xy + xz$. (They also have names – this is the *distributive law* – but those names are seldom required in practical mathematics.)

This law can be extended:

Example 1.9   Expand $(a + b)(c + d)$. Use the law twice:

$$a(c + d) + b(c + d) = ac + ad + bc + bd.$$

■

More often we have to reverse this by locating **common factors** – parts that are contained as multipliers in all terms – and *factoring them out*.

Example 1.10   The following show how to detect and extract common factors. The third example shows how disguised the factors may be.

$$ab + a = a(b + 1)$$
$$xy - y^2 = (x - y)y \qquad \text{or} \qquad y(x - y)$$
$$xy + x + y + 1 = x(y + 1) + (y + 1) = (x + 1)(y + 1)$$
$$\frac{x^2}{y} - \frac{x^4}{y^3} = \frac{x^2}{y}\left(1 - \frac{x^2}{y^2}\right) = \frac{x^2}{y}\left(1 - \frac{x}{y}\right)\left(1 + \frac{x}{y}\right)$$

This last case uses the identity (1.2) to extract further factors.

■

When division is involved, factorisation can help achieve significant simplification.

Example 1.11   Simplify:

$$\frac{uv^3 - u^2v^2}{vu^3 - v^2u^2} = \frac{uv^2(v - u)}{vu^2(u - v)} = -\frac{v}{u},$$

since $(v - u) = -(u - v)$.

■

Two *linear* terms in x, i.e., of the form $ax+b$, multiply to give a *quadratic* term:

Example 1.12   Using Example 1.9,

$$(x-2)(2x+1) = 2x^2 + x - 4x - 2 = 2x^2 - 3x - 2.$$

■

This can sometimes be reversed, but may involve non-integers; that case will be covered in Chapter 4. For now, we can seek integer-based factors:

$$ax^2 + bx + c = (\ x \quad\quad)(\ x \quad\quad).$$
↓ product is c ↓
↑ product is a ↑

Now try all factorisations of a and c, to seek one that delivers the desired middle term, that in x.

Example 1.13

$$x^2 - 7x + 12 = (\ x\ )(\ x\ )$$
↓ 1/2, 2/6, 3/4, +/+, −/− ↓
$$= (x-3)(x-4),$$

since $1 \times (-4) - 3 \times 1 = -7$.

$$6x^2 - 11x - 10 = (\ x\ )(\ x\ )$$
↓ 1/10, 2/5, +/−, −/+ ↓   1/6, 2/3
$$= (2x-5)(3x+2),$$

since $2 \times 2 - 5 \times 3 = -11$.   ■

Factorisations such as these can help simplify expressions.

Example 1.14

$$\frac{x^2 - 5x + 6}{x^2 - 4x + 4} = \frac{(x-2)(x-3)}{(x-2)^2} = \frac{x-3}{x-2}.$$

Note that we ought to insist that $x \neq 2$ to avoid a *division by zero*.   ■

Ex 1.2

(a) Simplify: $4xy - (3x+2y)(x-2y)$.

(b) Expand: $(x-2)(x+3)$.

(c) Factorise: $x^2 + 8x + 15, \quad \dfrac{1}{z} - \dfrac{2}{z^2}, \quad 25x^2 - 9$.

Ex 1.3 Expand the following:

$$\left(\left(\left(\left((2x+3)x+4\right)x+5\right)x+6\right)\right).$$

Use a calculator to evaluate this at $x = 2$, using both forms. How many $+$, $\times$, x^y key presses did each require?

Verify that the calculator gives the same answer using the sequence:

$$2 \;\times\; 2 + 3 = \times\; 2 + 4 = \times\; 2 + 5 = \times\; 2 + 6 = .$$

Ex 1.4

(a) Expand: $(1-x)(4+x)$, $x(x+1)(x+2)$.

(b) Simplify: $\dfrac{x^2y + xy^2}{xy^2 - x^2y}$, $\dfrac{x^2 - x - 12}{x^2 - 16}$.

Ex 1.5 Factorise: $x^2 - 2x - 8$, $u^2 - u + \frac{1}{4}$, $x^3 - x$, $(x+2)^2 - 4$.

1.5 Index Laws

We now examine what happens when we multiply and divide powers of the same number. Multiplication is easy: $a^m \times a^n$ will produce a product of $m+n$ copies of a. This result, with two others, are known as the **Index laws**.

Frame 1.2   Index laws

$$a^m \times a^n = a^{m+n} \tag{1.3}$$

$$\frac{a^m}{a^n} = a^{m-n} \tag{1.4}$$

$$(a^m)^n = a^{mn} \tag{1.5}$$

Example 1.15 The following is an illustration of (1.5):

$$\left(a^2\right)^3 = (a \times a) \times (a \times a) \times (a \times a) = a^6.$$

∎

The division law is proved by using cancellation:

$$\frac{a^m}{a^n} = \frac{\overset{m \text{ copies}}{\overbrace{a \times a \times \cdots \times a}}}{\underset{n \text{ copies}}{\underbrace{a \times a \times \cdots \times a}}} = a^{m-n}$$

after cancelling those on the bottom with some of those on the top. This, of course, can work only if $m > n$, else we run out of a terms on the top. This condition is not listed in Frame 1.2 because it, and others like it, are bypassed by adopting the following *conventions*:

Frame 1.3   Negative and fractional powers

$$a^{-n} = \frac{1}{a^n}, \qquad a^{1/n} = \sqrt[n]{a}, \qquad a^{m/n} = \sqrt[n]{a^m} = \left(\sqrt[n]{a}\right)^m, \qquad a^0 = 1$$

Example 1.16

$$1 = \frac{a^n}{a^n} = a^{n-n} = a^0,$$

$$1 = a^0 = a^{n-n} = a^n \times a^{-n} \quad \text{so} \quad a^{-n} = \frac{1}{a^n},$$

$$a^{1/2} \times a^{1/2} = a^{1/2+1/2} = a^1 \quad \text{so} \quad a^{1/2} = \sqrt{a}.$$

■

Think about it like this

These laws appear unusual, since multiplication and division are turned into addition and subtraction. Working in the 'power' or 'index' position in algebra is difficult, since the quantities that appear there cannot be accessed in the same way as others. Indeed, this is one of the reasons why **logarithms** are a key tool in mathematics: they allow us to access those quantities. The Index laws bear a resemblance to the logarithm rules that is not accidental; they are used to prove those rules.

Note that $\left(a^m\right)^n$ requires the bracketing if a^{mn} is intended, since a^{m^n} is interpreted as $a^{(m^n)}$:

$$a^{2^3} = a^8, \qquad \text{while} \qquad \left(a^2\right)^3 = a^6.$$

The rationale for this is that *working in the index position implies insertion of brackets*, consistent with the rules of precedence giving top priority to powering.

The following pair of rules are particularly useful:

$$(ab)^m = a^m b^m, \qquad \left(\frac{a}{b}\right)^m = \frac{a^m}{b^m}. \tag{1.6}$$

Note, however, that there are **no simple rules** for $(a \pm b)^m$:

$$\text{including} \qquad \sqrt{a+b} \ \ (m = \tfrac{1}{2}), \qquad \frac{1}{a+b} \ \ (m = -1).$$

Notation

In this connection, note that the horizontal lines in these expressions are, in fact, **brackets**, a remnant of an old-fashioned bracketing notation: $a - \overline{b+c}$ is the same as $a - (b+c)$. Thus, in $\sqrt{a+b}$ the addition must be done *before* the square root.

Basic Algebra 9

Think about it like this

You may find the following a useful rule of thumb. In *arithmetic*, addition and subtraction are much easier operations than multiplication and division. But in *algebra*, the opposite is the case: there are many simple and useful rules for multiplication and division, such as those in (1.6), while there are few simple rules for addition and subtraction, as we see in the 'non-rules' above. Be on your guard!

Example 1.17

$$(-3)^4 = (-1)^4 \times 3^4 = 81$$

$$8^{-2/3} = \frac{1}{8^{2/3}} = \frac{1}{\sqrt[3]{8^2}} = \frac{1}{\sqrt[3]{64}} = \frac{1}{4}$$

$$or = \frac{1}{\left(\sqrt[3]{8}\right)^2} = \frac{1}{2^2} = \frac{1}{4}$$

$$2^{1/3}(54)^{2/3} = 2^{1/3}\left(2 \times 3^3\right)^{2/3} = 2^{1/3} \cdot 2^{2/3} \cdot 3^{2/3 \cdot 3} = 2^1 \cdot 3^2 = 18$$

$$(2x)^3 = 2^3 x^3 = 8x^3 \qquad NOT \qquad 2x^3$$

$$\left(\frac{2}{x}\right)^4 = \frac{2^4}{x^4} = 16x^{-4}$$

∎

Notation

In one calculation in this example, $a \cdot b$ has been used in place of $a \times b$; this, and also $a.b$, are standard conventions for multiplication.

Example 1.18   Write, in the form $A \times 3^n$:

$$\left(3^4\right)^3 + \left(3^4 \times 3^3\right)^2 + \left(3^3\right)^4 = 3^{12} + \left(3^7\right)^2 + 3^{12}$$
$$= 3^{12} + 3^{14} + 3^{12} = 3^{12}\left(1 + 3^2 + 1\right) = 11 \times 3^{12}.$$

∎

Great care is needed to distinguish between:

$$x^{3/2} = \left(\sqrt{x}\right)^3, \qquad x^{2/3} = \left(\sqrt[3]{x}\right)^2, \qquad x^{-2/3} = \frac{1}{x^{2/3}},$$

and other similar examples.

A helpful simplification is one of the identities in Example 1.7. It is justified, in two ways, as follows:

$$\frac{x}{\sqrt{x}} = \frac{x^1}{x^{1/2}} = x^{1-1/2} = x^{1/2} = \sqrt{x},$$

$$or \quad \frac{x}{\sqrt{x}} = \frac{\sqrt{x} \times \sqrt{x}}{\sqrt{x}} = \sqrt{x}.$$

Ex 1.6

  (a) Simplify: $\;x^3 \times x^{-4}, \quad x^{1/3} \times y^3 / (xy^2), \quad (-y^{-2})(-y).$

  (b) Simplify: $\;(3\sqrt{x})^4, \quad \left(\dfrac{27}{t^3}\right)^{1/3}.$

Ex 1.7 Simplify the following:

$$y \times y^2 \times y^4 \times y^8, \quad t^8/t^4, \quad x^3/x^0, \quad (abc)^3/(a^2b^2c^2), \quad t^{-2}/t^{-3}, \quad \frac{x}{x^{-3}},$$

$$(-2t)^2, \quad (-2x^{-1})(-3x^{-2}), \quad (y^{-2})^3, \quad \left(-\frac{2}{x}\right)^4.$$

1.6   Roots

Although the previous section has used **roots** without comment, we must remember that $\sqrt[n]{a} = a^{1/n}$ may not exist:

    $a^{1/n}$ is always defined and is unique, when n is **ODD**;

    $a^{1/n}$ is defined **only if** $a \geqslant 0$, when n is **EVEN**, then there are **two** answers (for $a > 0$): one $+$, one $-$.

Example 1.19 $36^{1/2} = 6 \text{ or } -6, \qquad 16^{1/4} = 2 \text{ or } -2$ ■

    There is an agreed convention: when $\sqrt[n]{a}$ is written, it is the **positive** value that is intended (when n is even). If the other value is needed – and there are circumstances when we know this is the case – the minus sign must be given explicitly, $-\sqrt[n]{a}$.

Example 1.20 $(-8)^{2/3} = \left(\sqrt[3]{-8}\right)^2 = (-2)^2 = 4.$

    Some older calculators fail to evaluate this when we use the sequence:

$$8 \;\; +\!/\!- \;\; \boxed{x^y} \;\; [\;2\; \div\; 3\;]\;\; =$$

because $2 \div 3$ is rounded to a number that is equivalent to an even root and -8 is negative.   ■

    By far the most common roots are square roots; in practical mathematics there are good reasons for why this is the case. It is often necessary to move factors in an out of a square root. The rules for this follow from (1.6) and are simple to state: an x outside becomes x^2 inside, while a y inside becomes $\sqrt{y}$ outside. But there are dangers involved, as the final part of the next example shows.

Example 1.21

$$\sqrt{72} - \sqrt{50} + \sqrt{18} = \sqrt{36}\sqrt{2} - \sqrt{25}\sqrt{2} + \sqrt{9}\sqrt{2} = 6\sqrt{2} - 5\sqrt{2} + 3\sqrt{2} = 4\sqrt{2}$$

$$\sqrt{4x} = \sqrt{4}\sqrt{x} = 2\sqrt{x}$$

$$x\sqrt{\frac{1}{x} - \frac{1}{x^2}} = \sqrt{x^2}\sqrt{\frac{1}{x} - \frac{1}{x^2}} = \sqrt{x^2\left(\frac{1}{x} - \frac{1}{x^2}\right)} = \sqrt{x - 1}$$

$$\sqrt{x^2 - x^3} = \sqrt{x^2(1-x)} = \sqrt{x^2}\sqrt{1-x} = |x|\sqrt{1-x}$$

In this last case we must use $|x|$, the **size** of x, since both $\sqrt{x^2 - x^3}$ and $\sqrt{1-x}$ are $\geqslant 0$, while x could be negative. ∎

Ex 1.8 Simplify: $\left(\frac{a^2}{b^4}\right)^{1/2}$, $\left(\frac{k^{-1.5}}{4}\right)^{-2}$, $(p^2 q^{-3})^{-3/2}$.

1.7   Fractions

We now consider how to apply arithmetic operations to **fractions**, starting with the numerical fractions contained in the set of rational numbers $\mathbb{Q}$.

One outcome of this is that we will be able to treat *division* as a type of multiplication, i.e., $\frac{a}{b} = a \times \frac{1}{b}$. Since subtraction can also be regarded as a type of addition, i.e., $a - b = a + (-b)$, we shall often find we need consider only two of the four basic operations.

Addition/Subtraction: Find a common **denominator** (bottom part), in which to rewrite the fractions, then add or subtract the **numerators** (top parts). (We then use quantities of the same basic type, halves, sixths, etc.)

Example 1.22

$$\frac{1}{2} + \frac{1}{3} = \frac{3}{6} + \frac{2}{6} = \frac{3+2}{6} = \frac{5}{6}$$
$$\frac{1}{6} - \frac{1}{8} = \frac{8}{48} - \frac{6}{48} = \frac{2}{48} = \frac{1}{24}$$
$$or = \frac{4}{24} - \frac{3}{24} = \frac{1}{24}$$

∎

In the final case, the common denominator was first found by simply multiplying the original ones, while the second calculation avoided a final tidying up by using the **lowest common denominator**.

Multiplication: Multiply the top and bottom parts separately. Sometimes it is possible to cancel common factors between the two numbers beforehand, avoiding the need to tidy up at the end, when it may be harder to do so.

Example 1.23

$$\frac{3}{7} \times \frac{14}{15} = \frac{42}{105} = \frac{2}{5}$$
$$or = \frac{\cancel{3}^1}{\cancel{7}_1} \times \frac{\cancel{14}^2}{\cancel{15}_5} = \frac{2}{5}$$

∎

Division: Multiply by the **reciprocal** of the dividing fraction, i.e., the fraction with its top and bottom parts swapped over.

Whole numbers: Treat n as $\dfrac{n}{1}$.

Example 1.24

$$4 - \frac{8}{3} = \frac{4}{1} - \frac{8}{3} = \frac{12}{3} - \frac{8}{3} = \frac{4}{3}$$

$$\frac{3}{35} \times 10 = \frac{3}{35} \times \frac{10}{1} = \frac{6}{7}$$

$$\frac{7}{10} \div \frac{1}{2} = \frac{7}{10} \times \frac{2}{1} = \frac{7}{5}$$

∎

All of these devices extend to fractions involving symbols.

Example 1.25

$$\frac{1}{a} + \frac{1}{b} = \frac{b}{ab} + \frac{a}{ab} = \frac{b+a}{ab} \quad or \quad \frac{a+b}{ab}$$

$$\frac{1}{x-1} - \frac{1}{x} = \frac{x-(x-1)}{(x-1)x} = \frac{1}{x(x-1)}$$

$$\frac{1}{x(x+1)} - \frac{1}{(x+1)(x+2)} = \frac{x+2-x}{x(x+1)(x+2)} = \frac{2}{x(x+1)(x+2)}$$

In this last case the work was made easier by using a **lowest** common denominator. ∎

The value of a fraction is left unchanged if *BOTH* numerator and denominator are multiplied or divided by the same quantity:

$$\frac{A}{B} = \frac{A}{B} \times \frac{X}{X} = \frac{AX}{BX}, \quad \text{since} \quad \frac{X}{X} = 1.$$

Think about it like this

> This is sometimes extended to all the individual terms in the fraction, where terms are linked by + or −. Thus, we can multiply every such part of a fraction by the same quantity without changing its value. For example, a numerator or denominator $a+b$, when multiplied by x, becomes $ax+bx$.

Example 1.26

$$\frac{\sqrt{x}}{\frac{1}{\sqrt{x}} + \sqrt{x}} \left(\times \frac{\sqrt{x}}{\sqrt{x}} \right) = \frac{x}{1+x}$$

$$\frac{1-\cos x}{\sin^2 x} = \frac{1-\cos x}{1-\cos^2 x} = \frac{1-\cos x}{(1-\cos x)(1+\cos x)} = \frac{1}{1+\cos x}$$

on *dividing* both top and bottom by $1 - \cos x$. ∎

This trick helps **rationalise the denominator** for some fractions containing irrational quantities, using

$$\left(\sqrt{x} - \sqrt{y} \right) \left(\sqrt{x} + \sqrt{y} \right) = \left(\sqrt{x} \right)^2 - \left(\sqrt{y} \right)^2 = x - y.$$

If the denominator is $\sqrt{x} - \sqrt{y}$, multiply "above and below" by $\sqrt{x} + \sqrt{y}$, and *vice versa*.

Example 1.27

$$\frac{1}{\sqrt{3} - \sqrt{2}} = \frac{1}{\sqrt{3} - \sqrt{2}} \times \frac{\sqrt{3} + \sqrt{2}}{\sqrt{3} + \sqrt{2}}$$

$$= \frac{\sqrt{3} + \sqrt{2}}{3 - 2} = \sqrt{3} + \sqrt{2}$$

∎

Ex 1.9

(a) Write as single fractions: $\dfrac{x}{3} - \dfrac{x}{12}$, $\dfrac{2}{x^2} - \dfrac{1}{x}$.

(b) Rationalise the denominators in: $\dfrac{1}{\sqrt{17} - \sqrt{15}}$, $\dfrac{1}{\sqrt{13} + 2\sqrt{5}}$.

Ex 1.10

(a) Evaluate the following:

$$\frac{1}{2} \div \frac{1}{4}, \quad \frac{5}{6} - \frac{2}{3}, \quad \frac{15}{16} \times \frac{4}{5}, \quad \frac{8}{9} + \frac{1}{5} + \frac{1}{6}, \quad \frac{3}{4} \div \frac{3}{4}, \quad \frac{3}{4} \div \frac{4}{3}, \quad \frac{3/4}{4}, \quad \frac{3}{4} \times 2.$$

(b) Simplify the following:

$$\frac{1}{2}\left(\frac{9}{x} - \frac{5}{x}\right), \quad \frac{2}{x - 1} + \frac{1}{(x - 1)^2}, \quad \frac{a}{\frac{1}{b} + \frac{1}{c}},$$

$$\frac{1}{x^2 + 3x - 10} + \frac{1}{x^2 + 17x + 60}, \quad \frac{\frac{1}{x+1}}{2 - \frac{1}{x+1}}.$$

1.8 Formulae

The name **formula** is usually reserved for an equation where just one symbol appears on the left-hand side of the equals sign, called the **subject** of the formula. Such an equation is normally intended for calculation of the value of the subject, given values of the remaining symbols.

Example 1.28 Einstein's famous formula $E = mc^2$ gives values of E from those of m and c. ∎

An important procedure with a formula is to *change its subject*, i.e., use algebraic steps to make one of the other symbols the subject, so that the formula can be used in a different context.

Example 1.29 The **Cosine Rule**, $a^2 = b^2 + c^2 - 2bc \cos A$, can be used to calculate the subject a^2 and hence the value of a. We could take the square root of both sides to get a direct formula for a, but that is clumsy.

To make $\cos A$ the subject, and hence to allow calculation of A from a, b and c, perform the following steps on both sides:

add $2bc \cos A$: $\qquad 2bc \cos A + a^2 = b^2 + c^2,$

subtract a^2 : $\qquad 2bc \cos A = b^2 + c^2 - a^2,$

divide by $2bc$: $\qquad \cos A = \dfrac{b^2 + c^2 - a^2}{2bc}.$

■

Example 1.30   The **period** of a pendulum, length L, is $T = 2\pi\sqrt{\dfrac{L}{g}}.$

Square both sides: $\qquad T^2 = 4\pi^2 \dfrac{L}{g},$

Multiply by $\dfrac{g}{4\pi^2}$ and swap sides: $L = \dfrac{gT^2}{4\pi^2}.$

■

Think about it like this

In these examples we have used various operations to treat both sides of the equation in the same way. Thus, if $X = Y$, then

$$\alpha X = \alpha Y, \qquad \frac{1}{X} = \frac{1}{Y}, \qquad X^2 = Y^2, \qquad X + Z = Y + Z, \qquad \text{etc.}$$

Do not push this idea too far:

$$X = Y + Z \quad \text{does \textbf{not} lead to} \quad \frac{1}{X} = \frac{1}{Y} + \frac{1}{Z}$$

since the two sides have been treated differently. Remember (§1.5) that there is no simple formula for $1/(Y + Z)$.

Example 1.31   A second-order chemical reaction has concentration and time linked by

$$\frac{1}{C} = at + b,$$

with a and b measured by using a graph of experimental data. We **cannot** deduce that $C = \dfrac{1}{at} + \dfrac{1}{b}$, a formula that is not even defined when $t = 0$. The correct deduction is

$$C = \frac{1}{at + b},$$

which produces the behaviour we expect: the concentration starts at $1/b$ and falls away to zero as t increases.   ■

There is a device called **cross-multiplication** that speeds up calculations using fractions. It removes them in one big step rather than two smaller ones.

Frame 1.4   *Cross-multiplication*

$$\text{If} \qquad \frac{a}{b} = \frac{c}{d} \qquad \text{then} \qquad ad = bc$$

Example 1.32   Solve $\dfrac{x-1}{4} = \dfrac{2}{x+1}$.

Cross-multiplying gives: $(x-1)(x+1) = 2 \times 4 = 8$. Then:

$$x^2 - 1 = 8, \qquad x^2 = 9, \qquad x = \pm 3.$$

■

Ex 1.11 Find y, where $\quad \dfrac{1}{y} = 1 + \dfrac{1}{x}$.

Ex 1.12 Which of the following are *always* true (assuming x and y are not zero)?

$$(2-x)^3 = 8 - x^3, \quad \left(\frac{2}{x}\right)^3 = \frac{8}{x^3}, \quad \frac{1}{x} + \frac{1}{y} = \frac{x+y}{xy}, \quad \sqrt{x^2 + y^2} = x + y.$$

Ex 1.13 Make s the subject of $\quad m = p\sqrt{\dfrac{s+t}{s-t}}$.

Ex 1.14 A pizzeria switches from making circular pizzas, radius r and crust length $C = 2\pi r$, to square pizzas with the same area. Find a formulae for the side x in the new format (in terms of r) and one for the length of the crust K (in terms of C).

1.9   Substitution

There is a widely used technique summed up by the word **substitution**, where every instance of a particular symbol in an expression is replaced by a number or some formula involving numbers and/or other symbols. In some cases this is to find a numerical value, while in others it is to change the expression into a simpler form. It may even be used to produce a more complicated form, when a simple 'standard' formula has its application extended to cover other cases.

Think about it like this

This word is used to describe an important technique in calculus. But there it is a shortening of the correct title: *integration by substitution*. Indeed the first stages of that method are precisely the manoeuvres we shall now examine.

1.9.1   Verification

It is much easier to *check* that something satisfies requirements than to derive it from scratch. Thus, if asked to **verify** that something is a solution to an equation, **substitute** it into the equation and check that both sides agree.

Example 1.33   Verify that $x = 2$ is a solution of $x^3 - 3x - 2 = 0$.

Substitute $x = 2$: $2^3 - 3 \times 2 - 2 = 8 - 6 - 2 = 0$, as required.   ∎

Example 1.34   Verify that $x = at^2$, $y = 2at$ satisfy $y^2 = 4ax$.

Substitute: $y^2 = (2at)^2 = 4a^2t^2$, $4ax = 4a \times at^2 = 4a^2t^2$, as required.

Note: $y^2 = 4ax$ is one way of specifying a *parabola*, like the familiar $y - ax^2$, but rotated through $90°$ clockwise. The equations given here are called **parametric equations**, defining the parabola in terms of an intermediate variable t. If you think of t as *time*, then the (x, y) points can be seen to move along the curve.   ∎

1.9.2   Simplifying expressions

A carefully chosen substitution can make complicated expressions easier by exploiting possible cancellations or taking advantage of useful identities.

Example 1.35   Substitute $y = \sqrt{z}$ in $x^2 - 2xy^2 + y^4$.

$$x^2 - 2x\left(\sqrt{z}\right)^2 + \left(\sqrt{z}\right)^4 = x^2 - 2xz + z^2 = (x - z)^2.$$

Having spotted this neat answer we can, if we wish, return to y using $z = y^2$: $\left(x - y^2\right)^2$.   ∎

Example 1.36   Substitute $x = \sin\theta$ in $\sqrt{1 - x^2}$:

$$\sqrt{1 - \sin^2\theta} = \sqrt{\cos^2\theta} = \cos\theta,$$

using the **identity** $\sin^2\theta + \cos^2\theta \equiv 1$.

Note: this result requires θ to lie between $-90°$ and $+90°$, to ensure $\cos\theta \geqslant 0$ to match the sign of the original square root. Quoting the answer $|\cos\theta|$ (the *size* of $\cos x$) would give a result that is always correct.   ∎

1.9.3   Extending standard formulae

There are a host of simple formulae whose scope can be extended by replacing (substituting for) the symbols therein.

Example 1.37   Expand $(2x - 3y)^2$.

We can use (1.1): $(a + b)^2 = a^2 + 2ab + b^2$, by **substituting** $a = 2x$ and $b = -3y$:

$$(2x)^2 + 2 \times (2x) \times (-3y) + (-3y)^2 = 4x^2 - 12xy + 9y^2.$$

(Note that $(-3y)^2 = (-3)^2 y^2 = +9y^2$.)   ∎

Note the careful use of **brackets** here. This is strongly recommended when using substitution. When we replace a symbol by an expression, that expression is tied to the symbol *before* any other calculation, i.e., it has the highest priority in any final calculation, which can only be safeguarded by using brackets.

Example 1.38 Substitute $x = a+1$ in $x(1-x)$. Enclose $a+1$ in brackets, then carefully remove them:

$$(a+1)\left[1-(a+1)\right] = (a+1)\left[1-a-1\right] = -a(a+1),$$

NOT $a + 1(1 - a + 1) = a + 2 - a = 2$, which contains two errors. It is obviously wrong: the original version varies with x, while 2 is constant. ∎

Ex 1.15 *Verify* that $x = 1$ and $x = -3$ satisfy $x^3 - 7x + 6 = 0$.
Find a third such value of x.

Ex 1.16 Substitute $x = y^3$ in $\dfrac{x}{x - y^2}$ and simplify your answer.

Ex 1.17 Use $x = \tan\theta$ and the trigonometric identity $\sec^2\theta = \tan^2\theta + 1$ (where $\sec\theta = 1/\cos\theta$) to simplify $\dfrac{1}{\sqrt{x^2 + 1}}$.
How could one simplify $\dfrac{1}{\sqrt{x^2 - 1}}$?

1.10 Identities

Identities, as introduced in §1.3, provide a powerful tool for **rearrangement**, where an expression is rewritten in an equivalent, but more useful, form. For example, in calculus, identities of the form

$$2\sin 2x \cos x = \sin 3x + \sin x$$

are regularly used, since the right-hand side is much easier to use than the left.

In constructing such rearrangements, the nature of an identity is helpful. Thus, if an expression involving a variable x is written as $f(x)$ and we seek to write it as $g(x)$, but do not know the values of some of the quantities involved in $g(x)$, we can use the fact that $f(x) = g(x)$ for **all** x to argue that $f(\alpha) = g(\alpha)$ for some carefully chosen α, which will help determine parts of $g(x)$.

Example 1.39 Find A and B for which

$$A(x + 1) + B(x + 2) \equiv 3x + 7, \tag{1.7}$$

the sort of task required to determine *partial fractions*, as we shall see in Chapter 4. There are two methods, the second of which is much easier.

Method 1   Equate, separately, the coefficients of x and 1 in (1.7):

$$A + B = 3 \qquad \text{with solution}$$
$$A + 2B = 7 \qquad A = -1, \ B = 4$$

This requires the solution of *simultaneous equations*. Although this example is straightforward, it can be time-consuming.

Method 2   Substitute sample values for x in (1.7). There are two clever choices:

$$x = -1: \quad A \times 0 + B \times 1 = 3 \times (-1) + 7, \ \text{giving } B = 4,$$
$$x = -2: \quad A \times (-1) + B \times 0 = 3 \times (-2) + 7, \ \text{giving } A = -1.$$

∎

Before looking at a further example, this is an appropriate time to introduce a popular, though often misused, notational device. This last example used "giving" to show the logical connection between two statements. There are a plethora of other words or phrases such as "showing", "proving", "leading to", "and hence" and "so that". All of these can be replaced by a single symbol '$\Rightarrow$', borrowed from *Logic*. It is read as "implies". When we write

$$A \ \Rightarrow \ B$$

we mean that "A true" implies "B true", so that the truth of A guarantees that of B e.g.,

$$3x = 12 \ \Rightarrow \ x = 4.$$

This symbol can link *ONLY* true/false statements, never *numbers* or expressions (which are often numbers whose values we do not yet know). Thus:

$$x = 2^3 - 3 \times 2 - 2 \Rightarrow 8 - 6 - 2 \Rightarrow 0 \quad \textit{MAKES NO SENSE.}$$

Less common is the reverse implication $A \Leftarrow B$, where the truth of B implies that of A.

These ideas can be joined in $A \Leftrightarrow B$, which means that A and B are *equivalent* statements: if either is true, the other must be. (This is a different use of 'equivalent' from that in the identity $f(x) \equiv g(x)$, where we do mean the equality of numbers.)

Example 1.40

$$x^2 = 1 \ \Leftarrow \ x = 1$$

is true since if $x = 1$ then $x^2 = x \times x = 1 \times 1 = 1$. But we cannot reverse this since, if $x^2 = 1$ then x may be -1. Correct is

$$x^2 = 1 \ \Leftrightarrow \ |x| = 1.$$

These *logical connectives* can be used for non-numerical statements:

My birthday is 29th Feb $\Leftrightarrow$ I have a birthday only in a leap year.

∎

The second example of the use of identities concerns the division of linear and quadratic terms, for which we shall find a general systematic method in Chapter 4.

Example 1.41 Find A, B and C so that

$$\frac{x^2}{x+2} \equiv Ax + B + \frac{C}{x+2}.$$

First, multiply by $x+2$:

$$x^2 \equiv (Ax+B)(x+2) + C.$$

Now choose special values for x, starting with 'clever' values that deliver information immediately, then using small whole numbers. This time we shall use $\Rightarrow$ to save on words:

$$\begin{aligned}
x = -2 : \quad & 4 = (-2A+B) \times 0 + C && \Rightarrow C = 4, \\
x = 0 : \quad & 0 = 2B + C && \Rightarrow B = -2, \\
x = 1 : \quad & 1 = (A+B) \times 3 + C && \Rightarrow A = 1.
\end{aligned}$$

■

Ex 1.18 Find A and B such that $\quad x - 3 \equiv A(x+1) + B$.

Ex 1.19 Find constants A, B, C and D such that:

(a) $3x + 2 \equiv A(x-1) + B(x-2)$,

(b) $\dfrac{x^3}{x^2+1} \equiv Ax + B + \dfrac{Cx+D}{x^2+1}$.

1.11 Inequalities

It is often the case that we do not have precise information about a quantity, e.g., when it has been measured, and we seek to **bound** it, by stating a region in which it must lie. A useful tool is the set of **inequality** relations:

Frame 1.5   *Inequality relations*

$<$: less than	$\leqslant$ or $\leq$: less than or equal to
$>$: greater than	$\geqslant$ or $\geq$: greater than or equal to

Example 1.42 $\quad 2 < 3, \quad -0.001 < 0.002, \quad -2 > -3, \quad 1 \leqslant 1, \quad 1 \geqslant 1$

Inequalities can be portrayed on the number line.

$x < 2$

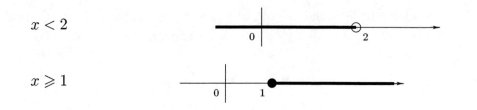

$x \geqslant 1$

■

Notation

In this example, ∘ showed that point $x = 2$ was not included, while • showed that $x = 1$ was. This use of ∘ to show non-inclusion and • to show inclusion is common in graph-drawing.

Several rules are similar to those for equalities, e.g.,

$$a < b \quad \Rightarrow \quad a + c < b + c, \qquad a - c < b - c,$$

but one in particular does not:

$$a < b \quad \Rightarrow \quad ac < bc \;\; \text{if } c > 0, \qquad ac > bc \;\; \text{if } c < 0.$$

Example 1.43 We know that $-1 < 2$. Multiplying by 2 gives: $-2 < 4$, which is correct; multiplying by -2 and *reversing the inequality* gives $2 > -4$, which is correct. ■

We can 'solve' inequalities, much in the way we solve equations.

Example 1.44

$$3x + 1 \leqslant 13 \quad \Rightarrow \quad 3x \leqslant 13 - 1 = 12$$
$$\Rightarrow \quad x \leqslant 4 \qquad \text{(on multiplying by } \tfrac{1}{3} > 0)$$

$$1 - 2x < 7 \quad \Rightarrow \quad 1 < 7 + 2x \quad \Rightarrow \quad -6 < 2x$$
$$\Rightarrow \quad -3 < x \quad \text{i.e., } x > -3$$

OR

$$1 - 2x < 7 \quad \Rightarrow \quad -2x < 7 - 1 = 6$$
$$\Rightarrow \quad x > \frac{6}{-2} = -3 \qquad \text{(reversing inequality: } -2 < 0)$$

■

Particular care is needed when multiplication or division is by a symbol, since we must ask what sign that quantity may have. Usually this means treating two separate cases.

Example 1.45 $\dfrac{6}{x} < 2$. Note that we cannot allow $x = 0$.

$$x > 0: \qquad 6 < 2x \quad \Rightarrow \quad x > 3 \quad \text{(multiplying by } x > 0)$$
$$x < 0: \qquad 6 > 2x \quad \Rightarrow \quad x < 3 \quad \text{(multiplying by } x < 0, \text{ reversing } <)$$

The solution is $x < 0$ **or** $x > 3$. Note that, in the second calculation $x < 3$ is redundant since we already know the stronger bound $x < 0$.

A similar calculation for $6/x > 2$ leads to $x > 0$, $x < 3$ or $x < 0$, $x > 3$. This time the entire second case is contradictory and thus impossible, so the answer is simply the first case, written more neatly as $0 < x < 3$. ■

Ex 1.20 Suppose that $a < b$ and $c < d$. Decide which of the following are always true and which may be false; in each of the 'false' cases, give an example to justify your answer:

$$\text{(a) } a + c < b + d, \quad \text{(b) } a - c < b - d, \quad \text{(c) } ac < bd, \quad \text{(d) } \frac{1}{b} < \frac{1}{a}.$$

Suppose, now, that a, b, c and d are all greater than zero. How does that affect your answers?

1.12 Absolute Values

It is common, especially when treating errors, to bound a number as lying within a certain distance of a known number. One way to express this uses the **absolute value** or **modulus** function. This returns the *size* of the number, ignoring any minus sign that may be attached.

Frame 1.6   *Absolute value function*

$$|x| = \begin{cases} -x, & \text{if } x < 0; \\ x, & \text{if } x \geqslant 0. \end{cases} \tag{1.8}$$

Notation

> The notation $|.|$ is a good example of one that has multiple uses. In some cases there is a strong relationship between the uses, which makes it apt, e.g., the magnitude of a vector $|\mathbf{v}|$ and the modulus of a complex number $|z|$ are really extensions of the absolute value of a number. The determinant of a matrix is sometimes written $|A|$, but is entirely different; there are potential dangers in using that notation.

An immediate application is to the measurement of **distance** on the real line, since distance is not regarded as having a sign. The distance between x and y is $|x - y|$ or, equivalently, $|y - x|$.

Example 1.46   Let $x = -3$ and $y = 2$. Then $|x| = 3$ and $y = 2$.

$$|xy| = |(-3) \times 2| = |-6| = 6 = |x|\,|y|,$$
$$|x - y| = |-3 - 2| = |-5| = 5 = |2 - (-3)| = |y - x|.$$

■

The following properties of $|x|$ are often used in practical calculations:

$$|x| \geqslant 0, \qquad\qquad |x| = 0 \quad \text{only if} \quad x = 0$$
$$|x| = |-x|, \qquad\quad |xy| = |x|\,|y|$$
$$|x + y| \leqslant |x| + |y| \quad \text{(triangle inequality)}$$

Think about it like this

Note that, although there is a simple rule for $|xy|$, there is none for $x + y$. This reflects a general tendency for algebraic rules to be better disposed to multiplication and division than to addition and subtraction. The **triangle inequality**, which is the best we can offer, is so-named because of a similar inequality for *vectors*, which can be illustrated by the lengths of the sides of a triangle; see Chapter 5.

Example 1.47   Returning to the data in the previous example, $|-3+2| = |-1| = 1 < |-3| + |2| = 5$. Had we used $x = 3$ instead, we would find $|x + y| = 5 = |x| + |y|$.   ∎

Ex 1.21   When is $|-x| = x$?

1.13   Intervals

An **interval** is a segment of the real line, with no gaps. There are two main types:

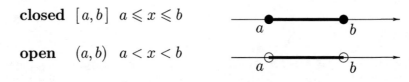

closed $[a, b]$ $a \leqslant x \leqslant b$

open (a, b) $a < x < b$

There are also hybrid types, such as $[a, b)$, which includes a but not b.

The notation used here is **end-point form**. There is an alternative – **centred form** – that is more useful when dealing with symmetrically disposed intervals, such as those that apply to errors:

$$|x - c| \leqslant r \qquad (\text{or} \ < r \ \text{for an open interval}),$$

where c is the **centre** and r is the **radius**.

Conversion between end-point and centred forms can be deduced from the diagram below, recalling that $|x - c|$ measures the distance between x and c.

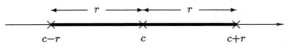

Centred to end-point: The end-point form for $|x - c| \leqslant r$ is $[c - r, c + r]$.

End-point to centred: The centre of $[a, b]$ is the average of the end-points, while the radius is half the width, $b - a$:

Frame 1.7   *Conversion from end-point to centred form*

$$[a,b] \quad \text{is} \quad |x - c| \leqslant r, \quad \text{where} \quad c = \frac{1}{2}(a+b), \quad r = \frac{1}{2}(b-a)$$

Example 1.48

$$|x - 1| \leqslant 2 \quad \Rightarrow \quad -2 \leqslant x - 1 \leqslant 2 \quad \Rightarrow \quad -1 \leqslant x \leqslant 3 \quad \Rightarrow \quad -1 \leqslant x \leqslant 3.$$

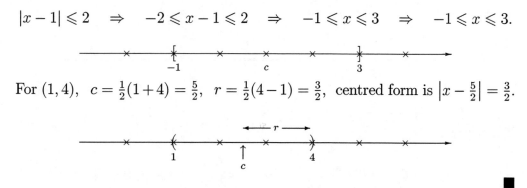

For $(1, 4)$, $c = \frac{1}{2}(1 + 4) = \frac{5}{2}$, $r = \frac{1}{2}(4 - 1) = \frac{3}{2}$, centred form is $\left| x - \frac{5}{2} \right| = \frac{3}{2}$.

∎

Ex 1.22

(a) Write in end-point form $|x - 2| \leqslant 5$.

(b) Write in centred form $(-4, 2)$.

Ex 1.23

(a) Express, in end-point form, $|x - 6| < 6$, $|x + \frac{1}{2}| \leqslant \frac{7}{2}$.

(b) Convert the following intervals to centred form, i.e., $|x - c| < r$ or $|x - c| \leqslant r$:

i. $(3, 11)$, ii. $[-2, 4]$, iii. $(-3, 6)$, iv. $[-\frac{1}{3}, \frac{1}{6}]$.

1.14   Errors and Rounding

Suppose that a quantity Q we seek is measured as $\overline{Q}$ with a maximum error ϵ [*epsilon*]. Then we know the correct value lies in the interval

$$[\overline{Q} - \epsilon, \overline{Q} + \epsilon] \quad \text{or} \quad |Q - \overline{Q}| \leqslant \epsilon.$$

This is often written $Q = \overline{Q} \pm \epsilon$, which is a special, *non-standard*, use of $\pm$, which would normally signal only the two end-points of the interval, without the points between.

> *Think about it like this*
>
> This approach assumes 100% certainty that the correct value lies in this interval. In some practical work, where a value is the result of averaging several readings, the convention is that the correct value lies in this interval with 68% (around two-thirds) certainty. Much of what follows still applies, provided one bears this in mind when interpreting the results. There is a real difference when these measured quantities are subjected to arithmetic, when there are different rules for the two approaches.

The value ϵ is an **(absolute) error bound**. It is more usual for this maximum error to be given as a **percentage** error bound: $p\%$, where ϵ is $p\%$ of Q. (Usually we have to work with $\overline{Q}$ since Q is not known.) Conversion between these error bounds is straightforward.

Frame 1.8   *Absolute and percentage error bounds*

$$p = \frac{\epsilon}{\overline{Q}} \times 100, \qquad\qquad \epsilon = \overline{Q} \times \frac{p}{100}$$

The difference between these two measures is usually flagged by the presence or absence of '%'.

Example 1.49

$$Q = 7.83 \pm 0.05, \qquad\qquad p = \frac{0.05}{7.83} \times 100 = 0.64\%$$

$$Q = 217.1 \pm 2\%, \qquad\qquad \epsilon = 217.1 \times \frac{2}{100} = 4.4$$

This last answer has been nudged slightly upwards when rounded off; this is often done for error bounds, to err on the safe side.   ■

An important advantage of using the percentage bound is that it has no units: it is a *pure* number. The absolute bound shares the same units as Q and so will change if we scale Q, e.g., moving from metres to millimetres. The percentage bound is unchanged.

Think about it like this

You can think of the difference between these error measures as follows. Suppose x is the size of your overdraft, then ϵ_x is the interest you pay on it and $100r_x$ is the interest rate expressed (as is usual) as a percentage. The absolute bounds contains units: you may pay interest in different numbers of pounds or euros depending on the currency of x. The percentage bound is independent of this: the interest rate is the same in both instances. More importantly, most people are familiar with how to convert between interest payments and interest rates: the calculations required for conversion, in Frame 1.8, are identical in nature.

Another difference is illustrated by unit conversion. Suppose we have measured a distance in kilometres and wish to convert it to metres. We do this by multiplying by the scale factor 1000. Clearly, the *absolute* error bound in the measurement – which inherits the same units – should also be converted to metres and thus must also be multiplied by 1000. The *percentage* bound contains no units. The fundamental quality of the measurement has not changed by the conversion, so the percentage bound must stay the same.

Some errors are due to our inability to measure quantities exactly. Others arise because numbers cannot be written exactly using decimal notation, or using a reasonably short decimal form. In such cases we **round** the number x to find $\overline{x}$.

Frame 1.9   *Rounding numbers*

(1) Decide on number n of **decimal places (dp)** after the point
(2) Copy out the first n digits after the point
(3) Finish, if remaining digits are less than $5000\cdots$
(4) Otherwise, add 1 to the final digit

Example 1.50

$$\tfrac{2}{3} = 0.66\big|6666\cdots \qquad = 0.67 \qquad \text{to 2 dp}$$

$$\sqrt{2} = 1.414\big|2135\cdots \qquad = 1.414 \qquad \text{to 3 dp}$$

$$\pi = 3.1415\big|926\cdots \qquad = 3.1416 \qquad \text{to 4 dp}$$

∎

In each case, the maximum error that could have been made is $\tfrac{1}{2}$ unit in the last place quoted (5 units in the first not used).

Example 1.51

$$\tfrac{2}{3} = 0.67 \pm 0.005, \qquad\qquad \sqrt{2} = 1.414 \pm 0.0005$$
$$\text{or } \tfrac{1}{2} \times 10^{-2} \qquad\qquad\qquad \text{or } \tfrac{1}{2} \times 10^{-3}$$

∎

The general rule for the error due to rounding to n dp is:

Frame 1.10   *Error due to rounding*

$$\epsilon = \tfrac{1}{2} \times 10^{-n}, \qquad\qquad |x - \bar{x}| \leqslant \tfrac{1}{2} 10^{-n}$$

In 'real' calculations, numbers can inhabit a wide range of values. It is therefore common to use **scientific notation**:

$$x = a \times 10^n, \qquad (1 \leqslant |a| < 10, \ n \text{ an integer}).$$

The quoted number has $m + 1$ **significant figures (sf)** if a has m dp. The figures with significance are all of those after the decimal point *and* the single non-zero digit before it.

Example 1.52

$$\text{mass of electron} \quad 9.11 \times 10^{-31}\,\text{kg} \quad 3\,\text{sf}$$
$$\text{speed of light} \quad 2.9978 \times 10^8\,\text{ms}^{-1} \ 5\,\text{sf}$$

$$472.6154 = 4.726\,154 \times 10^2 \quad 4\,\mathrm{dp},\ 7\,\mathrm{sf}$$
$$0.005\,720 = 5.720 \times 10^{-3} \qquad 6\,\mathrm{dp},\ 4\,\mathrm{sf}$$

■

In the last case in this example, the final '0' *is* significant, else it would not have been quoted. This means we know that this is indeed 0 and not 9 or 1. Leading zeros, however, are *never* significant. They are merely 'padding' between the point and the first significant number; they disappear when scientific notation is used.

A more insidious problem concerns large integers: how can we show which of any trailing zeros are significant? Again, scientific notation is the key.

Example 1.53 The mean distance from the earth to the sun, D, could be written as $150,000,000\,\mathrm{km}$. How many of the zeros are significant? This number is better written:

$$D = 1.50 \times 10^8\,\mathrm{km},$$

which shows there are $3\,\mathrm{sf}$, since the first zero is known to be significant. ■

Think about it like this

Finally, it is misleading to give a numerical answer to more decimal places or significant figures than can be justified. Resist the temptation to reproduce all that your calculator gives. Thus, $235.12 \times 0.531 = 124.84872$ promises more information than can be relied on if the input numbers are correctly rounded.

Ex 1.24

(a) Round to $3\,\mathrm{dp}$, $4\,\mathrm{dp}$, $10\,\mathrm{dp}$: $e = 2.71828\,18284\,59045\ \ldots\,$.

(b) 2.39 has been correctly rounded to $2\,\mathrm{dp}$. Find the absolute and percentage error bounds.

(c) What is the absolute error bound in $4.12 \pm 5\%$?

Ex 1.25

(a) State the numbers of *decimal places* and *significant figures* in each of the following:

$$980.665, \quad 1.759 \times 10^7, \quad 6.67 \times 10^{-8}, \quad 2.00 \times 10^{20}.$$

(b) Find the *percentage error bound* for $x = 35\,\mathrm{min} \pm 5\,\mathrm{sec}$.

(c) Find the *absolute error bound* for $x = 35\,\mathrm{min} \pm 4\%$.

1.15   Revision Exercises

Ex 1.26 Without using a calculator, simplify the following expressions, to obtain answers in as simple a form as possible. **Show all working**.

$$\text{(a)} \quad \frac{\sqrt{2}}{3 - \sqrt{8}}, \qquad \text{(b)} \quad \frac{\sqrt{12}}{\sqrt{3} - 1/\sqrt{3}}.$$

Ex 1.27 Expand: $(x^2 - x + 1)^2$.

Ex 1.28 Expand, to obtain a polynomial without brackets:

$$\left(1 - x^3\right)^2 \left(1 + x^3\right)^2.$$

Ex 1.29 Find a formula for y in terms of x, where:

$$x = \sqrt{\frac{y}{1 - y}}.$$

Your answer must be as neat as possible, e.g., avoid using more than one division.

Ex 1.30 Use the substitution $y = x^2/z$ to simplify the expression:

$$\frac{x^2 \left(x^4/y^2 - 1\right)}{y \left(x^2/y + 1\right)}.$$

Ex 1.31 Find values of A and B to make the following identity true:

$$A(x - 2)^2 + B(x + 1)^2 \equiv 6x - 3.$$

Ex 1.32 Solve the following inequality, to find those x for which it is true:

$$\frac{3}{1 - x} < -1.$$

Ex 1.33 A measured quantity is known to lie in the interval $[\,16.84, 17.42\,]$. Write this interval in **centred-form** and hence calculate the **percentage** error bound when the centre is used as to estimate the quantity.

Ex 1.34 A number x is known to satisfy $|x - 3.42| \leqslant 0.24$. Find the interval, in end-point form, in which x must lie. Also, find the **percentage error bound** when 3.42 is used as an approximation to x.

2   SEQUENCES AND SERIES

This chapter considers how to specify sequences of numbers or expressions and how to add them up. It concentrates on two particularly useful types.

2.1   Sequences

A **sequence** is like a *set*, but with two differences. The elements are in a definite order and duplicates are allowed. It is the same as what computer scientists call a **list** and we shall adopt their notation:

$$[\, a_0, \, a_1, \, a_2, \, \ldots \, a_k, \, \ldots \,],$$

where the sequence may be **finite**, ending at a_n, or **infinite**, with no 'last' member.

Notation

There is no generally agreed notation for sequences. Some use $\{\ldots\}$, which is a standard notation for sets, while some use no bracketing at all. The set notation is dangerous because sets and sequences are different entities: sets have no sense of *order*.

The subscript k in a_k is an **index** or **counter** and the three dots, $\ldots$, is an *ellipsis*, which usually indicates omitted text and here can be read as "and so on [until]", depending on whether the sequence is finite or not.

Think about it like this

Sequences play a part in everyday life and may be textual, as in a list of world record holders in the 100 metres, or numerical, as in a list of their times. The most common case is where the ordering is chronological, but other factors can be involved, e.g., a list of scheduled stops for an Edinburgh–London train, or a list of the distances between those stops. In this increasingly digital age, sequences can reflect intermittent *sampling* from a continuous process, as in a music CD.

We shall explore mathematical sequences, initially using the following five illustrations.

Example 2.1

$$0, 1, 2, 3, 4, \ldots \qquad\qquad\qquad (2.1)$$
$$1, 4, 9, 16, \ldots \qquad\qquad\qquad (2.2)$$
$$0, 1, 1, 2, 3, 5, 8, \ldots \qquad\qquad\qquad (2.3)$$
$$1003, 998, 995, 999, 1002, \ldots \qquad\qquad\qquad (2.4)$$
$$1, 2, 4, 8, 16, \ldots \qquad\qquad\qquad (2.5)$$

∎

There is one feature of the specification that is unclear and must remain so: where does the sequence start? In some cases $r = 0$ is best, while in others it is better to use $r = 1$. Choosing either as a compulsory convention would occasionally causes difficulties, so we shall adopt the solution of making a_0 the first term by default, with other cases allowed as stated exceptions.

An immediate outcome is that care is required in counting: a_k is the $(k+1)^{\text{st}}$ term in the default case.

Example 2.2   Presuming that (2.1) satisfies a simple pattern, we have

$$a_k = k, \quad a_7 = 7 \text{ is the } 8^{\text{th}} \text{ term.}$$

Similarly, for (2.2):

$$a_k = (k+1)^2, \quad a_3 = 4^2 \text{ is the } 4^{\text{th}} \text{ term,}$$

although this is a case where it may be better to declare that the sequence starts at 1, so that $a_k = k^2$. ∎

Our chosen notation can be adapted to indicate the start and end of a sequence. We write, for a finite sequence,

$$[\, a_0, \, a_1, \, \ldots, \, a_n \,] = [\, a_k \,]_{k=0}^n \,,$$

and for an infinite sequence,

$$[\, a_0, \, a_1, \, \ldots \,] = [\, a_k \,]_{k=0}^\infty \,.$$

This notation extends to provide a neat way to define only part of the sequence, a **subsequence**:

$$[\, a_m, \, a_{m+1}, \, \ldots, \, a_n \,] = [\, a_k \,]_{k=m}^n \qquad (n \geqslant m),$$

which contains $n - m + 1$ terms.

Notation

> In this definition the closing expression in brackets is used to show the set of values for which the given equation is true. Here, it states that the starting count cannot exceed the finishing count, but in other contexts we may find restrictions such as $(x > 0)$ or $(x \neq 1)$.

Think about it like this

> If this seems a strange formula, recall that, when quoting a page range from a book, we must subtract then add 1 to obtain the page count: pages 21–30 contain $30 - 21 + 1 = 10$ pages.

Example 2.3   For (2.3):

$$[\, 1, \, 2, \, 3, \, 5 \,] = [\, a_k \,]_{k=2}^5 \text{ contains } 5 - 2 + 1 = 4 \text{ terms.}$$

∎

In this notation, k is called a **dummy index** (or **variable**, to tie in with a similar concept in calculus). It plays no part in the final answer and is used only as an intermediate tool. Thus:

$$[\,a_k\,]_{k=1}^{3} = [\,a_r\,]_{r=1}^{3} = [\,a_1,\,a_2,\,a_3\,],$$

the final version referring to neither k nor r.

A formula for a_k, if one exists, is preferred to the '...' use, since the latter can be uninformative or even dangerous.

Example 2.4

(a) The sequence $[\,4,\,3,\,3,\,5,\,4,\,4,\,3,\,5,\,\ldots\,]$ has no obvious pattern. What is the next term? We could answer '5', arguing that these numbers count the letters in "zero", "one", "two", etc.

(b) Surely the next term in (2.5) is $2^5 = 32$? That is most likely, but count the number of distinct parts in each of the following diagrams:

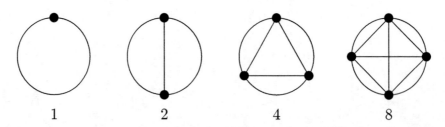

       1   2   4   8

A diagram with 5 points has 16 parts, but one with 6 points has only 31. There is a formula for this particular sequence and it has nothing to do with 2^n. That said, in most cases, e.g., a model of bacterial growth, $a_5 = 32$ would be the correct continuation.

■

There are three principal ways in which a sequence can be constructed.

(a) The elements may be measured as they occur. Thus, in (2.4), a_k could represent the atmospheric pressure at a fixed location at noon on day k. There is no pattern and future values are unknown. The best we can do is to tabulate the values.

(b) A formula can be derived for a_k in terms of k:

$$a_k = f(k)$$

for some function f. Thus, in (2.1), $f(k) = k$ and in (2.2), $f(k) = (k+1)^2$.

(c) An iteration or recursion can be used, to define one a_k value in terms of preceding ones.

This last possibility is often the easiest to use and it is sometimes possible to use a mathematical argument to deduce a formula from it. It forms the subject of the next section.

Ex 2.1

(a) Write out, in full, the sequences: $[a_r]_{r=2}^3$, $[x_k]_{k=0}^2$, $[u_m]_{m=4}^4$.

(b) Write down a formulae for the nth term (start at x_0) for: $[1, -\frac{1}{3}, \frac{1}{5}, -\frac{1}{7}, \dots]$.

Ex 2.2 The *triangular numbers* are defined by: $T_n = 1 + 2 + 3 + 4 + \cdots + n$. They count the number of balls in an n row snooker triangle, as in ⚬.

We can find a formula for T_n as follows. Consider a square array of dots, such as: ⚬. Now show that the number of dots in T_n, counted twice, is the same as that for the square plus its diagonal and hence find T_n.

Count the dots in the same square, divided up in a special way, to find a formula for
$$S_n = 1 + 3 + 5 + \cdots + (2n - 1).$$

2.2 Iteration

The simplest form of **iteration** or **recursion** is defined by the **recurrence relation**:
$$x_{k+1} = g(x_k), \qquad x_0 = \alpha, \tag{2.6}$$
where g is a known function and α a known constant. Again k is a *dummy* variable and other letters could be used.

Setting $k = 0$ gives $x_1 = g(\alpha)$, so we now know x_1. Setting $k = 1$ gives $x_2 = g(x_1)$, so we now know x_2, and so on. In this way we can calculate as many terms as we wish in the sequence $[x_k]$.

There are many applications of iteration, e.g., for solving equations. We shall concentrate on some simple examples.

Example 2.5 A cell splits in two after one time unit. There are P cells initially. How many are there after n time units?

Let x_n be that number. After one further time unit, each has split into two. Also, there are P cells after zero time units:
$$x_0 = P, \qquad x_{k+1} = 2x_k. \tag{2.7}$$

We can use this to build up a list of values:
$$x_1 = 2x_0 = 2P, \qquad x_2 = 2x_1 = 2(2P) = 4P,$$

and so on, suggesting the general formula $x_n = 2^n P$.

There are ways of deriving this from (2.7), but the easiest approach is to *verify* the formula by *substitution* in (2.7):
$$2^0 P = 1 \times P = P, \qquad 2^{n+1} P = 2(2^n P),$$

which are clearly correct. ∎

Example 2.6 The sequence (2.3) extends this idea, in that it uses *two* previous values and hence needs *two* starting values to enable further values to be calculated:

$$x_0 = 0, \quad x_1 = 0, \qquad x_{k+1} = x_k + x_{k-1}.$$

This is the **Fibonacci sequence**, which has applications in many areas, e.g., in modelling biological phenomena.

Again, we can find a formula from this recurrence, although it is much more difficult than in the previous example and leads to a more complicated result:

$$x_n = \frac{1}{\sqrt{5}} \left[\left(\frac{1 + \sqrt{5}}{2} \right)^n - \left(\frac{1 - \sqrt{5}}{2} \right)^n \right].$$

The two numbers in this formula are also well-known in mathematical and in design work: $\frac{1}{2}\left(1 + \sqrt{5}\right) = 1.618\cdots$ is the **golden mean** and $\frac{1}{2}\left(\sqrt{5} - 1\right)$ is its reciprocal. ∎

Example 2.7   Towers of Hanoi

The object in this puzzle is to move the disks from peg T_1 to peg T_2, but a disk can only be placed on top of a larger disk. How many moves are required?

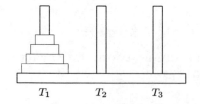

Let M_n be the number required for n disks. The method for solving this puzzle can be described recursively:

> move $n - 1$ disks from T_1 to T_3, using T_2 as spare peg,
>
> move bottom disk from T_1 to T_2,
>
> move $n - 1$ disks from T_3 to T_2, using T_1 as spare peg.

Adding up the moves required gives the recurrence relation:

$$M_n = M_{n-1} + 1 + M_{n-1} = 2M_{n-1} + 1. \qquad (2.8)$$

Clearly, with just one disk we require just one move, so $M_1 = 1$. That allows us to calculate using (2.8):

$$M_2 = 2 \times 1 + 1 = 3, \qquad M_3 = 2 \times 3 + 1 = 7,$$

and so on. The values suggest that $M_n = 2^n - 1$. This, by the way, produces $M_0 = 2^0 - 1 = 0$, which makes sense.

It is possible to prove that this answer is correct, using *substitution*. Let

$$x_n = M_n + 1 \quad \Rightarrow \quad M_n = x_n - 1.$$

Substitute this into (2.8):

$$x_n - 1 = 2\left(x_{n-1} - 1\right) + 1 = 2x_{n-1} - 1 \quad \Rightarrow \quad x_n = 2x_{n-1}.$$

This is equivalent to the recurrence relation in Example 2.5, with $x_1 = M_1 + 1 = 1 + 1 = 2$ agreeing with the value there, if $P = 1$. Hence we can use the solution found in that Example:

$$x_n = 2^n \quad \Rightarrow \quad M_n = x_n - 1 = 2^n - 1,$$

as we conjectured. ∎

Ex 2.3 Find, to 4 dp, the sequence $[x_r]_{r=1}^4$, where $x_{r+1} = \dfrac{2}{x_r + 1}$, $x_0 = 1.1$.

Ex 2.4 A ball is dropped from a height 8 m above the ground. It rebounds many times and on each bounce reaches a maximum height of r times its previous maximum height. The maximum height reached after the third bounce is 1.728 m. Assuming r is constant, find the maximum height after 6 bounces and after n bounces.

Ex 2.5 The square root of a can be approximated by calculation using the sequence:

$$x_{n+1} = \frac{1}{2}\left[x_n + \frac{a}{x_n}\right].$$

Using $x_0 = 4$, estimate $\sqrt{17}$ correct to 6 dp.

2.3 Arithmetic Progression

There are two simple recurrence relations that define particularly important sequences or, as they are usually referred to, *progressions*, an old-fashioned name. The first of these is an **arithmetic progression**, often abbreviated as **AP**, where each term differs from the previous one by a constant amount.

> *Frame 2.1*   Arithmetic progression
>
> $$x_{k+1} = x_k + d, \tag{2.9}$$
> $$x_n = a + nd, \tag{2.10}$$
>
> d is the **common difference** and $a = x_0$ is the **first term**

The explicit formula follows from the recurrence relation on noting that by the time we reach x_n we have added d on n times. Alternatively, it can be verified by substitution.

Example 2.8   A person starts with £1000 in the bank and, each month, earns £1500, pays £500 by direct debit and withdraws £700. Find a formula for the bank balance, ignoring any interest added.

The recurrence relation is

$$x_{k+1} = x_k + 1500 - 500 - 700 = x_k + 300,$$

with $x_0 = 1000$. This is an AP with common difference 300 and first term 1000. Hence, after n months, $x_n = 1000 + 300n$ is the bank balance. ∎

APs can also *decrease*. This is tantamount to a recurrence relation in which subtraction is used, but is better regarded as a normal AP with a negative common difference.

Example 2.9 A photocopy card has 100 copies credited. A person photocopies a 12 page magazine every week. When will the card need to be replaced?

The recurrence relation is

$$x_{k+1} = x_k - 12, \qquad x_0 = 100,$$

so the formula for the remaining credit is $x_n = 100 - 12n$.

We seek $x_n = 0$, i.e., $n = 100/12 = 8\frac{1}{3}$, so the card runs out during the 9th week. ∎

Ex 2.6 Find a formula for x_n (start at x_0) for the arithmetic progression: $[11, 8, 5, 2, \ldots]$.

Ex 2.7 Find the second and fifth terms of an arithmetic progression whose first term is -2 and third term is 4.

Ex 2.8 Show that $\dfrac{1}{1+\sqrt{x}}, \dfrac{1}{1-x}, \dfrac{1}{1-\sqrt{x}}$ are in arithmetic progression and find the nth term, if these are the first three, i.e., a_1, a_2, a_3.

2.4   Geometric Progression

The second special case is a **geometric progression**, often abbreviated as **GP**, where each term differs from the previous one by a constant *ratio*. By that we mean

$$\frac{x_{k+1}}{x_k} = r,$$

with r a constant.

Frame 2.2   *Geometric progression*

$$x_{k+1} = rx_k, \tag{2.11}$$
$$x_k = ar^k, \tag{2.12}$$

r is the **common ratio** and $a = x_0$ is the **first term**

The explicit formula follows from the recurrence relation on noting that by the time we reach x_n we have multiplied by r, n times. Alternatively, it can be verified by substitution.

Think about it like this

It is arguable that r would be better called the common *multiple*, since that would make it clear how to get from x_k to x_{k+1}: we *multiply* by the common (multiple) ratio. 'Ratio' is rather ambiguous since it doesn't make it clear which way round the division is.

We have already seen a GP: Example 2.5 (cell division) has first term P and common ratio 2.

Example 2.10 Suppose that fish reproduce 20% new stock each year, while 10% die and 30% are caught. Suppose that P_n is the number of fish after n years:

$$P_{k+1} = P_k + 0.2P_k - 0.1P_k - 0.3P_k = 0.8P_k,$$

and hence

$$P_n = (0.8)^n P_0.$$

In particular $P_{10} \simeq 0.1P_0$, where '$\simeq$' means "is nearly equal to". Thus only 10% of the stock remains after 10 years. ∎

Example 2.11 Suppose that £Q is invested at a **compound interest** rate of $i\%$. Then, in one year,

$$Q \text{ becomes } Q\left(1 + \frac{i}{100}\right).$$

This produces the GP, $[P_k]$, with first term Q and common ratio $\left(1 + \frac{i}{100}\right)$. Hence

$$P_n = Q\left(1 + \frac{i}{100}\right)^n.$$

Some sample results, over a 10 year period, are, to the nearest pound:

$$2\%: \quad £1000 \rightarrow (1.02)^{10} \times 1000 = £1219,$$
$$10\%: \quad £1000 \rightarrow (1.10)^{10} \times 1000 = £2594.$$

∎

Think about it like this

There is a significant difference between APs and GPs: this last example shows a much greater than five-fold return from a five-fold increase in interest rate, unlike the AP case. This can make GPs rather harder to work with, although the *logarithm* can help: if x_n is a GP, then $\log x_n$ is an AP:

$$\log x_n = \log(ar^n) = \log a + n\log r : \text{ similar to } y_n = b + nd.$$

Our perception of the passage of time is consistent with an AP, but it is more common for other physical processes to behave like a GP, e.g., radioactive decay, first-order chemical reactions, bacterial growth and, of course, compound interest.

Ex 2.9 Find a formula for x_n (start at x_0) for the geometric progression: $[64, 48, 36, 27, \ldots]$.

Ex 2.10 The second and seventh terms of a geometric progression are 5 and 160, respectively. Find the terms in between these.

2.5   Series

A **series** or **sum** is the result of adding the terms in a sequence. For example, a saver making regular yearly deposits of an identical amount would have to sum the terms in the geometric series in Example 2.11.

There are two notational devices: write the sum out as a sequence, linked with '+' and possibly using $\cdots$ in the middle, or replace $[\ ]_{k=m}^{n}$ by a similar notation based on $\sum$ [capital *sigma*, equivalent to S], which is an abbreviation for "sum". (Note that the ellipsis is now raised, since it is continuing the plus sign in the sum, rather than the comma in a sequence.)

Frame 2.3   *Sigma notation*

$$\sum_{k=m}^{n} a_k = a_m + a_{m+1} + \cdots + a_{n-1} + a_n$$

As for sequences, k is a dummy variable and the same result would ensue using $\sum_{r=m}^{n} a_r$. The extreme values of the index, m and n, are **not** dummy variables; they affect the final result. They are called the **limits** for the sum.

Example 2.12

$$\sum_{k=1}^{n} k^2 = 1^2 + 2^2 + 3^2 + \cdots + n^2$$

$$\sum_{j=2}^{4} b_j = b_2 + b_3 + b_4$$

$$\sum_{r=1}^{3} a_r b_r = a_1 b_1 + a_2 b_2 + a_3 b_3$$

The first of these sums part of the sequence (2.2). The last represents the *dot product* of two vectors, as we shall see in Chapter 5.   ∎

Like the sequence it sums, a series may never stop, leading to an **infinite series**:

$$\sum_{k=0}^{\infty} a_k = a_0 + a_1 + a_2 + \cdots, \qquad (2.13)$$

which is sometimes abbreviated as $\sum a_k$.

It is not immediately clear that such a sum can have any sensible meaning. The key to answering this is to construct a sequence based on its **partial sums**:

$$S_n = \sum_{k=0}^{n} = a_0 + a_1 + \cdots + a_n.$$

Note that, given this sequence, we can recover the original sum:

$$a_0 = S_0, \qquad a_n = S_n - S_{n-1} \ (n > 0).$$

If the values S_n approach ever nearer a finite number as n increases, the series is **convergent** and this number is the **sum to infinity**. Otherwise it is **divergent**. The strict definition relies on the idea of a *limit*, as used in calculus; this is a different use of the word from the use for the *limits* in the sigma notation. Since we shall, at this time, use only one such sum, we shall not explore this further. That it is a difficult topic is shown in the following.

Example 2.13   The series

$$\sum k^2 = 1^2 + 2^2 + 3^2 + \cdots$$

would seem to be divergent since the terms get ever larger. That is indeed the case. It can be shown that

$$S_n = 1^2 + 2^2 + \cdots + n^2 = \frac{1}{6}n(n+1)(2n+1)$$

and this blows up as n gets larger.

On the other hand, the series

$$\sum_{k=1}^{\infty} \frac{1}{k^2} = \frac{1}{1^2} + \frac{1}{2^2} + \frac{1}{3^3} + \cdots$$

has terms that decrease towards zero. It is convergent and, by some difficult calculations, can be shown to have sum to infinity $\pi^2/6$. Note that, in this case, we wrote out the limits on the sum since $k = 0$ is not allowed as it would lead to a division by zero.

This argument would appear to extend to

$$\sum_{k=1}^{\infty} \frac{1}{k} = \frac{1}{1} + \frac{1}{2} + \frac{1}{3} + \cdots,$$

but this is notoriously divergent. It is called the **harmonic series** and lies on the boundary between convergence and divergence.   ∎

The sigma notation has several advantages: it is neat, using less room than writing out the sum; it provides a formula for the kth term; it avoids a need to guess what is to follow. There are a couple of useful tricks that extend its use.

An **alternating series** is one with alternate '+' and '−' signs between elements. This can be accommodated using $(-1)^k$ or $(-1)^{k+1}$.

Example 2.14

$$\sum_{k=0}^{\infty} (-1)^k a_k = a_0 - a_1 + a_2 - a_3 + \cdots$$

$$\sum_{k=1}^{\infty} (-1)^{k+1} \frac{1}{k} = \frac{1}{1} - \frac{1}{2} + \frac{1}{3} - \frac{1}{4} + \cdots$$

The latter series, although appearing to be similar to the harmonic series, converges with sum to infinity $\ln 2$. ■

We can also select "every other" term by using index $2r$, to obtain the *even* terms and $2r + 1$ to obtain the *odd* terms.

Example 2.15

$$\sum_{r=0}^{\infty} c_{2r} = c_0 + c_2 + c_4 + \cdots$$

$$\sum_{n=0}^{\infty} \frac{(-1)^n x^{2n+1}}{2^{2n+1}} - \frac{x}{2} - \frac{x^3}{2^3} + \frac{x^5}{2^5} - \cdots$$

To expand this last case, substitute $n = 0,\ 1,\ 2,\ \ldots$ into the formula for the nth term:

$$\frac{(-1)^0 x^{0+1}}{2^{0+1}} = \frac{1 \times x}{2}, \qquad \frac{(-1)^1 x^{2+1}}{2^{2+1}} = \frac{(-1) \times x^3}{2^3}, \quad \text{etc.,}$$

then add the results. ■

Ex 2.11

(a) Calculate $\displaystyle\sum_{r=1}^{5} x_r$, where: $\quad x_r = r^2 + (-1)^r$.

(b) Given $a_0 = 2$, $a_1 = -1$, $a_2 = -4$, $a_3 = 5$, $a_4 = 3$; $b_0 = 1$, $b_1 = 3$, $b_2 = 2$, $b_3 = -1$, $b_4 = 2$, calculate:

$$\sum_{k=0}^{4} a_k, \qquad \sum_{i=1}^{3} a_i, \qquad \sum_{k=1}^{2} a_k b_k, \qquad \sum_{j=0}^{4} b_j^2.$$

Ex 2.12

(a) Write out, using $\sum$ notation,

$$S = \frac{x}{1 \times 2} + \frac{x^2}{2 \times 3} + \frac{x^3}{3 \times 4} + \cdots .$$

(b) Write in a shorter form, using $\sum$ notation, $\quad x - 2x^2 + 3x^3 - 4x^4 + \cdots .$

2.6   Arithmetic Series

As for sequences, we shall concentrate on two series: those obtained by adding up terms in an AP or GP. We face the same starting-point uncertainty as for sequences: since it is most usual to talk of the "sum of n terms", this means we seek S_{n-1} rather than S_n. One objective will be to find a version where we do not need to use the counter in this way.

First, then, we seek a formula for the sum of an **arithmetic series**, where the underlying sequence starts at a and has common difference d. Write this sum out twice, once in reverse:

$$S_{n-1} = a \qquad\qquad + (a+d) \qquad + (a+2d) \qquad +\cdots + [a+(n-1)d]$$
$$S_{n-1} = [a+(n-1)d] + [a+(n-2)d] + [a+(n-3)d] + \cdots + a$$

When we add these, each of the corresponding terms is the same, $2a+(n-1)d$, and there are n of them. Dividing by two gives the result we seek.

Frame 2.4   *Sum of n terms of an arithmetic series*

$$S_{n-1} = \frac{n}{2}\left[2a + (n-1)d\right] \qquad\qquad (2.14)$$

$$= n \quad \times \quad \frac{1}{2}[a \quad + \quad \{a+(n-1)d\}] \qquad (2.15)$$

$$= \text{no. of terms} \times \text{average of first and last}$$

The version (2.15) is a simple rearrangement of (2.14) and allows us to calculate sums without knowing the common difference: all we require is the first and last terms and how many there are.

Example 2.16   The sum of the first n natural numbers, 1 to n, is

$$S_{n-1} = n \times \frac{1}{2}(1+n) = \frac{1}{2}n(n+1).$$

■

Example 2.17   To sum the first n **odd** numbers, use $a=1$ and $d=2$:

$$S_{n-1} = 1 + 3 + 5 + \cdots + (2n-1)$$
$$= \frac{n}{2}\left[2 \times 1 + (n-1)2\right] = n^2.$$

■

The formulae even produce sensible answers for a zero difference:

$$\sum_{k=1}^{n} 1 = 1 + 1 + \cdots + 1 = \frac{n}{2}\left[2 + (n-1) \times 0\right] = n.$$

as expected, since we have n copies of 1 to add up.

Example 2.18   An AP has $a_3 = 11$ and $a_7 = -9$. Find $\sum_{k=0}^{9} a_k$.

First, use $a_k = a + kd$:

$$k = 3: \quad a + 3d = 11 \qquad\qquad \text{subtract these to find } d, \text{ then } a:$$
$$k = 7: \quad a + 7d = -9 \qquad\qquad 4d = -20 \quad \Rightarrow \quad d = -5, \ a = 26$$

The series is:

$$26 + 21 + 16 + 11 + 6 + 1 - 4 - 9 - \cdots .$$

We now have the data for (2.14):

$$S_9 = \frac{10}{2} \left[2 \times 26 - 9 \times 5 \right] = 35.$$

Alternatively, the first term is 26, the last is -19 and there are 10 terms to add: $10 \times \frac{1}{2} \left[26 + (-19) \right] = 35.$ ∎

Ex 2.13 Sum all multiples of 3, less than 100.

Ex 2.14 Calculate the following sums:

(a) $1 + 2 + 3 + \cdots + 99$ (b) $1^2 + 2^2 + 3^2 + \cdots + 99^2$

(c) $95 + 85 + \cdots + 15 + 5$ (d) $2 - 1 + 4 - 2 + 6 - 3 + \cdots + 20 - 10$

2.7 Geometric Series

We now sum a **geometric series**, where the underlying GP has first term a and common ratio r. There is a different trick required:

$$S_{n-1} = a + ar + ar^2 + \cdots + ar^{n-1}$$
$$rS_{n-1} = \quad\;\; ar + ar^2 + \cdots + ar^{n-1} + ar^n.$$

Subtract these:

$$S_{n-1} - rS_{n-1} = (1 - r)S_{n-1} = a - ar^n.$$

Divide by $1 - r$ to obtain the result we seek.

Frame 2.5   *Sum of n terms of a geometric series*

$$S_{n-1} = a \frac{1 - r^n}{1 - r} \qquad\qquad (2.16)$$

$$= \frac{1}{1 - r} \left[a \quad - \quad ar^n \right] \qquad\qquad (2.17)$$

a is the first term

ar^n is the first term **not** used (after the end of the series)

Example 2.19 Sum the geometric series

$$1 - \frac{1}{3} + \frac{1}{9} - \frac{1}{27} + \frac{1}{81}.$$

Here the first term is $a = 1$, while the common ratio is $r = -1/3$ (e.g., $-1/27 \div 1/9 = -1/3$). The "next" term in the series is $\frac{1}{81} \times \left(-\frac{1}{3}\right) = -\frac{1}{243}$.

$$S = \frac{1}{1 + 1/3}\left[1 - \left(-\frac{1}{243}\right)\right] = \frac{3}{4}\left[1 + \frac{1}{243}\right]$$
$$= \frac{3}{4}\frac{244}{243} = \frac{61}{81}$$

■

Example 2.20 A GP has $a_2 = 2$ and $a_5 = 432$. Find $\sum_{k=0}^{9} a_k$.

First, use $a_k = ar^k$:

$$k = 2: \quad ar^2 = 2 \qquad \text{divide these to find } r, \text{ then } a:$$
$$k = 5: \quad ar^5 = 432 \qquad r^3 = 216 \quad \Rightarrow \quad r = 6, \ a = 1/18$$

The series is:
$$1/18 + 1/3 + 2 + 12 + 72 + 432 + \cdots.$$

We now have the data for (2.17):

$$S_9 = \frac{1}{1 - 6}\left[\frac{1}{18} - \frac{1}{18} \times 6^{10}\right] = \frac{1}{90}\left(6^{10} - 1\right) = 671\,846\tfrac{7}{18}.$$

■

Example 2.21 Return to compound interest, as in Example 2.11.

A student borrows £1000 at 5% interest at the start of each of four years. Each amount attracts interest, leading to, at the end of successive years, amounts

$$1000 \times 1.05, \qquad 1000 \times 1.05^2, \qquad 1000 \times 1.05^3, \qquad \text{etc.}$$

On graduation, the debt is:

$$1000 \times 1.05^4 + 1000 \times 1.05^3 + 1000 \times 1.05^2 + 1000 \times 1.05$$
$$= \frac{1000}{1 - 1.05}\left[1.05 - 1.05^5\right] = £4525.63$$

In this calculation, the sum was read in reverse, since it was easier to use $r = 1.05$ than $r = 1/1.05$. The common factor of 1000 was taken out to make the structure clearer. ■

Now suppose that the common ratio satisfies $|r| < 1$, i.e., $-1 < r < 1$. Then r^n dies away as n gets larger; in other words it "tends to zero". If we consider the *infinite series* that results, the "next term" at the end is zero, loosely expressed as $ar^\infty = 0$. The series **converges** with a simple expression for its sum.

Frame 2.6   *Sum to infinity for a geometric series*

$$S_\infty = \frac{a}{1-r} \qquad (-1 < r < 1)$$

Example 2.22   Using common ratio $\tfrac{1}{2}$:

$$1 + \frac{1}{2} + \frac{1}{4} + \frac{1}{8} + \cdots = \sum_{k=0}^{\infty} \frac{1}{2^k} = \frac{1}{1 - \tfrac{1}{2}} = 2.$$

∎

Series can involve symbols as well as numbers. The next example shows this and collects together several other ideas, e.g., alternating signs and 'odd' terms only.

Example 2.23   When does the second series in Example 2.15 converge and what is its sum to infinity when it does?

$$\sum_{n=0}^{\infty} \frac{(-1)^n x^{2n+1}}{2^{2n+1}} = \frac{x}{2}\left[1 - \frac{x^2}{2^2} + \frac{x^4}{2^4} - \cdots \right]$$

and the sum in brackets is geometric, with common ratio $-x^2/4$. This converges if

$$-1 < -\frac{x^2}{4} < 1 \quad \Rightarrow \quad \frac{x^2}{4} < 1 \quad \Rightarrow \quad -2 < x < 2.$$

Then the sum is

$$S_\infty = \frac{x}{2} \frac{1}{1 + \frac{x^2}{4}} = \frac{2x}{x^2 + 4}.$$

This has given us a series for the sort of function we shall examine in Chapter 4. This is, in certain contexts, a very useful device.   ∎

Infinite geometric series can be used to discover the fractions generating *repeating decimals*.

Example 2.24   Consider $x = 0.15151515\cdots = \frac{1}{10} + \frac{5}{10^2} + \frac{1}{10^3} + \frac{5}{10^4} + \cdots$.

This expression, derived by using the idea behind decimal notation, can be separated into two geometric series and summed independently. It is easier to rewrite it as follows, summing it as one:

$$x = \frac{15}{100} + \frac{15}{100^2} + \frac{15}{100^3} + \cdots$$

$$= \frac{15}{100} \frac{1}{1 - \frac{1}{100}} = \frac{15}{100 - 1} = \frac{5}{33}.$$

Again, it proved helpful to extract a common factor before summing. The result can easily be verified using $5 \div 33$ on a calculator.   ∎

Ex 2.15

(a) Sum, giving the answer as a fraction: $1 + 0.1 + 0.01 + 0.001 + \cdots$.

(b) Calculate $\frac{1}{2} + \frac{1}{4} + \frac{1}{8} + \cdots + \left(\frac{1}{2}\right)^{99}$.

(c) Calculate $2 + 6 + 18 + 54 + \cdots$; (there are 10 terms in all).

Ex 2.16 For the ball in Exercise 2.4, find the total distance travelled in an upward direction by the time maximum height has been reached after the nth bounce. What is the total distance travelled upwards by the time it has come to rest?

Ex 2.17 Decide which of the following geometric series are convergent and, for such, find the sum to infinity.

(a) $4 + \frac{4}{5} + \frac{4}{25} + \frac{4}{125} + \frac{4}{625} + \cdots$ (b) $1 - \frac{4}{3} + \frac{16}{9} - \frac{64}{27} + \cdots$

(c) $1 + 1.1 + 1.21 + 1.331 + \cdots$ (d) $10 - 9 + 8.1 - 7.29 + \cdots$

2.8 Revision Exercises

Ex 2.18 An **arithmetic progression** has terms $a_4 = 10$ and $a_7 = 22$. Find the values of a_0 and a_{10}.

Calculate the sum: $\displaystyle\sum_{k=0}^{10} a_k$.

Ex 2.19 Find, as an **exact** expression, the sum: $\displaystyle\sum_{k=1}^{10} 0.2^k$.

Ex 2.20 Find the sum to infinity for the **geometric** series:

$$9 - 3 + 1 - \frac{1}{3} + \frac{1}{9} - \cdots .$$

Ex 2.21 A **geometric progression** $\{a_r\}_{r=0}^{\infty}$ with positive elements has $a_2 = 8$ and $a_6 = \frac{1}{2}$. Find a_0 and the common ratio.

Calculate $\displaystyle\sum_{r=0}^{\infty} a_r$ and $\displaystyle\sum_{r=0}^{\infty} a_{2r}$.

3   COMBINATORICS

The topic of **combinatorics** is sometimes called "counting" because its objectives are simply to do that. It seeks to answer questions such as:

- How many possibilities are there?

- In how many ways can objects be arranged?

- How many steps are involved in a process?

We have already seen an example of the last of these: solving the *Towers of Hanoi* problem in Example 2.7 requires $2^n - 1$ steps.

Combinatorics provides information for organisational activities such as *logistics* and *computer programming*. It also helps in the creation of statistical models using *probability*. We shall need it now to deliver a key piece of algebra: the *Binomial Theorem*.

3.1   Permutations

Our first analysis concerns the choice of items from a collection, with a definite order in the result.

Example 3.1   A CD player is set to *Random* mode, whereby it will play all the tracks in a random order, without repeating any. How many different ordered playlists are there for a CD single with three tracks?

Call the tracks A, B and C. We can represent all the possibilities in a *tree diagram*.

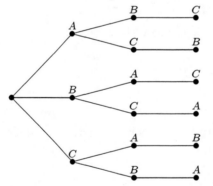

Number of possibilities is six:

ABC, ACB, BAC, BCA, CAB, CBA

We can readily count up, and list the details for, all **six** possibilities. If we wish only to know the total, we can argue there are:

3 choices for the first slot
2 choices for the second slot
1 choice for the third slot

Then we use the key step that these individual counts are *multiplied* to give the final number. The reason for multiplying is clear from the tree diagram: each early decision spawns a number of further ones in each of which it is a part.   ∎

The number $6 = 3 \times 2 \times 1$ has a very special and common form: it is written 3! and is a value from a sequence with general term $n!$, pronounced **n-factorial**:

$$n! = n \times (n-1) \times (n-2) \times \cdots \times 3 \times 2 \times 1. \tag{3.1}$$

Example 3.2 The following are some sample values

$$4! = 4 \times 3 \times 2 \times 1 = 24, \qquad 1! = 1, \qquad 20! \simeq 2.4329 \times 10^{18}.$$

$\blacksquare$

Think about it like this

> This last value shows that $n!$ grows very rapidly. It is typical of a phenomenon known as the *combinatorial explosion*, where the number of possibilities grows so rapidly that we cannot keep track of them. That is why it is so difficult to write a program to play chess: there are too many possible moves to analyse them all.

The factorial satisfies a **recurrence relation**, which follows easily from (3.1):

$$(n+1)! = (n+1)n!, \qquad 0! = 1. \tag{3.2}$$

The value of 0! is a *convention*. There is no argument using 'choices' to support it, but it fits in with the recurrence and allows it to start the sequence: $1! = 1 \times 0! = 1$ holds true.

Example 3.3 Following on from Example 3.2,

$$5! = 5 \times 4! = 5 \times 24 = 120.$$

$\blacksquare$

Returning to the CD situation, we can see that a CD with n tracks will generate $n!$ different play orders. The number of ways of ordering n distinct objects, of any type, is $n!$. This is the number of **permutations** of n objects.

Example 3.4 Now, suppose the CD has 5 tracks, but we have time only to play 3. How many playlists are there? We can try a tree diagram:

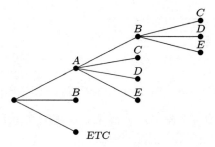

This tree is clearly becoming too dense to complete and it is better to use the logical approach:

5 choices for the first slot

4 choices for the second slot

3 choice for the third slot

This gives a total of $5 \times 4 \times 3 = 60$ possibilities. ∎

We can extend this to obtain the following general formula.

Frame 3.1   *Number of permutations of r items from n*

$$^nP_r = n(n-1)(n-2)\cdots(n-r+1) \qquad\qquad (3.3)$$

Notation

The notation ^nP_r is a standard one and, like $n!$, will be found on many 'scientific' calculators, which may therefore be used to calculate it. Otherwise, the formula (3.3) is recommended. Starting with n, write down r decreasing numbers; this is an easier way of working out when to stop, than trying to deduce the value of $n-r+1$.

There is an alternative formula that is often quoted:

$$n(n-1)\cdots(n-r+1) = \frac{n(n-1)\cdots(n-r+1)(n-r)\cdots3\cdot2\cdot1}{(n-r)\cdots3\cdot2\cdot1}$$

$$= \frac{n!}{(n-r)!}$$

This is best avoided in computational work due to the large size of the component factorials. Note the need for the brackets in $(n-r)!$: the value of $n-r$ must be calculated before the factorial. This also applies to terms such as $(2r)!$, which is different from (and much larger than) $2r! = 2(r!)$.

Example 3.5   How many 4-letter 'words', with distinct letters, can be made using the letters in SWEARING?

$$^8P_4 = \frac{8!}{4!} = 8 \times 7 \times 6 \times 5 = 1680.$$

Note that if repetition of letters is allowed, there are far more: $8 \times 8 \times 8 \times 8 = 4096$. (This is shown using exactly the same logical argument as above, but there is no need to reduce the count at each step.) ∎

Ex 3.1   Evaluate: $5!$, $6!$, $\dfrac{9!}{6!}$, $^7P_3$, $^{15}P_2$.

Ex 3.2   Evaluate the following:

(a) the number of different ways to order the letters in PROBLEMS;

(b) the number of different four-letter 'words' with no repeated letters, which can be formed from the letters in PROBLEMS.

Ex 3.3   How many numbers x, $(1 \leqslant x < 10)$, have distinct digits when quoted to 5 significant figures?

3.2 Combinations

Now suppose that we are not concerned about the *order* in which the items are listed, only the constituents of the chosen subset. Thus, we seek the number of **combinations** or **selections** of r items from n, by which we mean that only the final set of r items is relevant, not the order in which they were chosen.

Example 3.6 Consider the case of listening to three tracks from a CD with five tracks (Example 3.4), where the order is irrelevant.

The 60 possible *ordered* playlists contain the following:

$$ABC, \ ACB, \ BAC, \ BCA, \ CAB, \ CBA,$$

all of which are now to be regarded as the same. There are $6 = 3!$ of them, and there can be no more since that is the number of permutations of A, B, C.

This happens for every different combination of three tracks, so there are only $60/6 = 10$ different *combinations*. ■

Extending this argument to the general case of selecting r items from n, we obtain the second, and much more important, counting measure. We start with ^nP_r and divide by $r!$, the number of times each selection appears therein.

Frame 3.2   *Number of combinations of r items from n*

$$\binom{n}{r} = \frac{n(n-1)(n-2)\cdots(n-r+1)}{r!} = \frac{n!}{r!(n-r)!} \qquad (3.4)$$

Notation

There is an alternative notation, ^nC_r, in line with that for permutations, but this is rarely used in modern texts. It does persist as a label for a key in some calculators.

The number $\binom{n}{r}$ is called a **binomial coefficient** and is pronounced "n choose r", which is a brief statement of its meaning: *the number of ways of, when given n items, choosing r of them.*

As in the case of permutations, the full factorial form is reserved for theoretical work, since we try to avoid using factorials directly, on account of their size. The best way to evaluate these is to use the first version in (3.4):

$$\binom{n}{r} = \frac{n(n-1)(n-2)\cdots(n-r+1)}{r!},$$

the top line of which is constructed by starting with n, then writing down further values, decreasing by one at each stage, until there are r in all; dividing by $r!$ completes the calculation.

Example 3.7 A CD shop has 1000 CD titles in stock. How many different purchases of three distinct CDs can be made?

$$\binom{1000}{3} = \frac{1000 \times 999 \times 998}{3 \times 2 \times 1} = 166,167,000.$$

■

The binomial coefficients are involved in several topics in mathematics. They have many properties, although we shall look at only a few. The simplest is the *symmetry* property:

$$\binom{n}{n-r} = \binom{n}{r}, \tag{3.5}$$

which is very useful in calculations.

Think about it like this

> This can be proved directly from (3.4), or by using a *combinatorial* argument: we can select r items either directly, in $\binom{n}{r}$ ways, or by selecting $n-r$ items, in $\binom{n}{n-r}$ ways and throwing them away. Such arguments can be very powerful, giving results much more quickly than using symbolic algebra.

The most common use of (3.5) is when r is large, since we then have a large number of factors on the top and a large factorial on the bottom, while $n - r$ is small and gives few factors.

Example 3.8 $\binom{11}{8}$ would have 8 factors on the top and 8! on the bottom, but:

$$\binom{11}{8} = \binom{11}{3} = \frac{11 \times 10 \times 9}{3 \times 2 \times 1} = 165.$$

■

Note how, in the last two examples, the factorial on the bottom was expanded. This allows cancellations to be made before the fraction is evaluated.

Care is needed to avoid confusing **permutations** with **combinations**, since these terms are used imprecisely in everyday speech:

- A *combination lock* would be better called a *permutation* lock, since the order of the digits is important: a lock with code 4321 will not be opened by 3421. But even that is not accurate since numbers can be repeated, not just jumbled; 4221 is a valid code.

- *Permutations* in football pools are really *combinations*.

  Example 3.9 Someone declaring 11 potential "score draws", so that a win occurs should any 8 of the 11 matches be a score draw, will refer to "perm any 8 from 11", although the true number of possibilities (and hence the number of stakes that must be paid for) is $\binom{11}{8} = 165$, since the order in which the matches are chosen is irrelevant. This binomial coefficient was evaluated in Example 3.8; further values, where more matches are chosen, are $\binom{12}{8} = 495$ and $\binom{13}{8} = 1287$, so the cost rises quickly: the *combinatorial explosion* once again. ■

There are four simple values that should be known without the need to use the formulae:

$$\binom{n}{0} = \frac{n!}{0!\,n!} = 1, \qquad \binom{n}{1} = \frac{n!}{1!(n-1)!} = n,$$

using the recurrence (3.2), with $n+1$ replaced by n. These then gives, using (3.5), $\binom{n}{n} = 1$ and $\binom{n}{n-1} = n$.

One of their uses is to start (or end) one or other of the various *recurrences* satisfied by $\binom{n}{r}$. The following is typical:

$$\binom{n}{r} = \frac{n!}{r!(n-r)!} = \frac{n(n-1)!}{r(r-1)!(n-r)!}$$
$$= \frac{n}{r}\binom{n-1}{r-1}. \tag{3.6}$$

Using this enables evaluation of binomial coefficients without any need to calculate factorials.

Example 3.10 Calculate $\binom{1000}{997}$. First, convert to $\binom{1000}{1000-997}$ and continue, using (3.6):

$$\binom{1000}{3} = \frac{1000}{3}\binom{999}{2} = \frac{1000}{3}\frac{999}{2}\binom{998}{1}$$
$$= \frac{1000}{3}\frac{999}{2} \times 998 = 166,167,000$$

as before. We terminated this recursion on reaching $\binom{998}{1}$, using $\binom{n}{1} = n$, although we could have continued to reach $\frac{998}{1}\binom{997}{0}$ and used $\binom{n}{0} = 1$. ∎

Example 3.11 Calculate the number of different selections for the UK National Lottery.

We choose 6 *different* numbers out of 49, and the order is irrelevant, which gives:

$$\binom{49}{6} = \frac{49}{6}\binom{48}{5} = \frac{49}{6}\frac{48}{5}\binom{47}{4} = \cdots$$
$$= \frac{49}{6}\frac{48}{5}\frac{47}{4}\frac{46}{3}\frac{45}{2}\frac{44}{1} = 13,983,816,$$

a number usually quoted as 14 million. ∎

We can now reveal the true formula for the circle division problem in Example 2.4. For number of points n, with $n \geq 4$:

$$\text{number of parts} = 1 + \binom{n}{2} + \binom{n}{4} \neq 2^{n+1},$$

for example $n = 5$ gives $1 + 10 + 5 = 16$, but $n = 6$ gives $1 + 15 + 15 = 31$, as we noted.

The 'counting' we have pursued here is simple and structured: selections of r items from a set of n, with and without the order being significant. It is possible to combine these in more complex contexts, or even to construct different counting models. In these, we can often fall back on the logical "How many ways can we choose ...?" analysis.

Example 3.12 A menu has **three** starters, **four** main courses and **two** desserts. How many different three-course meals are possible?

Multiply the possibilities for each course: $3 \times 4 \times 2 = 24$. ∎

Ex 3.4 Evaluate $\binom{3}{2}$, $\binom{6}{2}$, $\binom{7}{3}$, $\binom{5}{2}$, $\binom{8}{3}$, $\binom{20}{2}$, $\binom{20}{17}$.

Ex 3.5 In how many ways can one order the **seven** colours of the rainbow?

In how many ways can one select *ordered* triplets of them?

In how many ways can one select three different colours from the seven?

Ex 3.6 Find the number of different **sets** of four letters – with no repeats and where the order is irrelevant – that can be chosen from those in PROBLEMS.

Ex 3.7 We are given n balls, numbered 1 to n and wish to select 3. This can be done in $\binom{n}{3}$ ways.

Suppose we count this differently. How many selections have 1 as the smallest numbered ball? How many have 2 as the smallest numbered ball? Pursue this argument to deduce that

$$\binom{n}{3} = \binom{n-1}{2} + \binom{n-2}{2} + \cdots + \binom{3}{2} + \binom{2}{2}.$$

Verify this when $n = 6$.

Ex 3.8 Show that, for $1 \leqslant r \leqslant n$,

$$\binom{n}{r} = \frac{n-r+1}{r}\binom{n}{r-1}.$$

Given $\binom{n}{0} = 1$, use this formula to evaluate $\binom{5}{3}$ and $\binom{9}{6}$.

3.3   Pascal's Triangle

The binomial coefficients satisfy a further, more complicated but still useful, recurrence:

$$\binom{n+1}{r} = \binom{n}{r} + \binom{n}{r-1}. \tag{3.7}$$

This can be proved using the factorial definition in (3.4), but there is a simpler approach using the counting technique. This is an opportune time to introduce the notation # [hash] for "number".

$$\binom{n+1}{r} = \# \text{ of ways of selecting } r \text{ items from } n+1.$$

Now label one of these items as 'special', S say. The following two enumerations cover all possibilities:

$$\binom{n}{r-1} = \# \text{ of ways of selecting } S \text{ and } (r-1) \text{ other items,}$$

$$\binom{n}{r} = \# \text{ of ways of selecting } r \text{ non-special items.}$$

Adding these should give the same count as the direct calculation, proving (3.7).

Example 3.13 $\quad \binom{5}{2} = \dfrac{5 \times 4}{2} = 10$, while

$$\binom{4}{2} + \binom{4}{1} = \frac{4 \times 3}{2} + 4 = 6 + 4 = 10.$$

∎

This recurrence is the basis for the array of numbers known as **Pascal's triangle**:

```
n = 0                    1
n = 1                 1     1
n = 2              1     2     1
n = 3           1     3     3     1
n = 4        1     4     6     4     1
n = 5     1     5    10    10     5     1
  etc.
```

This array is bounded by the lines containing 1s, while each internal number is the sum of the two immediately above and to each side of it. Each row provides, in order, the full set of binomial coefficients $\binom{n}{r}$ for the corresponding value of n.

Example 3.14 The row labelled "$n = 3$" contains 1, 3, 3, 1, which are the four binomial coefficients $\binom{3}{r}$.

The third number (10) in the row "$n = 5$" is the sum of the 4 and 6 above: $\binom{5}{2} = \binom{4}{1} + \binom{4}{2}$ as we saw in Example 3.13. ∎

In general, the nth row (starting counting at $n = 0$) contains

$$\binom{n}{0} \quad \binom{n}{1} \quad \cdots \quad \binom{n}{n-1} \quad \binom{n}{n},$$

and the symmetry in the table is what we would expect, since $\binom{n}{r} = \binom{n}{n-r}$.

Useful guidance about Pascal's triangle is that it should be used when we require **all** values of $\binom{n}{r}$ for a small n, as in the next section. Otherwise, use (3.4) or the recurrence (3.6).

Ex 3.9 Construct the 6th row of Pascal's Triangle.

3.4 Binomial Theorem

Elementary algebra produces the following results:

$$(a+b)^0 = 1$$
$$(a+b)^1 = a+b$$
$$(a+b)^2 = a^2 + 2ab + b^2$$
$$(a+b)^3 = a^3 + 3a^2b + 3ab^2 + b^3$$

The coefficients in these formulae mimic precisely the numbers in Pascal's triangle and lead us to conjecture that the following result, known as the **Binomial Theorem**, is true:

Frame 3.3   *The Binomial Theorem*

$$(a+b)^n = a^n + \binom{n}{1}a^{n-1}b + \binom{n}{2}a^{n-2}b^2 + \cdots + \binom{n}{r}a^{n-r}b^r + \cdots + b^n$$

$$(3.8)$$

To complete the pattern the first and last terms should have coefficients $\binom{n}{0}$ and $\binom{n}{n}$, but these are often omitted since they are both 1.

The key to using the Binomial Theorem is not to memorise the formula, but to understand its **structure**.

- Start with the first term, to the full power: a^n.

- Move right, losing one power in a, gaining one in b at each step:

$$a^n \quad \to \quad a^{n-1}b \quad \to \quad a^{n-2}b^2 \quad \to \quad \text{etc.},$$

noting that the indexes always add to n, e.g., $(n-2)+2 = n$.

- Insert the binomial coefficient $\binom{n}{r}$ in the term involving b^r.

Think about it like this

It is now clear why $\binom{n}{r}$ has its name, but why should it be involved here? Consider

$$(a+b)^n = (a+b)(a+b)\cdots(a+b)(a+b).$$

On removing the brackets on the right, each term is a product of n terms, chosen as one of the two from each bracket. Every possibility must be used. Example 1.9 illustrates this for $(a+b)(c+d)$.

To obtain $a^{n-r}b^r$, we must choose $(n-r)$ copies of a and r copies of b. There are n brackets from which to choose the r copies of b, which can therefore be done in $\binom{n}{r}$ different ways; the brackets for the copies of a are then fixed. Hence the result contains $\binom{n}{r}$ instances of $a^{n-r}b^r$.

All expansions of $(X \pm Y)^n$, for a natural number n, can be done using (3.8), no matter how complicated X and Y are. We use the **substitutions** $a = X$ and $b = \pm Y$.

Example 3.15 $(a - b)^n$: keep a as it is and change every b to $-b$.

$$a^n + \binom{n}{1}a^{n-1}(-b) + \binom{n}{2}a^{n-2}(-b)^2 + \cdots + (-b)^n$$
$$= a^n - \binom{n}{1}a^{n-1}b + \binom{n}{2}a^{n-2}b^2 - \cdots + (-1)^n b^n.$$

∎

Hence, having a minus sign between the terms generates an **alternating sum**. This is generally true: every binomial expansion (3.8) has either all plus signs or alternating plus/minus signs.

Example 3.16 $(2x + 3y)^4$: let $a = 2x$, $b = 3y$, $n = 4$.

$$(2x)^4 + \binom{4}{1}(2x)^3(3y) + \binom{4}{2}(2x)^2(3y)^2 + \binom{4}{3}(2x)(3y)^3 + (3y)^4$$
$$= 16x^4 + 4 \times 8 \times 3x^3 y + 6 \times 4 \times 9x^2 y^2 + 4 \times 2 \times 27xy^3 + 81y^4$$
$$= 16x^4 + 96x^3 y + 216x^2 y^2 + 216xy^3 + 81y^4,$$

on reading the binomial coefficients from Pascal's triangle. ∎

Note the careful way in which the substituted terms have been placed in brackets initially, as recommended in §1.9.3. Writing $2x^4$ is wrong, even if one thinks that it represents the fourth power of $2x$; that can soon be forgotten later in the calculation.

Example 3.17 $(2p - q)^5$: let $a = 2p$, $b = -q$, $n = 5$.

$$(2p)^5 + 5(2p)^4(-q) + 10(2p)^3(-q)^2 + 10(2p)^2(-q)^3 + 5(2p)(-q)^4 + (-q)^5$$
$$= 32p^5 - 80p^4 q + 80p^3 q^2 - 40p^2 q^3 + 10pq^4 - q^5,$$

on reading the binomial coefficients $\binom{5}{r} = 1, 5, 10, 10, 5, 1$ from Pascal's triangle. ∎

A common use of the Binomial Theorem is when one of a and b is small and the expansion can be truncated after a few terms, giving an approximate, but acceptably accurate, answer.

Example 3.18 Find 0.999^{10} correct to 6 dp.

Use $a = 1$ and $b = -0.001$, with $n = 10$. This time we do not need to build Pascal's triangle as far as $n = 10$, since we need only a few binomial coefficients; these can be calculated directly from (3.4).

$$(1 - 0.001)^{10} = 1 - \binom{10}{1}(0.001) + \binom{10}{2}(0.001)^2 - \binom{10}{3}(0.001)^3 + \cdots$$
$$= 1 - 10 \times 0.001 + 45 \times 0.000\,001 - 120 \times 0.000\,000\,001 + \cdots$$
$$\simeq 1 - 0.01 + 0.000\,045 = 0.990\,045,$$

since the fourth term, and presumably all later terms, are too small to contribute to 6 dp accuracy. ∎

The Binomial Theorem can also be written using 'sigma' notation, which is particularly useful for calculations where we wish a formula for the *general* term.

Frame 3.4   *Binomial Theorem using sigma notation*

$$(a+b)^n = \sum_{k=0}^{n} \binom{n}{k} a^{n-k} b^k \qquad (3.9)$$

Example 3.19   Find the term with no x in $\left(2x^2 - \dfrac{1}{x}\right)^9$.

Firstly, why should there be such a term? We start with $(2x^2)^9 = 2^9 x^{18}$ and end with $-x^{-9}$. At each step we lose a factor of $2x^2$ and gain one of $-1/x$, which is a net loss of *three* factors of x. The powers are thus 18, 15, 12, ... and so should pass through zero.

Use the general term from (3.9):

$$\binom{9}{k}(2x^2)^{9-k}\left(-\frac{1}{x}\right)^k = (-1)^k \binom{9}{k} 2^{9-k} x^{18-2k} x^{-k}$$
$$= (-1)^k \binom{9}{k} 2^{9-k} x^{18-3k},$$

on carefully removing the brackets and using the index laws to calculate and bring together the various powers of x.

We wish a term with no x, i.e., one in x^0, which forces $18 - 3k = 0$. Hence $k = 6$. (If we obtain a fraction at this stage, that tells us there is no such term and the question is inappropriate.)

The final answer is thus

$$(-1)^6 \binom{9}{6} 2^3 x^0 = \binom{9}{3} 2^3 = \frac{9 \times 8 \times 7}{6} \times 8 = 672.$$

■

The expansion used in Example 3.18 started in fairly simple form, since one of the terms was 1. That leads to a special case of the Binomial Theorem, with $a = 1$ and $b = x$. Using x indicates that the result is an **identity**. (In fact, the Binomial Theorem is always an identity, which we take advantage of by using substitution; using x just makes it more obvious.)

$$(1+x)^n \equiv \sum_{k=1}^{n} \binom{n}{k} x^k \qquad (3.10)$$

$$\equiv 1 + \binom{n}{1}x + \binom{n}{2}x^2 + \cdots + \binom{n}{k}x^k + \cdots + x^n \qquad (3.11)$$

Example 3.20 Let $x = 1$ and $x = -1$ in the **identity** (3.10):

$$2^n = \sum_{k=0}^{n} \binom{n}{k}, \qquad 0 = \sum_{k=0}^{n} (-1)^k \binom{n}{k},$$

which give values for adding rows of Pascal's triangle directly and with alternating signs.

For example,

$$n = 4: \quad 1 + 4 + 6 + 4 + 1 = 16 = 2^4$$
$$1 - 4 + 6 - 4 + 1 = 0$$
$$n = 5: \quad 1 + 5 + 10 + 10 + 5 + 1 = 32 = 2^5$$
$$1 - 5 + 10 - 10 + 5 - 1 = 0$$

The second result is trivially true for odd n, by symmetry, but that is not the case for even n, where the result is more surprising. ∎

Ex 3.10 Expand $(x + 2)^6$ using the Binomial Theorem.

Ex 3.11 Use the general binomial theorem to expand the following:

(a) $(x + \frac{1}{2})^3$, (b) $(2x + 3)^5$, (c) $(x - \frac{1}{2})^5$, (d) $(3 - 2x)^6$, (e) $(3x + 2y)^4$.

Ex 3.12 Without using a calculator, evaluate $(2.001)^4$ correct to 3 decimal places.

Ex 3.13 Show that

$$(1 + \epsilon)^n \simeq 1 + n\epsilon + \frac{1}{2}n(n-1)\epsilon^2$$

for small ϵ.

For each of $n = 5$, 10, 15, find the largest value of ϵ such that $(1+\epsilon)^n = 1+n\epsilon$ correct to 4 decimal places. (Assume that the resultant error is dominated by the next term, which must therefore be less than $\frac{1}{2}10^{-4}$.)

Ex 3.14

(a) Using factorials, write down an expression for the coefficient of x^3 in the expansion of $(1 + x)^{17}$. Evaluate the coefficient. Which other term in the expansion has the same coefficient?

(b) Find the term in x^2 in the expansion of $\left(x + \dfrac{2}{x^2}\right)^8$.

3.5   Revision Exercises

Ex 3.15 There are 12 different notes in an octave on a piano. How many distinct tunes, consisting of **four** different notes, could be composed within this octave? (Ignore note durations, rhythms and other variations.)

Ex 3.16

 (a) How many arrangements can be made using all the letters of **COMPUTER**, once only?

 (b) Calculate, **showing detailed working**, the values of the binomial coefficients:
$$\binom{9}{2}, \quad \binom{7}{4}, \quad \binom{11}{7}.$$

Ex 3.17 Calculate, **showing detailed working**, the values of the binomial coefficients:
$$\binom{6}{3}, \quad \binom{10}{8}, \quad \binom{15}{4}.$$

Ex 3.18 Use the **binomial theorem** to expand: $(x^2 - 2)^4$.

Ex 3.19 Use the **binomial theorem** to expand: $(2 - y)^5$.

Ex 3.20 Use the **binomial theorem** to expand: $(2x + 1)^6$.

4 POLYNOMIALS

A **polynomial** is a function of the following form.

Frame 4.1   *Standard form for a polynomial*

$$f(x) = a_0 + a_1 x + a_2 x^2 + \cdots + a_n x^n = \sum_{k=0}^{n} a_k x^k \qquad (4.1)$$

If $a_n \neq 0$ the **degree** of the polynomial is n. The factors a_k are the **coefficients** of the polynomial.

Polynomials are easy to evaluate and manipulate, e.g., using calculus, and have strong properties. This makes them popular for providing approximations to other, more complicated, functions.

Example 4.1 $\sin x \simeq x - \frac{1}{6} x^3$ for small x, measured in *radians*. ∎

4.1 Linear Polynomials

We start with the case $n = 1$, which delivers a **linear polynomial**. Its formula $f(x) = a_0 + a_1 x$ has a straight line graph.

This is often written

$$f(x) = mx + c,$$

where:

m is the **gradient** of the line,

c is the **intercept** on the y-axis.

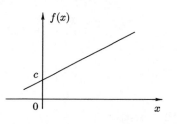

This graph is fixed by knowing the gradient m and one point on the line.

Frame 4.2   *Equation of straight line, gradient m, through (x_1,y_1)*

$$y - y_1 = m(x - x_1) \quad \Rightarrow \quad y = y_1 + m(x - x_1) \qquad (4.2)$$

Given two points on the line, (x_1, y_1) and (x_2, y_2), we can calculate

$$m = \frac{y_2 - y_1}{x_2 - x_1}$$

and hence

$$y = y_1 + \frac{y_2 - y_1}{x_2 - x_1}(x - x_1). \qquad (4.3)$$

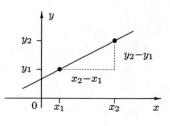

There are many applications of linear functions, principally as rough but convenient approximations.

Example 4.2 In thermodynamics, the **molar heat capacity** of a gas, C_p, varies with temperature T. Certain calculations require a formula for this relationship. Suppose that, for ammonia, $C_p = 35.5$ at $T = 300$ and $C_p = 38.7$ at $T = 400$, in appropriate units; T is in °K.

Then, from (4.3),

$$C_p \simeq 35.5 + \frac{38.7 - 35.5}{400 - 300}\,(T - 300) = 25.9 + 0.032T,$$

a reasonable approximation for T in $[\,250, 450\,]$. ∎

Most **mathematical tables** are designed to allow **linear interpolation**. This is a technique that effectively finds a linear function agreeing with two adjacent entries, then uses that formula to fill in values between them. The table designer will usually try to ensure the resulting error is no worse than that involved in rounding the published entries.

A small rearrangement in (4.3) gives

x	$f(x)$
x_1	y_1
x_2	y_2
x_3	y_3
⋮	⋮

$$y = y_1 + \frac{x - x_1}{x_2 - x_1}\,(y_2 - y_1).$$

This can be interpreted as follows:

$x_2 - x_1 =$ difference between x values,

$y_2 - y_1 =$ difference between y values,

$\dfrac{x - x_1}{x_2 - x_1} =$ proportion of $[\,x_1, x_2\,]$ used.

$x \rightarrow$ $\leftarrow y$

The easiest way to implement linear interpolation is to calculate this proportion, then add the same proportion of the width of $[\,y_1, y_2\,]$ to y_1.

Example 4.3 Use the following excerpt from a table of $f(x) = \tan x$ to estimate $\tan 0.327$.

The proportion required is

$$\frac{0.327 - 0.32}{0.33 - 0.32} = 0.7,$$

x	$\tan x$
0.32	0.3314
0.33	0.3425

which could be seen without explicit calculation, by thinking of where 0.327 would lie in the table.

Now take 0.7 of $(0.3425 - 0.3314)$ and add it to first value of $\tan x$:

$$0.3314 + 0.7(0.3425 - 0.3314) = 0.3392,$$

which is correct to 4 dp.

The simplest way to look at this is: $x = 0.327$ is $^7/_{10}$ of the way between 0.32 and 0.33, so choose y to be $^7/_{10}$ of the way between 0.3314 and 0.3425. ∎

This can be used in reverse – **inverse interpolation** – to estimate x values delivering specific $f(x)$ values. All that needs to be done is to swap the columns round or, more realistically, to *think* of them in the opposite order. The results are usually less reliable since such use is not likely to have been anticipated in the design.

Example 4.4   Use the following excerpt from a table of $f(x) = \tan x$ to estimate that x for which $\tan x = 0.5$.

x	$\tan x$
0.46	0.4954
0.47	0.5080

The proportion required is
$$\frac{0.5 - 0.4954}{0.5080 - 0.4954}.$$

We seek the corresponding proportion of $[\,0.46, 0.47\,]$, with a width of 0.01. Adding that proportion to the first x value gives:

$$0.46 + \frac{0.5 - 0.4954}{0.5080 - 0.4954}\, 0.01 = 0.4637.$$

The correct answer, to 4 dp, is 0.4636, but both numbers round to 0.46365 to 5 dp, so they are in close agreement.   ∎

Ex 4.1 Find a **linear function** $f(x)$, such that $f(-1) = 7$, $f(1) = 3$.

Ex 4.2 Use *linear interpolation* to estimate $f(5.43)$ from the data:
$f(5.40) = 1.6864$, $f(5.45) = 1.6956$.

Ex 4.3 The following is an except from a table of e^x:

x	0.5	0.52	0.54
e^x	1.649	1.682	1.716

Use linear interpolation to estimate $e^{0.508}$ and the x such that $e^x = 1.7$.

4.2 Quadratic Polynomials

The next case to consider is $n = 2$, where it is again normal to simplify the notation, writing the highest power first:

$$f(x) = ax^2 + bx + c \qquad (a \neq 0). \tag{4.4}$$

This **quadratic** is also used for 'filling in values'. Quadratics underpin many computer programs for finding maxima and minima; they approximate a function near its turning point by a quadratic, then find its turning point instead. We shall see in the next section that this is very easy to do.

Quadratics can do this because, unlike the linear functions in the previous section, their graphs are *curves*; they are **parabolas**. The graphs on the right show $y = ax^2$.

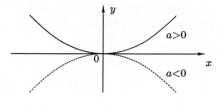

To determine a general parabola, we need *three* points: to fix the three values a, b and c.

Example 4.5 Fit a quadratic to the data:

x	1	2	3
$f(x)$	4	7	2

The simplest approach is to set, in turn, $x = 1$, 2, 3 in (4.4). This gives a set of **simultaneous equations**:

$$a + b + c = 4$$
$$a + 2b + 4c = 7 \qquad a = -4, \ b = 15, \ c = -7,$$
$$a + 3b + 9c = 2 \qquad \text{after much work,}$$

and so $f(x) = -4x^2 + 15x - 7$.

It is much easier to "shift the origin" to the middle point of the x values ($x = 2$), i.e., we try to fit

$$f(x) = A(x - 2)^2 + B(x - 2) + C$$

to the data. We now obtain:

$$A - B + C = 4 \qquad \text{Hence } C = 7 \text{ immediately; then}$$
$$C = 7 \qquad A = -4, \ B = -1,$$
$$A + B + C = 2 \qquad \text{after much less work.}$$

The result is

$$\begin{aligned} f(x) &= -4(x - 2)^2 - (x - 2) + 7 \\ &= -4x^2 + 16x - 16 - x + 2 + 7 \\ &= -4x^2 + 15x - 7, \end{aligned}$$

as before. ∎

Ex 4.4 Fit the quadratic $y = Ax^2 + Bx + C$ to the data: $(-1, 2)$, $(0, -1)$, $(1, 0)$.

Ex 4.5 Find a quadratic $Q(x)$, such that: $Q(1) = 9$, $Q(3) = 7$, $Q(5) = -3$.
(You may find it easier to start with $Q(x) = A(x - 3)^2 + B(x - 3) + C$.)

4.3 Completing the Square

The simple parabola $f(x) = ax^2 + c$ is easy to deal with: we can find its **roots** as $x = \pm\sqrt{-c/a}$ (if a and c have opposite signs); also, its **minimum** (if $a > 0$) or **maximum** (if $a < 0$) are at $x = 0$.

These key values are much less clear when we have a **middle term** bx. But there is a piece of basic algebra that overcomes this, by rewriting the quadratic in a new form:

$$f(x) = ax^2 + bx + c = \alpha(x + \beta)^2 + \gamma \qquad (4.5)$$

for some α, β and γ [gamma].

This manoeuvre, called **completing the square**, is tantamount to "moving the origin" to $x = -\beta$ and delivers several advantages:

- easier to graph $f(x)$;

- easy to find maxima/minima/roots;

- very useful in calculus, for integration.

In the following method it is the *procedure* that is important, not the general formulae obtained.

Step 1 Factor out a:

$$f(x) = a\left[x^2 + \frac{b}{a}x + \frac{c}{a}\right].$$

Step 2 Compare what is inside the brackets with $(x+p)^2 = x^2 + 2px + p^2$: $p = \frac{b}{2a}$. Add and subtract $p^2 = \frac{b^2}{4a^2}$ and rewrite:

$$f(x) = a\left[\left(x + \frac{b}{2a}\right)^2 - \frac{b^2}{4a^2} + \frac{c}{a}\right].$$

Step 3 Remove brackets (if $a \neq 1$) and tidy up:

$$f(x) = a\left(x + \frac{b}{2a}\right)^2 - \frac{b^2}{4a} + c.$$

The key part is at the heart of Step 2, **halving the coefficient of** x. Quadratics with **leading coefficient** $a = 1$ do not need Steps 1 and 3, as the first case in the following example shows.

Example 4.6

(a) The coefficient of x in $x^2 + 2x - 3$ is 2, halved to 1:

$$x^2 + 2x - 3 = (x+1)^2 - 1 - 3 = (x+1)^2 - 4.$$

(b) Now consider a leading coefficient 2:

$$2x^2 - 3x - 5 = 2\left[x^2 - \frac{3}{2}x - \frac{5}{2}\right]$$
$$= 2\left[\left(x - \frac{3}{4}\right)^2 - \frac{9}{16} - \frac{5}{2}\right]$$
$$= 2\left(x - \frac{3}{4}\right)^2 - \frac{49}{8}$$

(c) A quadratic with first term $-x^2$ can be handled directly, but it is safer to treat is as having leading coefficient -1 and proceed as in (b):

$$-x^2 + 4x - 5 = -\left[x^2 - 4x + 5\right]$$
$$= -\left[(x-2)^2 - 4 + 5\right]$$
$$= -(x-2)^2 - 1$$

∎

4.4   Properties of Quadratics

It is now straightforward, using the *completed square* form, to find the roots (if any), and maxima/minima for quadratics, *without the use of calculus*. We start with the form in (4.5):

$$f(x) = \alpha(x + \beta)^2 + \gamma.$$

Now, being a square, $(x + \beta)^2 \geqslant 0$ for **every** value of x. Also, $(x + \beta)^2 = 0$ if (and only if) $x = -\beta$. There are two cases to consider:

$\boxed{\alpha > 0}$ maintains $\alpha(x + \beta)^2 \geqslant 0$. Hence

$\quad f(x) \geqslant \gamma \quad$ (for all x),

$\qquad$ showing a **minimum** value and

$\quad f(x) = 0 \quad$ if $x = -\beta$,

$\qquad$ gives its location.

$\boxed{\alpha < 0}$ forces $\alpha(x + \beta)^2 \leqslant 0$. Hence

$\quad f(x) \leqslant \gamma \quad$ (for all x),

$\qquad$ showing a **maximum** value and

$\quad f(x) = 0 \quad$ if $x = -\beta$,

$\qquad$ gives its location.

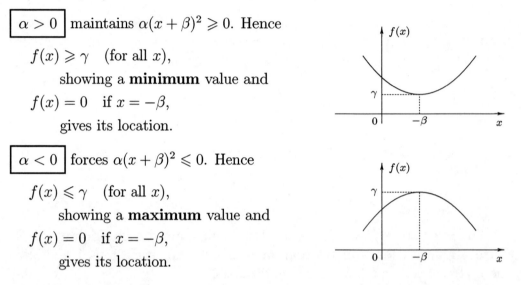

The other key feature of quadratics is the position of their **roots**, if any, i.e., the values of x such that $f(x) = 0$. Using the completed square form:

$$\alpha(x + \beta)^2 = -\gamma$$
$$\Rightarrow \quad (x + \beta)^2 = -\frac{\gamma}{\alpha}$$
$$\Rightarrow \quad x + \beta = \pm\sqrt{-\frac{\gamma}{\alpha}}$$
$$\Rightarrow \quad x = -\beta \pm \sqrt{-\frac{\gamma}{\alpha}},$$

provided that $-\gamma/\alpha \geqslant 0$, to ensure the square root exists.

Although it is straightforward to derive these roots from the completed square form, which is recommended if the square has already been completed, there is a well-known formula, in terms of the original a, b and c. First, consider the condition for existence:

$$-\frac{\gamma}{\alpha} = \frac{b^2}{4ac} - \frac{c}{a} = \frac{b^2 - 4ac}{4a^2},$$

so the condition become $b^2 - 4ac \geqslant 0$, since $a^2 > 0$ always.

This value $b^2 - 4ac$, often written Δ [capital delta], is the **discriminant** for the quadratic. It 'discriminates' between three distinct cases, as set out

in the following 'Frame', which also contains the well-known formula for the
roots of a quadratic.

Frame 4.3   *Roots of a Quadratic*

$\Delta > 0$ *two roots* $x_1, x_2 = \dfrac{-b \pm \sqrt{b^2 - 4ac}}{2a}$ (4.6)

$\Delta = 0$ *one (double) root* $x_1, x_2 = -\dfrac{b}{2a}$ (4.7)

$\Delta < 0$ *no roots*   (4.8)

In the last case, the quadratic is called **irreducible**: it cannot be 're-
duced' by factorisation. In the other cases we can write $f(x)$ in **linear**
factors:

$$f(x) = a\,(x - x_1)\,(x - x_2).\qquad(4.9)$$

The right-hand side shows that $f(x_1) = f(x_2) = 0$.

The three cases can be illustrated graphically:

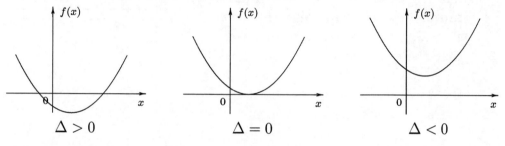

$\Delta > 0$ $\Delta = 0$ $\Delta < 0$

Example 4.7 The first three of the four cases analysed here are those
where the square was completed in Example 4.6, results we now use.

(a) $x^2 + 2x - 3$ has discriminant $\Delta = 2^2 - 4 \times 1 \times (-3) = 16 > 0$.

The roots are:

$$x = \frac{-2 \pm \sqrt{16}}{2} = 1,\ -3$$

giving the factorisation

$$(x - 1)(x + 3).$$

The completed square form found before, $(x+1)^2 - 4$, shows a **minimum**
($a = 1 > 0$) value of -4 at $x = -1$.
Also, we can use this for the roots:

$$(x + 1)^2 = 4 \quad \Rightarrow \quad x + 1 = \pm 2,$$

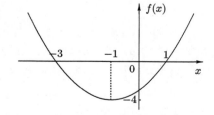

leading to the same values as above.

(b) $2x^2 - 3x - 5$ has discriminant $\Delta = (-3)^2 - 4 \times 2 \times (-5) = 49 > 0$.

The roots are:

$$x = \frac{-3 \pm \sqrt{49}}{4} = \frac{5}{2}, \ -1$$

giving the factorisation

$$2\left(x - \tfrac{5}{2}\right)(x + 3) = (2x - 5)(x + 1).$$

The completed square form found be-
fore, $2(x - \tfrac{3}{4})^2 - \tfrac{49}{8}$, shows a **minimum** ($a = 2 > 0$) value of $-\tfrac{49}{8}$ at
$x = \tfrac{3}{4}$. Also, we can use this for
the roots, as in the previous case, although the arithmetic is not quite as
straightforward.

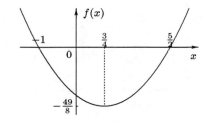

(c) $-x^2 + 4x - 5$ has discriminant $\Delta = 4^2 - 4 \times (-1) \times (-5) = -4 < 0$.

There are therefore no roots: the quadratic is *irreducible*.

The completed square form found before, $-(x - 2)^2 - 1$, shows a **maximum** ($a = -1 < 0$) value of -1 at
$x = 2$. Also, we can see from this
that there are no roots, since both
$-(x - 2)^2$ and -1 are negative, so
the quadratic must always be negative and cannot cross the x-axis.

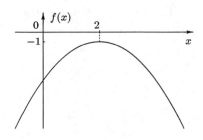

(d) $x^2 - 6x + 9$ has discriminant $\Delta = (-6)^2 - 4 \times 1 \times 9 = 0$.

There is a double root at:

$$x = \frac{6}{2} = 3$$

giving the factorisation

$$(x - 3)(x - 3) = (x - 3)^2.$$

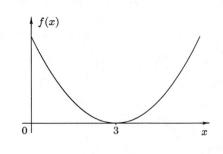

∎

In the cases where there are roots, the maximum or minimum occurs
precisely halfway between the roots. This can be seen from (4.6), since $-\frac{b}{2a}$
is the value of $-\beta$, the point at which the maximum or minimum occurs.

Ex 4.6 Complete the square for the quadratic $x^2 - 2x - 15$.

Hence determine its roots, its maximum or minimum value and sketch its
graph.

Ex 4.7 For each of the following quadratics, *complete the square*. **Hence** find its roots (if any), find its maximum or minimum value (and where it occurs), and draw its graph.

(a) $x^2 + 4x + 5$ (b) $6 - x - 2x^2$ (c) $9x^2 - 12x + 4$ (d) $-3 + 3x - x^2$

Ex 4.8 Sketch $f(x) = x^2 - ax + 1$ for $a = -4$, $a = 0$ and $a = 4$.

For which values of a does $x^2 - ax + 1 = 0$ have (a) no real roots or (b) exactly one root?

4.5 Applications of Quadratics

Quadratic polynomials appear in many 'real' situations, for various reasons, both physical and mathematical. Two of these are now presented, chosen to illustrate the different types.

4.5.1 Projectiles

A **projectile** is a mass launched into the earth's atmosphere with speed V at an initial angle α to the horizontal, as in the diagram. It is affected by gravity, assumed to be a constant g. Among the questions we can ask is: "What are the **range** R and maximum height H?"

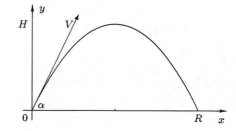

The initial velocities are

(horizontal:) $u_0 = V\cos\alpha,$ (vertical:) $v_0 = V\sin\alpha,$

which lead, using simple equations of motion, to the coordinates of the mass, as functions of time:

$$x = u_0 t, \qquad y = v_0 t - \frac{1}{2}gt^2.$$

The first of these gives $t = x/u_0$, which can then be substituted into the second, to **eliminate** t from it:

$$y = \frac{v_0}{u_0}x - \frac{g}{2u_0^2}x^2,$$

which is the equation of a **parabola**.

We can now complete the square for this quadratic, leading to a more informative version:

$$
\begin{aligned}
y &= -\frac{g}{2u_0^2}\left[x^2 - \frac{2u_0 v_0}{g}x\right] \\
&= -\frac{g}{2u_0^2}\left[\left(x - \frac{u_0 v_0}{g}\right)^2 - \frac{u_0^2 v_0^2}{g^2}\right] \\
&= \frac{v_0^2}{2g} - \frac{g}{2u_0^2}\left(x - \frac{u_0 v_0}{g}\right)^2.
\end{aligned}
$$

From this final version we can read off the maximum height H and when it occurs, as shown in the previous section:

$$H = \frac{v_0^2}{2g} = \frac{V^2 \sin^2 \alpha}{2g}, \quad \text{when } x = \frac{u_0 x_0}{g}, \quad t = \frac{v_0}{g}.$$

For this symmetric case, where the initial and final heights are the same, the range is twice the distance to where the maximum height occurs:

$$R = 2\frac{u_0 v_0}{g} = \frac{2V \cos \alpha V \sin \alpha}{g} = \frac{V^2}{g} \sin 2\alpha.$$

It is clear from this result that the range will be largest when

$$\sin 2\alpha = 1 \quad \Rightarrow \quad 2\alpha = 90° \quad \Rightarrow \quad \alpha = 45°.$$

Ex 4.9 Find the range and the maximum height reached for a projectile launched at $30°$, with velocity $10\,\text{ms}^{-1}$. (Use the value $g = 10\,\text{ms}^{-2}$.)

4.5.2   Data Fitting

Consider the following data, where the extension of a spring is measured, in some units, after the application of various loads.

Load (x)	1	2	3	4	5
Extension (y)	0.9	1.9	2.9	4.0	5.0

Hooke's Law states that $y = mx$. Assuming it applies, what value should we deduce for m?

Consider the general situation, with data plotted as on the right. Assume that this represents the data:

$$\left[(x_k, y_k) \right]_{k=1}^n .$$

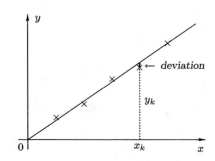

We seek to estimate and then minimise the total error measured by the deviations, such as that shown on the graph.

The simplest, and most popular, method is to add the **squares** of the individual deviations: we use the squares since they are guaranteed to be non-negative and hence we will avoid cancellation between positive and negative deviations when we add them.

The values from the graph are mx_k and the measured values are y_k. The deviations are the differences between these:

$$\begin{aligned} S &= (y_1 - mx_1)^2 + (y_2 - mx_2)^2 + \cdots + (y_n - mx_n)^2 \\ &= \left(y_1^2 - 2mx_1 y_1 + m^2 x_1^2\right) + \cdots + \left(y_n^2 - 2mx_n y_n + m^2 x_n^2\right) \\ &= am^2 + bm + c, \end{aligned}$$

where

$$a = x_1^2 + \cdots + x_n^2 \qquad = \sum_{k=1}^{n} x_k^2$$

$$b = -2x_1y_1 - \cdots - 2x_ny_n = -2\sum_{k=1}^{n} x_ky_k$$

$$c = y_1^2 + \cdots + y_n^2 \qquad = \sum_{k=1}^{n} y_k^2.$$

We wish to find that value of m (the gradient of the line) which will minimise S. Since S is a quadratic, we can use the results from the previous section: $m = -\frac{b}{2a}$, i.e.,

$$m = \frac{\sum x_ky_k}{\sum x_k^2}, \qquad (4.10)$$

where the limits for the sums have been suppressed to make the result clearer.

Example 4.8 For the data given at the start,

$$\sum x_ky_k = 1 \times 0.9 + 2 \times 1.9 + 3 \times 2.9 + 4 \times 4.0 + 5 \times 5.0$$

$$= 54.6$$

$$\sum x_k^2 = 1^2 + 2^2 + 3^2 + 4^2 + 5^2$$

$$= 55.$$

We now use these two sums to calculate:

$$m = \frac{54.6}{55} = 0.9927.$$

The data, and this 'best' line, are shown in the graph on the right.

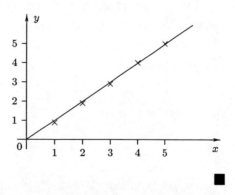

■

This is a special case of the **method of least squares**, for fitting a straight line to given data. It is special since it relies on the fact that the origin $(0,0)$ *must* lie on the line: no load, no extension. The calculation for the general case where the origin is unlikely to lie on the line is more complicated, but can be carried out by a clever adaptation of the special case.

Ex 4.10 Ohm's Law states that voltage (V) is proportional to current (i), i.e., $V = iR$, where R is a constant, the **resistance**. An experiment used different voltages and measured the corresponding currents (in conventional units), to find the following data:

V	15	30	45	60
i	0.20	0.36	0.56	0.80

Find a value of R that minimises the sum of the squares of the deviations calculated using $V = iR$ from the measured data. (Note that this data should be read in reverse, i.e., the rows should be swapped.)

Using this value, calculate the values of i it predicts, for each V in the table.

4.6   Cubic Polynomials

Polynomials of degree three are called **cubics**. The task of finding their maxima and minima is usually the business of *Calculus*, but finding their roots remains an algebraic challenge.

The previous sentence does not use the condition "if any" since every cubic has *at least* one root. This is because the value is dominated, for large $|x|$, by x^3, which forces the cubic to go from $-\infty$ to $+\infty$ (or *vice versa*) and must therefore pass through zero.

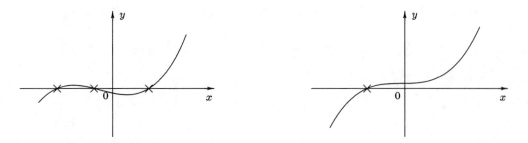

The above graphs show two of the cases; a mirror image in either axis shows the others. (The possibility of a double or triple root does not upset this observation.)

Suppose that

$$f(x) = a_0 + a_1 x + a_2 x^2 + a_3 x^3$$

has a root $x = \alpha$, so $f(\alpha) = 0$. Then $f(x)$ must have a factor $(x - \alpha)$ and so

$$f(x) = (x - \alpha)Q(x),$$

where, on checking the degrees on each side, $Q(x)$ must be a *quadratic*. We can then complete the job of finding the roots by finding those for $Q(x)$.

The above description does not explain how to find α and $Q(x)$. This is little different from what is required for the case of a general polynomial, to which we now turn.

4.7   General Polynomials

Suppose we have a general polynomial $P(x)$ and seek to find its roots and to factorise it. The gist of our method is as follows.

- Locate a root α, and hence a linear factor $(x - \alpha)$.

- Factorise $P(x)$:

$$P(x) = (x - \alpha)Q(x). \qquad (4.11)$$

- Repeat the above using $Q(x)$ until no more roots are found.

Sometimes this process provides a full set of n roots for $P(x)$ and we end up with

$$P(x) = a_n(x - \alpha_1)(x - \alpha_2) \cdots (x - \alpha_n),$$

while in some cases $P(x)$ has are no roots at all. The latter case cannot happen with n odd, when there is always at least one root, for precisely the reason given for the cubic case in the previous section.

There are two parts of this process that need further specification: how can we find a root α and how do we perform the factorisation in (4.11)? Consider the second of these first.

There are two methods; the simpler is a by-product of an efficient technique for evaluating $P(x)$ for a given x. A simple count of the number of calculations involved shows that finding each of the powers x^r, then multiplying by a_r and adding, is more expensive in time than using the **nested multiplication** form:

$$P(x) = \left(\cdots \left(\big((a_n x + a_{n-1})x + a_{n-2} \big)x + a_{n-3} \right) \cdots \right) x + a_0.$$

Example 4.9 Rewrite:

$$P(x) = 5x^4 - 3x^3 + x^2 - x + 4$$

$$= \left(\big((5x - 3)x + 1 \big) - 1 \right) x + 4.$$

Now suppose that $x = 3$. The following sequence of calculator input quickly provides the answer, effectively using the form above, with the '=' key evaluating what is inside the brackets. The intermediate results are also shown.

$$\begin{array}{ccccc}
a_4 & a_3 & a_2 & a_1 & a_0 \\
5 \times 3 - 3 & = \times 3 + 1 & = \times 3 - 1 & = \times 3 + 4 & = P(3) \\
(12) & (37) & (110) & \mathbf{334}
\end{array}$$

Although this calculation, as set out above, can be carried out without any intermediate recording of numbers, there can be an advantage in using a table:

3	5	−3	1	−1	4	*coefficients of $P(x)$*
	0	15	36	111	330	*3 × previous sum*
	5	12	37	110	334	*addition of column*

The same polynomial, evaluated at $x = -1$ leads to $P(-1) = 14$, using the table:

−1	5	−3	1	−1	4
	0	−5	8	−9	10
	5	−8	9	−10	14

The reason why the table is so useful is that *all* the entries in the bottom row are informative, not just the 14 at the end. Use them as coefficients in the following expression, then expand:

$$(x - (-1)) \left(5x^3 - 8x^2 + 9x - 10\right) + 14$$
$$= 5x^4 - 8x^3 + 9x^2 - 10x + 14$$
$$+ 5x^3 - 8x^2 + 9x - 10$$
$$= 5x^4 - 3x^3 + x^2 - x + 4,$$

which is the original polynomial. That this is no accident can be seen from the coefficients for each power in the calculation above. These are the numbers in the corresponding columns in the table.

This equation (an identity, in fact) can be rewritten:

$$\frac{5x^4 - 3x^3 + x^2 - x + 4}{x + 1} = 5x^3 - 8x^2 + 9x - 10 + \frac{14}{x + 1},$$

which is a **division** with **quotient** and **remainder** (14). ∎

All of the detail in this example generalises. We construct a table:

α	a_n	a_{n-1}	$\cdots$	a_1	a_0	coefficients of $P(x)$
	0	αb_{n-1}	$\cdots$	αb_1	αb_0	$\alpha \times$ previous sum
	b_{n-1}	b_{n-2}	$\cdots$	b_0	r	addition of column:

$$b_k = a_{k+1} + \alpha b_{k+1}$$

From the entries in the table we can construct the identity:

$$P(x) = \left(x - \alpha\right)\left(b_{n-1}x^{n-1} + b_{n-2}x^{n-2} + \cdots + b_1 x + b_0\right) + r, \qquad (4.12)$$

where the b_k and r are the numbers in the bottom row and α is the value at which we wish to evaluate $P(x)$. This can be rewritten as

$$\frac{P(x)}{x - \alpha} = b_{n-1}x^{n-1} + b_{n-2}x^{n-2} + \cdots + b_1 x + b_0 + \frac{r}{x - \alpha}, \qquad (4.13)$$

which is a division result.

This method is called **synthetic division**, since it gives the result for a division without really doing division at all. When we examine the direct method for division, in §4.9, it will become clear that synthetic division is *much* easier to use.

Now, set $x = \alpha$ in (4.12):

$$P(\alpha) = (\alpha - \alpha)Q(\alpha) + r = r,$$

as given in the table. If, however, α is a **root** of $P(x)$, then $r = 0$ and

$$P(x) = \left(x - \alpha\right)\left(b_{n-1}x^{n-1} + \cdots + b_1 x + b_0\right), \qquad (4.14)$$

which is precisely the factorisation we set out to find, with the polynomial $b_{n-1}x^{n-1} + \cdots + b_0$ the factor $Q(x)$ in (4.11).

Take particular note of the minus sign in this factorisation: in $(x - \alpha)$ the minus is part of the structure. Thus, in Example 4.9, the factor $(x + 1)$ corresponds to $\big(x - (-1)\big)$.

It is now time to address the other, more difficult, question: how do we find a root α for a polynomial. *There is no guaranteed method for finding an exact root for a general polynomial.* Possible approaches are:

- Use a computer to draw up a table and look for zero values.

- Draw a graph of $P(x)$ and see where it cuts the x-axis.

- Use one of a group of standard methods that provide *approximate* roots, correct to any predetermined accuracy.

- Use trial and error to look for whole number or fractional roots of a simple form.

At this stage we shall restrict ourselves to the last of these, possibly supplemented by simple graphs. There is a useful observation that helps steer us towards possible trial values: from (4.14) we have $-\alpha b_0 = a_0$, so if b_0 and a_0 are whole numbers, α must be a factor of a_0. (This argument can be refined to show a root of a simple form must be a factor of a_0/a_n.)

Example 4.10 For $P(x) = x^3 + 3x^2 - 4$, try $x = \pm 1$, ± 2, ± 4, the factors of -4. The simplest of these works:

1	1	3	0	−4
	0	1	4	4
	1	4	4	**0**

Hence $P(x) = (x - 1)(x^2 + 4x + 4)$. We know how to find the roots and factors of a quadratic from §4.4, so there is no need to repeat the trial and error. The final answer is

$$P(x) = (x - 1)(x + 2)^2.$$

Note how the 'missing' term in x was represented by a zero in the first row of the table; this is essential. ∎

Example 4.11 For $P(x) = x^4 - 2x^2 - 3x - 2$, we try $x = \pm 1$, ± 2. This time it is -1 that provides the first hit.

−1	1	0	−2	−3	−2
	0	−1	1	1	2
	1	−1	−1	−2	**0**

Reading off the final row, and remembering that $-(-1) = +1$, we obtain:

$$P(x) = (x + 1)\left(x^3 - x^2 - x - 2\right),$$

and we now attack the cubic factor on the right. We try $x = -1$, ± 2: there is no point in trying $x = 1$ since it failed at the start. Now $x = 2$ provides the first hit.

2	1	−1	−1	−2
	0	2	2	2
	1	1	1	**0**

Reading off the final row we obtain:

$$P(x) = (x+1)(x-2)(x^2 + x + 1),$$

as the final result, since the quadratic on the right has discriminant -3 and hence is irreducible.

The two tables above can be run together to save space:

−1	1	0	−2	−3	−2
	0	−1	1	1	2
2	1	−1	−1	−2	**0**
	0	2	2	2	
	1	1	1	**0**	

∎

It can be shown that every polynomial $P(x)$ can, in theory, be factorised as a product of **linear** and **irreducible quadratic** factors.

Ex 4.11

(a) Show that $x = 3$ is a root of $\;f(x) = x^3 - x^2 - x - 15$.

   Hence find $f(x)/(x - 3)$. Are there any further roots?

(b) Divide $x^3 - 4x^2 + 3x - 10$ by $x - 4$ and state the remainder.

Ex 4.12 Factorise $x^4 - 3x^2 - 4$. (**Hint:** treat it as a quadratic in $u = x^2$.)

Ex 4.13 Solve the equation $2x^4 + 4x^3 - 5x^2 + 2x - 3 = 0$.

Ex 4.14 Factorise the following polynomials into linear and irreducible quadratic factors (if any):

(a) $x^3 - 4x^2 + x + 6$ (b) $x^4 + 2x^3 + 6x - 9$

(c) $2x^4 + 5x^3 + x^2 - 2x$ (d) $3x^4 - x^3 - 9x^2 - 3x + 2$

4.8   Rational Functions

Having introduced polynomials, the next type of function to consider has the form

$$\frac{P(x)}{Q(x)}, \qquad (P(x),\ Q(x) \text{ polynomials}). \qquad (4.15)$$

This is called a **rational function**. Its definition is an analogue of the way whole numbers were extended to produce rational numbers (fractions).

The first task concerned with these is to find a counterpart for writing:

$$\frac{17}{6} = 2 + \frac{5}{6},$$

i.e., the **improper fraction** $\frac{17}{6}$ is written in terms of the **proper** fraction $\frac{5}{6}$, so-called because $0 \leqslant 5 < 6$.

It is convenient to introduce some notation at this point: $\deg P(x)$ represents the **degree** of the polynomial $P(x)$. Then, if $\deg P(x) < \deg Q(x)$, the function $P(x)/Q(x)$ is a **proper** rational function. Otherwise, we seek to rewrite it as follows.

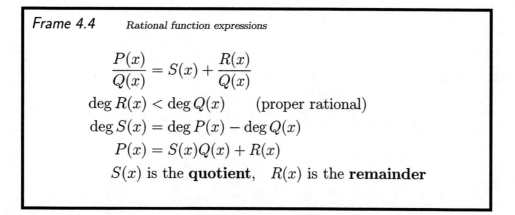

Frame 4.4   *Rational function expressions*

$$\frac{P(x)}{Q(x)} = S(x) + \frac{R(x)}{Q(x)}$$

$\deg R(x) < \deg Q(x)$ (proper rational)

$\deg S(x) = \deg P(x) - \deg Q(x)$

$$P(x) = S(x)Q(x) + R(x)$$

$S(x)$ is the **quotient**, $R(x)$ is the **remainder**

The names for $S(x)$ and $R(x)$ suggest how to achieve this: use *division*.

4.9   Division

Although synthetic division, as in §4.7, is a powerful technique for dividing polynomials by *linear* factors, we need to be able to divide by polynomials of any degree. Synthetic division can be extended, but it is more usual to adapt the technique for 'long division' of numbers, which is where we start.

This method is a *recursive* one, where we balance the most significant (for numbers, the largest) components, then repeat the calculation with the "error", i.e., what is left over. This is usually measured by the following:

$$\text{if } \frac{a}{b} \simeq c, \text{ then the error is } \frac{a}{b} - c,$$

but for these purposes we measure it as

$$b \times \left(\frac{a}{b} - c\right) = a - bc,$$

since that allows us to work only in integers. It retains the property that the "error" $a - bc = 0$ if $\frac{a}{b} = c$ exactly.

The method is best comprehended by example, rather than by a lengthy description in words.

Example 4.12   Divide 2716 by 43.

$$
\begin{array}{r}
6\,3 \\
43\,\overline{)\,2\,7\,1\,6} \\
\end{array}
$$

$6\times43\ \rightarrow$	$2\,5\,8\downarrow$	*Largest single digit multiple*
		of 43, less than 271, uses 6.
	$1\,3\,6$	*"Error" is 13 (units of 10)+6=136.*
$3\times43\ \rightarrow$	$1\,2\,9$	*Start again: largest multiple uses 3.*
	7	*"Error" is 7 (units of 1). 7<43, so STOP.*

The conclusion is that $\frac{2716}{43}$ has *quotient* 63 and *remainder* 7. This is expressed in two ways:

$$
\frac{2716}{43} = 63 + \frac{7}{43}, \qquad\qquad 2716 = 63 \times 43 + 7.
$$

■

Example 4.13   Divide 42731 by 113.

$$
\begin{array}{r}
3\,7\,8 \qquad\text{\small QUOTIENT}\\
113\,\overline{)\,4\,2\,7\,3\,1}\\
\end{array}
$$

$3\times113\ \rightarrow$	$3\,3\,9\downarrow\downarrow$	*Best multiple uses 3.*
	$8\,8\,3\downarrow$	*"Error" is 88 (units of 100)+31.*
$7\times113\ \rightarrow$	$7\,9\,1\downarrow$	*Best multiple uses 7.*
	$9\,2\,1$	*"Error" is 92 (units of 10)+1.*
$8\times113\ \rightarrow$	$9\,0\,4$	*Best multiple uses 8.*
REMAINDER	$1\,7$	*"Error" is 17<113, so STOP.*

The quotient and remainder are labelled in the tableau above. Also:

$$
\frac{42731}{113} = 378 + \frac{17}{113}, \qquad\qquad 42731 = 378 \times 113 + 17.
$$

■

Polynomials are divided by exactly the same process, except that the "multiple" is calculated by considering only the current *leading terms*, i.e., those of the highest degree in the two polynomials involved. Again this is best seen by an example.

Example 4.14   Divide $2x^3 - 3x^2 + 4$ by $x^2 + x + 1$. Note that the term in x is missing and should be replaced in the tableau by $0x$.

$$
\begin{array}{r}
2x - \ 5 \qquad\text{\small QUOTIENT}\\
x^2+x+1\,\overline{)\,2x^3 - 3x^2 + 0x + 4}\\
\end{array}
$$

$2x^3 + 2x^2 + 2x\ \downarrow$	*$(2x^3/x^2)\times Q(x)$*
$-5x^2 - 2x + 4$	*"Error"*
$-5x^2 - 5x - 5$	*$(-5x^2/x^2)\times Q(x)$*
$3x + 9$	*Final "Error", i.e., REMAINDER*

with $2x^3 - 3x^2 + 0x + 4$ labelled *Original polynomials P(x), Q(x)*.

This time we stop because the **degree** of the final "error" $(3x + 9)$ is less than the degree of the divisor $(x^2 + x + 1)$. We can make statements about the results, similar to those for numbers:

$$\frac{2x^3 - 3x^2 + 4}{x^2 + x + 1} = 2x - 5 + \frac{3x + 9}{x^2 + x + 1},$$

$$2x^3 - 3x^2 + 4 = (2x - 5)(x^2 + x + 1) + 3x + 9.$$

■

Example 4.15

$$
\begin{array}{r}
3x^2 + x + 2 \qquad\qquad \text{\small QUOTIENT} \\
x^2 - x + 2 \,\big|\, \overline{3x^4 - 2x^3 + 7x^2 + 3x - 2} \qquad \text{\small Original polynomials } P(x),\ Q(x) \\
\underline{3x^4 - 3x^3 + 6x^2} \qquad\qquad \text{\small } (3x^4/x^2) \times Q(x) \\
x^3 + x^2 + 3x \qquad\qquad \text{\small "Error"} \\
\underline{x^3 - x^2 + 2x} \qquad\qquad \text{\small } (x^3/x^2) \times Q(x) \\
2x^2 + x - 2 \qquad\qquad \text{\small "Error"} \\
\underline{2x^2 - 2x + 4} \qquad\qquad \text{\small } (2x^2/x^2) \times Q(x) \\
3x - 6 \qquad\qquad \text{\small Final "Error", i.e., REMAINDER}
\end{array}
$$

Again, we stop when the degree of the "error" is less than that of the divisor. Similar final deductions can be made. ■

The next example returns to a calculation performed in §4.7 (Example 4.9) using synthetic division.

Example 4.16 Divide $5x^4 - 3x^3 + x^2 - x + 4$ by $x + 1$.

$$
\begin{array}{r}
5x^3 - 8x^2 + 9x - 10 \qquad\qquad \text{\small QUOTIENT} \\
x + 1 \,\big|\, \overline{5x^4 - 3x^3 + x^2 - x + 4} \qquad \text{\small Original polynomials } P(x),\ Q(x) \\
\underline{5x^4 + 5x^3} \qquad\qquad \text{\small } (5x^4/x) \times Q(x) \\
-8x^3 + 1x^2 \qquad\qquad \text{\small "Error"} \\
\underline{-8x^3 - 8x^2} \qquad\qquad \text{\small } (-8x^3/x) \times Q(x) \\
9x^2 - 1x \qquad\qquad \text{\small "Error"} \\
\underline{9x^2 + 9x} \qquad\qquad \text{\small } (9x^2/x) \times Q(x) \\
-10x + 4 \qquad\qquad \text{\small "Error"} \\
\underline{-10x - 10} \qquad\qquad \text{\small } (-10x/x) \times Q(x) \\
14 \qquad\qquad \text{\small Final "Error", i.e., REMAINDER}
\end{array}
$$

The final remainder, also the value of $P(-1)$ is 14, as before. It is instructive to compare this calculation with that in Example 4.9, where the

2

same numbers appear, although sometimes with the opposite sign, reflecting a subtraction rather than an addition. ∎

Think about it like this

> The similarity between the number and polynomial methods is explained in part because we could tackle $\frac{2716}{43}$ by treating it as $(2x^3+7x^2+x+6)/(4x+3)$ with $x = 10$. But this allows negative coefficients, which are prohibited in the number calculation. As a result, the polynomial case is in fact easier: we do not have to avoid negative numbers and this makes it easier to determine the "multiple" at each stage.

Finally, consider the start of the general calculation $P(x)/Q(x)$. Suppose that $\deg P(x) = m$, $\deg Q(x) = n$. Then there is no division possible if $m < n$. Otherwise, we start:

$$q_n x^n + \cdots \enclose{longdiv}{ \begin{array}{l} \alpha x^{m-n}+\cdots \\ \hline p_m x^m + \cdots \end{array}} \qquad \alpha = p_m/q_n$$

This shows that:

the quotient has degree $m - n$,

the remainder has degree at most $n - 1$.

Ex 4.15

(a) Find the quotient and remainder for the division $\dfrac{427}{31}$.

(b) Divide $x^3 + 2x - 5$ by $x^2 + 1$ to obtain the form

$$Ax + B + \frac{Cx + D}{x^2 + 1}.$$

Ex 4.16 The *highest common factor* or *greatest common divisor* (**gcd**) of whole numbers a and b is the largest whole number that divides both. It can be calculated using the *Euclidean algorithm*.

Suppose $a > b$. Divide a by b to find a remainder r. Divide b by r to find remainder s. Continue dividing the previous divisor by the new remainder until one finds remainder zero. This last divisor is the gcd.

For example, let $a = 288$ and $b = 42$. Then:

$$288 = 6 \times 42 + 36, \quad 42 = 1 \times 36 + 6, \quad 36 = 6 \times 6 + 0, \quad \text{gcd is } 6.$$

Find the gcd for $(1891, 124)$ and $(244, 51)$.

Ex 4.17

(a) Divide $2x^3 + 3x^2 + 2x - 5$ by $2x^2 - x - 1$ and state the remainder.

(b) Divide $x^4 - x^3 + x^2 - x + 1$ by $x^2 + x + 1$ and state the remainder.

4.10   Application to Graph Drawing

The task of drawing a graph of a rational function is made easier if it is first expressed as a polynomial plus a proper rational function. The latter may have to be treated further, as in the next section.

Suppose, however, that the divisor is a **linear** function $ax + b$. Then we seek to graph

$$\frac{P(x)}{ax + b} = S(x) + \frac{\alpha}{ax + b}, \tag{4.16}$$

for a polynomial $S(x)$ and a constant α. The graph is dominated by two features.

(a) As x gets large in size – and so approaches either ∞ or $-\infty$ – the second term in (4.16) dies away and the function behaves like $S(x)$.

(b) As x gets near $-\frac{b}{a}$, the second term blows up in size since its denominator approaches zero. It approaches ∞ on one side and $-\infty$ on the other; which way round depends on the sign of α.

Thus the graph approaches that of $y = S(x)$ as x nears $\pm\infty$, and the vertical line $x = -\frac{b}{a}$ as x nears that value. Each of these graphical elements is called an **asymptote**: a line that a graph approaches ever closer to, but never meets. Identifying the asymptotes for a rational function is a large step towards finding its graph and often a few further points are all that is required to complete a sketch.

Example 4.17   Graph $y = \dfrac{2x - 1}{x + 1}$.

A division shows that

$$y = 2 - \frac{3}{x + 1}.$$

$$
\begin{array}{r}
2 \\
x + 1 \overline{\smash{)}\, 2x - 1} \\
\underline{2x + 2} \\
-3
\end{array}
$$

For large $|x|$, y approaches the value 2. For $|x|$ near -1,

$$-\frac{3}{x + 1} \text{ is } \begin{cases} \text{large and negative,} & \text{if } x > -1; \\ \text{large and positive,} & \text{if } x < -1. \end{cases}$$

Hence the graph has a horizontal asymptote $y = 2$ and a vertical asymptote $x = -1$. Two useful special points are where x and y are zero: $(0, -1)$ and $(0.5, 0)$. Finally, using calculus, $y' = 3/(x + 1)^2 > 0$ for all $x \neq -1$, so the function **increases** in both parts. It is now straightforward to sketch the graph.

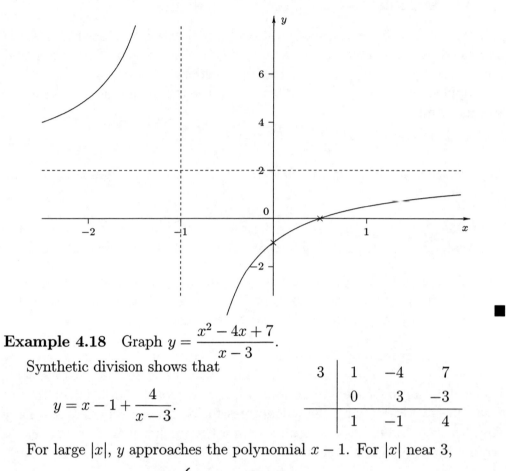

■

Example 4.18   Graph $y = \dfrac{x^2 - 4x + 7}{x - 3}$.

Synthetic division shows that

$$y = x - 1 + \frac{4}{x - 3}.$$

$$
\begin{array}{r|rrr}
3 & 1 & -4 & 7 \\
  & 0 & 3 & -3 \\
\hline
  & 1 & -1 & 4
\end{array}
$$

For large $|x|$, y approaches the polynomial $x - 1$. For $|x|$ near 3,

$$\frac{4}{x - 3} \text{ is } \begin{cases} \text{large and positive,} & \text{if } x > 3; \\ \text{large and negative,} & \text{if } x < 3. \end{cases}$$

The graph has a straight line asymptote $y = x - 1$ and a vertical asymptote $x = 3$. Two useful special points are the maximum $(1, -2)$ and minimum $(5, 6)$, found using calculus. It is now straightforward to sketch the graph.

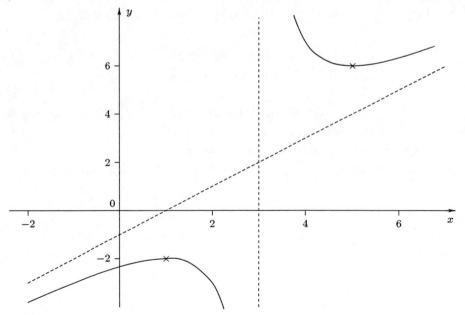

■

Ex 4.18 Write $y = \dfrac{x+2}{x+1}$ in the form $y = A + \dfrac{B}{x+1}$ and sketch its graph, identifying the asymptotes.

Ex 4.19 Divide $1 - x - x^2$ by $x + 1$. Hence sketch the graph of $y = \dfrac{1 - x - x^2}{x+1}$, identifying the asymptotes.

4.11 Partial Fractions

One further calculation is required for rational functions. Having isolated the *proper* part, this can often be broken into simpler fragments. This process is helpful in many contexts, e.g., in graph drawing and in calculus.

We start with an example based on §1.7.

Example 4.19 We can add the following fractions:

$$
\begin{aligned}
\frac{2}{x-1} - \frac{1}{x+2} &= \frac{2(x+2) - (x-1)}{(x-1)(x+2)} \\
&= \frac{2x + 4 - x + 1}{(x-1)(x+2)} \\
&= \frac{x+5}{(x^2 + x - 2)}
\end{aligned}
$$

The answer here is a *proper rational function*. Now suppose we are given this function, as a single fraction, and are asked to reverse the process.

The first step would be to factorise the bottom line:

$$
x^2 + x - 2 = (x-1)(x+2).
$$

Now seek *constants* A and B so that

$$
\begin{aligned}
\frac{x+5}{(x-1)(x+2)} &\equiv \frac{A}{x-1} + \frac{B}{x+2} \\
&\equiv \frac{A(x+2) + B(x-1)}{(x-1)(x+2)},
\end{aligned}
$$

after adding the simpler fractions together. Note the use of '$\equiv$', since this is indeed an **identity**, which we shall see is most helpful. The result would have no value unless it is true for **all** x.

We can deduce from this identity that

$$
x + 5 \equiv A(x+2) + B(x-1). \tag{4.17}
$$

There are two ways in which to deduce values of A and B from this.

Method 1

Rework (4.17) into

$$
x + 5 \equiv (A+B)x + (2A - B),
$$

then use the fact that it is an identity to argue that the terms in each power of x, i.e., x^1 and the constants, which contain x^0, must match *separately*:

$$A + B = 1 \qquad\qquad \text{add: } 3A = 6,$$
$$2A - B = 5 \qquad\qquad \text{so } A = 2, \ B = -1.$$

Method 2

Use some specific values of x in (4.17). Choosing clever values delivers A and B immediately:

$$x = 1: \qquad\qquad 6 = 3A + 0 \quad \Rightarrow \quad A = 2,$$
$$x = -2: \qquad\qquad 3 = 0 - 3B \quad \Rightarrow \quad B = -1.$$

The values used are precisely the roots of the quadratic in the denominator.

Both methods have recovered the original fractions with which we started, but the second method was rather easier. ∎

The simpler fractions in this example are called the **partial fractions** for the proper rational function. In general, suppose we start with the **proper** rational function:

$$\frac{P(x)}{Q(x)}: \qquad \deg P(x) < \deg Q(x).$$

Otherwise, divide $P(x)$ by $Q(x)$, as in §4.9.

We shall concentrate on Method 2, although there are occasions when some use of Method 1 is necessary.

Frame 4.5   *Finding partial fractions for $P(x)/Q(x)$*

(1) Factorise $Q(x)$

(2) Set up partial fractions, with factors of $Q(x)$ on bottom and unknown constants on top

(3) Recompose these into a single fraction

(4) Force the top line to match $P(x)$, to find values for the constants

---

This approach to finding new identities is a common one in mathematics and is sometimes called the *method of undetermined parameters*. We have already seen it in action, in §4.2, when we fitted quadratics to given data.

In the simplest case, on which we shall concentrate, all factors are **linear**.

Example 4.20 In this example the various steps are labelled with the numbers from Frame 4.5. We shall reduce the usage of '≡' to where it is essential.

$$\frac{x-6}{x^2-5x+6} =_{(1)} \frac{x-6}{(x-2)(x-3)} =_{(2)} \frac{A}{x-2} + \frac{B}{x-3}$$

$$=_{(3)} \frac{A(x-3)+B(x-2)}{(x-2)(x-3)}$$

$$\Rightarrow_{(4)} A(x-3)+B(x-2) \equiv x-6.$$

Now set x to be the roots of $(x-2)(x-3)$, in turn:

$$x=2: \qquad -A+0=-4 \quad \Rightarrow \quad A=4,$$
$$x=3: \qquad 0+B=-3 \quad \Rightarrow \quad B=-3,$$

delivering the answer

$$\frac{x-6}{x^2-5x+6} = \frac{4}{x-2} - \frac{3}{x-3}.$$

Steps (3) and (4) can be by-passed using the **cover-up rule**, which is simply a shorthand way of doing the calculations using Method 2:

$$\frac{x-6}{\boxed{(x-2)}(x-3)} \qquad \text{cover up box, set } x=2: \qquad \frac{-4}{-1}=4 \qquad (A)$$

$$\frac{x-6}{(x-2)\boxed{(x-3)}} \qquad \text{cover up box, set } x=3: \qquad \frac{-3}{1}=-3 \qquad (B)$$

■

Example 4.21 Returning to Example 4.19, we have the quicker calculation:

$$\left.\frac{x+5}{\boxed{(x-1)}(x+2)}\right|_{x=1} = \frac{6}{3} = 2 \qquad \left[\frac{2}{x-1}\right]$$

$$\left.\frac{x+5}{(x-1)\boxed{(x+2)}}\right|_{x=-2} = \frac{3}{-3} = -1 \qquad \left[\frac{-1}{x+2}\right]$$

Here we have used the notation $f(x)\big|_{x=a} = f(a)$, to reduce the amount of writing. ■

The cover-up rule becomes more and more useful as the degree of the bottom line increases.

Example 4.22 Find partial fractions for $\dfrac{4x^2+3x-4}{x(x-2)(x+1)}$.

$$\left.\frac{4x^2 + 3x - 4}{\boxed{x}(x-2)(x+1)}\right|_{x=0} = \frac{-4}{-2 \times 1} = 2$$

$$\left.\frac{4x^2 + 3x - 4}{x\boxed{(x-2)}(x+1)}\right|_{x=2} = \frac{18}{2 \times 3} = 3$$

$$\left.\frac{4x^2 + 3x - 4}{x(x-2)\boxed{(x+1)}}\right|_{x=-1} = \frac{-3}{-1 \times (-3)} = -1$$

The final answer is

$$\frac{2}{x} + \frac{3}{x-2} - \frac{1}{x+1}.$$

∎

There are two difficulties that can be encountered with this calculation. The bottom line may have an irreducible quadratic factor, such as $x^2 + 1$. This can be overcome, but we shall not pursue that, other than to note that the remedy is not very different from that for the second difficulty.

We may find that the bottom line has a *repeated* linear factor, e.g., $(x-1)^2$. There is no point in using two simple partial fractions, since $\frac{A}{x-1} + \frac{B}{x-1}$ is equivalent to $\frac{C}{x-1}$ and so we are one term short. The adaptation required is as follows.

Frame 4.6   *Partial fractions for a repeated linear factor*

If $Q(x)$ contains a factor $(x - \alpha)^r$ for $r > 1$, use terms

$$\frac{A_1}{x-\alpha}, \quad \frac{A_2}{(x-\alpha)^2}, \quad \cdots, \quad \frac{A_r}{(x-\alpha)^r}$$

For the case $r = 2$, this can be written in two ways:

$$\frac{A}{x-\alpha} + \frac{B}{(x-\alpha)^2} = \frac{A(x-\alpha) + B}{(x-\alpha)^2} \equiv \frac{Cx + D}{(x-\alpha)^2}.$$

This last version is not used, but has been shown here, since it is the method for dealing with irreducible quadratic factors, so $x^2 + 1$ generates $\frac{Cx+D}{x^2+1}$.

Unfortunately, Method 2 (and hence the cover-up rule) works only for one of the repeated factors and so we must resort to Method 1 to complete the calculation.

Example 4.23   Find partial fractions for $\dfrac{2x - 7}{(x-3)^2}$.

Using Frame 4.6, we start:

$$\frac{A}{x-3} + \frac{B}{(x-3)^2} = \frac{A(x-3) + B}{(x-3)^2},$$

and hence
$$A(x-3) + B \equiv 2x - 7.$$
Set $x = 3$ to find $0 + B = 6 - 7$, so $B = -1$.

Now balance either the coefficients of x or the constant terms. The former is easier: $Ax \equiv 2x$, so $A = 2$. Alternatively, another 'easy' value of x could be used, say $x = 0$: $-3A + B = -7$, also giving $A = 2$, using $B = -1$. The final answer is
$$\frac{2}{x-3} - \frac{1}{(x-3)^2}.$$

∎

A final example mixes a repeated factor with a non-repeated one.

Example 4.24 Find partial fractions for $\dfrac{4}{x^3 - 2x^2} = \dfrac{4}{x^2(x-2)}$.

The x factor is the repeated one, so we start
$$\frac{A}{x} + \frac{B}{x^2} + \frac{C}{x-2} = \frac{Ax(x-2) + B(x-2) + Cx^2}{x^2(x-2)},$$
from which we deduce
$$Ax(x-2) + B(x-2) + Cx^2 \equiv 4.$$

We complete the calculation using the two special values $x = 0$ and $x = 2$, as well as identifying the coefficients of one of the powers of x. (Note that we have to read the numerator as $0x^2 + 0x + 4$.) In this case we have already used $x = 0$ as a special value, so it cannot be used again: the coefficients of x^2 give the answer most quickly.

$$x = 0: \quad -2B = 4 \quad \Rightarrow \quad B = -2$$
$$x = 2: \quad 4C = 4 \quad \Rightarrow \quad C = 1$$
$$\text{coeff. of } x^2: \quad A + C = 0 \quad \Rightarrow \quad A = -1,$$

giving the final answer
$$-\frac{1}{x} - \frac{2}{x^2} + \frac{1}{x-2}.$$

∎

Ex 4.20 Express as partial fractions:

(a) $\dfrac{2x}{(x+1)(x-1)}$, (b) $\dfrac{x^2 - 4x}{(x+2)(x-1)(x-2)}$, (c) $\dfrac{x^2 - x + 2}{x(x-1)^2}$.

Ex 4.21 Find partial fractions for the following functions:

(a) $\dfrac{5x-4}{(x+1)(2x-1)}$, (b) $\dfrac{x+7}{(x-2)(x+1)^2}$, (c) $\dfrac{x^2 + 5x - 10}{x^3 + x^2 - 5x + 3}$, (d) $\dfrac{x^2 - 6x + 5}{x^2 - 7x + 12}$.

4.12   Applications of Partial Fractions

We end this chapter with two applications: the summing of series and the drawing of graphs.

Example 4.25   Sum the series $\frac{1}{1\cdot2} + \frac{1}{2\cdot3} + \frac{1}{3\cdot4} + \cdots$.

The general term in the series can be written using partial fractions:

$$\frac{1}{k(k+1)} = \frac{1}{k} - \frac{1}{k+1}.$$

Then the nth partial sum is

$$S_n = \left(\frac{1}{1} - \frac{1}{2}\right) + \left(\frac{1}{2} - \frac{1}{3}\right) + \left(\frac{1}{3} - \frac{1}{4}\right) + \cdots$$

$$\cdots + \left(\frac{1}{n-1} - \frac{1}{n}\right) + \left(\frac{1}{n} - \frac{1}{n+1}\right)$$

$$= 1 - \frac{1}{n+1},$$

since all other terms cancel.

Now let n tend to ∞: $\frac{1}{n+1}$ dies away and the sum to infinity is 1.   ∎

Example 4.26   Sketch the graph of $y = \dfrac{3x+2}{x^2+x-2} = \dfrac{^4\!/_3}{x+2} + \dfrac{^5\!/_3}{x-1}$.

The graph of $y = \frac{1}{x+2}$ is that of $y = \frac{1}{x}$ (shown on the right) but moved 2 units to the left (so the break is at the forbidden value of $x = -2$). Similarly, this graph is moved 1 unit to the right to obtain that for $y = \frac{1}{x-1}$.

These can be superimposed, to give the rough outline of the graph, with some special points, such as $(-1, ^1\!/_2)$, $(-^2\!/_3, 0)$ and $(0, -1)$, used where the two parts meet.

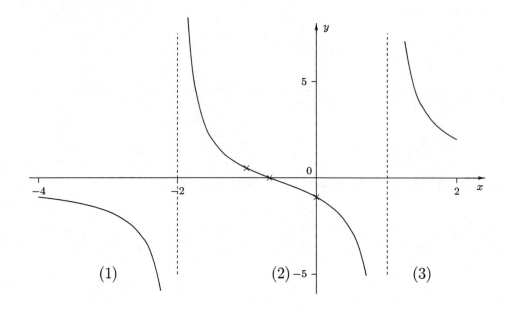

(1) is dominated by $\frac{4/3}{x+2}$; (3) is dominated by $\frac{5/3}{x-1}$, since, in each case, the other term has a very large bottom line and so is negligible.

(2) behaves like $\frac{4/3}{x+2}$ on the left and $\frac{5/3}{x-1}$ on the right. ■

Ex 4.22 Find the partial fractions for $y = \dfrac{x+4}{x^2-1}$ and hence its asymptotes. Sketch the graph of y.

Ex 4.23 Consider the infinite series $\dfrac{1}{1\times 2\times 3} + \dfrac{1}{2\times 3\times 4} + \cdots$.

Express the general term $\dfrac{1}{r(r+1)(r+2)}$ in partial fractions and hence show that

$$\sum_{r=1}^{\infty} \frac{1}{r(r+1)(r+2)} = \frac{1}{4}.$$

4.13 Revision Exercises

Ex 4.24 Use **linear interpolation** to estimate $f(1.175)$ for the function in the table below.

x	$f(x)$
1.14	0.8507
1.16	0.8593
1.18	0.8677

Ex 4.25 Complete the square for the quadratic: $4x^2 - 8x - 21$.
   Hence find its roots, its maximum or minimum point and sketch its graph.

Ex 4.26 Show that $(x-1)$ is a factor of the polynomial

$$f(x) = x^4 - 2x^3 + x^2 - 4x + 4.$$

Find $f(x)/(x-1)$, then find all real factors of $f(x)$.

Ex 4.27 Show that $(x+1)$ is a factor of the polynomial

$$f(x) = x^4 - 3x^3 + 2x^2 - 3x - 9.$$

Find $f(x)/(x+1)$, then find all real factors of $f(x)$.

Ex 4.28 Find the partial fractions for: $\dfrac{x+4}{(2x-1)(x+1)}$.

Ex 4.29 Find the partial fractions for: $\dfrac{x+19}{(x-2)(x+5)}$.

Ex 4.30 Find the partial fractions for: $\dfrac{4x^2 + x - 9}{x(x-1)(x+3)}$.

5 VECTORS

There are two kinds of physical quantity:

- **scalars**: these have only a 'size', called the **magnitude**;

- **vectors**: these have both a **magnitude** and **direction**.

Example 5.1 The following are typical:

    scalars: mass, radius, energy, electrical resistance;

    vectors: velocity, momentum, electric field, force.

Note that *speed* is a scalar, being the magnitude of *velocity*.   ■

Vectors are most powerful in a plane (two *dimensions*, 2-D) or space (3-D) or even, as in relativity, space and time (4-D).

Think about it like this
> There is a blurring between 1-D vectors and scalars that can be plus or minus, e.g., *temperature*. A simple rule in 1-D is that quantities that can be used in 2-D, such as velocity, are vectors, while those that cannot be given a direction in 2-D, such as temperature, are scalars.

Ex 5.1 Which of the following are vectors and which are scalars? acceleration, density, resistance, magnetic field, concentration in a solution, gravitational field, frequency

---

5.1 Addition of Vectors

Much of our work with vectors will concentrate on how to combine them, in similar ways to numbers, e.g., addition, subtraction and multiplication. In deciding on appropriate definitions for these operations, we place most emphasis on those that provide useful results.

Example 5.2 The first example is in 2-D, ignoring a minor complication at the start and finish of the model.

An aeroplane leaves Edinburgh (E), flies 60° West of South for 200 miles, due South for 300, due East for $100\sqrt{3}$, to arrive at London (L). (The minor complication is the take-off and landing, requiring a third dimension.)

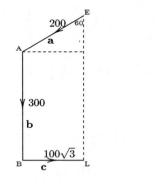

The net result is to fly 400 miles due South, a journey described by the **addition** of the three arrowed **vectors**.   ■

Before developing this further, it is necessary to address the issue of notation. There are two particularly common methods for writing vectors, both of which are used, depending on what is convenient in the context.

The vector from A to B is written $\overrightarrow{AB}$ or **v**.
In handwritten text the bold type format
is usually replaced by $\underline{v}$ or $\vec{v}$.

In the end-point format, the order of the letters is important and must agree with the direction of the arrow: $\overrightarrow{BA}$ has direction from B to A. In Example 5.2, we labelled the vector $\overrightarrow{AB}$ by **b**.

The **magnitude** of a vector uses the same notation as absolute value, $|\ |$, and is consistent with it, in the sense that the magnitude of a one-dimensional vector, consisting of the number x, is $|x|$, its absolute value (or size). Thus we write $|\overrightarrow{AB}|$ and $|\mathbf{v}|$. In Example 5.2, $|\mathbf{b}| = 300$.

Notation

> Some authors write AB or v for the magnitude, but this should normally be avoided since it can cause ambiguity, especially in handwriting, should an underline be carelessly omitted. Also, in some geometrical applications it will be convenient to use AB to refer to the line joining A and B and not necessarily its length.

There are two types of vector. For now, we shall use **free** or **displacement** vectors, almost always referring simply to **vectors**. These have their magnitude and direction fixed, but *not* their end-points.

Two (free) vectors are equal if they have the same magnitude and direction, i.e., their geometrical representations are **parallel** with the same length, so $\overrightarrow{AB} = \overrightarrow{A'B'}$.

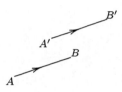

Example 5.3 Returning to the journey in Example 5.2, we can vary the order of the component vectors.

These two further examples (from $3! = 6$ possible orderings) produce the same final result: a flight of 400 miles due South. We can interpret this as the addition of the same three vectors, provided we regard them as free ones, since their end-points are not always the same.

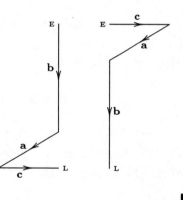

These two examples of possible flight paths provide a natural way to add the individual vectors involved: *join the tail of the second vector to the head of the first.*

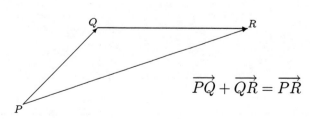

$$\overrightarrow{PQ} + \overrightarrow{QR} = \overrightarrow{PR}$$

Example 5.4 An aeroplane has speed $120\,\text{ms}^{-1}$ in a direction due North, represented by a vector $\overrightarrow{AB} = \mathbf{a}$. The wind blows at speed $50\,\text{ms}^{-1}$ in a direction due East, represented by a vector $\overrightarrow{BC} = \mathbf{b}$. Find the speed relative to the ground and the direction of travel.

The velocity vector for the aeroplane is found by adding these vectors:

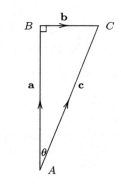

$$\mathbf{c} = \mathbf{a} + \mathbf{b}.$$

The speed is the magnitude, found by using Pythagoras's Theorem on the triangle in the diagram.

$$|\mathbf{c}| = \sqrt{120^2 + 50^2} = \sqrt{16900}$$
$$= 130 \text{ ms}^{-1}.$$

The direction of travel is that of $\mathbf{c}$, at angle θ, East of North:

$$\tan\theta = \frac{50}{120} \quad \Rightarrow \quad \theta = 22.6°.$$

∎

Using this idea of addition, $\overrightarrow{AB} + \overrightarrow{BA}$ does nothing: it moves us from A to A. Such a vector is the **zero vector**, written $\mathbf{0}$, which has magnitude 0 and no defined direction.

We can now argue that

$$\overrightarrow{AB} + \overrightarrow{BA} = \mathbf{0} \quad \Rightarrow \quad \overrightarrow{BA} = -\overrightarrow{AB},$$

where, as noted earlier, $\overrightarrow{BA}$ is precisely the *reverse* of $\overrightarrow{AB}$: it has the same magnitude but points in the opposite direction. This provides a method for **subtraction** of vectors:

$$\mathbf{a} - \mathbf{b} = \mathbf{a} + (-\mathbf{b}), \qquad -\mathbf{b} \text{ is the reverse of } \mathbf{b}.$$

Since the vectors we are using are *free*, we can move one of them, parallel to itself, so that its tail joins the tail of the other. If we complete, using parallel lines, a **parallelogram**, we find an alternative addition law.

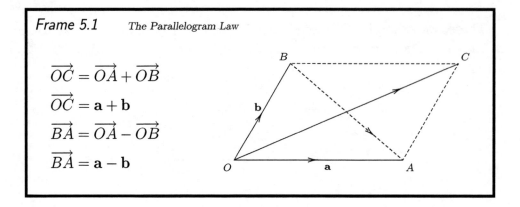

Frame 5.1   *The Parallelogram Law*

$$\overrightarrow{OC} = \overrightarrow{OA} + \overrightarrow{OB}$$
$$\overrightarrow{OC} = \mathbf{a} + \mathbf{b}$$
$$\overrightarrow{BA} = \overrightarrow{OA} - \overrightarrow{OB}$$
$$\overrightarrow{BA} = \mathbf{a} - \mathbf{b}$$

The addition rule is justified by noting that $\overrightarrow{AC} = \overrightarrow{OB}$, since they are equal in length and parallel, and using the head-to-tail addition method. The subtraction rule follows from

$$\overrightarrow{OB} + \overrightarrow{BA} = \overrightarrow{OA} \quad \Rightarrow \quad \overrightarrow{BA} = \overrightarrow{OA} - \overrightarrow{OB} = \mathbf{a} - \mathbf{b}.$$

Which of the two addition methods is used depends on the context of the calculation. A rough guide is that the "triangle" method is more common when using free vectors, while the parallelogram rule is invaluable with the position vectors in §5.3.

Also of great use, when working with position vectors, is the following expression for $\overrightarrow{AB}$, the reverse of $\overrightarrow{BA}$:

$$\overrightarrow{AB} = \overrightarrow{OB} - \overrightarrow{OA} = \mathbf{b} - \mathbf{a}. \qquad (5.1)$$

This vector is sometimes referred to as the position of B **relative to** A.

Developing this idea of relative position, vector addition is a useful way of **translating** a set of points, i.e., moving them all through the same distance in the same direction. This can sometimes make a problem much easier; it can then be solved and the points translated back to their original positions, by subtraction.

Example 5.5   Find the shortest pipeline from A to B, if the river must be crossed at right angles.

Let B' be the nearest point to B, on the river bank. Translate A to A' and B to B', using the vector $\overrightarrow{BB'}$.

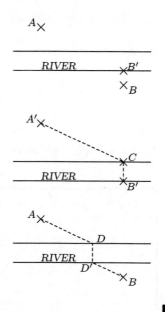

The answer is now clear: the pipeline goes from A' to C to B'.

We now translate back, using $-\overrightarrow{BB'}$. We retain the direction of the land-based pipeline until it meets the river at D; then cross the river to D' and continue to B in the initial direction.

We see that $|\overrightarrow{AD}| + |\overrightarrow{D'B}| = |\overrightarrow{A'C}|$ and $|\overrightarrow{CB'}| = |\overrightarrow{DD'}|$, so the pipeline lengths before and after the final translation are the same.

■

Finally, there is no simple rule for $|\mathbf{u} + \mathbf{v}|$. The best we can say is the following:

$$|\mathbf{u} + \mathbf{v}| \leqslant |\mathbf{u}| + |\mathbf{v}|, \qquad (5.2)$$

This is known as the **triangle inequality**. It gets that name since, in any triangle, one side cannot be longer than the sum of the lengths of the other two sides.

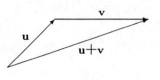

Ex 5.2 Consider a triangle ABC. Find the sum: $\overrightarrow{AB} + \overrightarrow{BC} + \overrightarrow{CA}$.

Ex 5.3 Three forces act on a body: $5\,\mathrm{N}$ in the positive x-direction, $7\,\mathrm{N}$ in the negative x-direction and $2\,\mathrm{N}$ in the negative y-direction. What is the net force?

Ex 5.4 Consider the cube shown below. Let $\mathbf{p} = \overrightarrow{AB}$, $\mathbf{q} = \overrightarrow{AD}$ and $\mathbf{r} = \overrightarrow{AE}$. Express $\overrightarrow{BD}$, $\overrightarrow{AC}$ and $\overrightarrow{AG}$ in terms of $\mathbf{p}$, $\mathbf{q}$ and $\mathbf{r}$. Which points are connected by the vector $\mathbf{p} - \mathbf{q} + \mathbf{r}$?

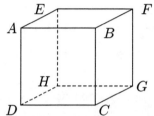

Ex 5.5 A force $\mathbf{F}_1$, with magnitude $3\,\mathrm{N}$, and a second force $\mathbf{F}_2$, with magnitude $5\,\mathrm{N}$ act on a particle; they make an angle of $60°$ with each other. Use trigonometric calculations to find the magnitude of the resultant force and the angle it makes to the force $\mathbf{F}_1$.

5.2   Scaling Vectors

Our concept of addition, applied to a single vector $\mathbf{a}$

$$\xrightarrow{\hspace{2cm}\mathbf{a}\hspace{2cm}\mathbf{a}\hspace{2cm}}$$

shows $2\mathbf{a} = \mathbf{a} + \mathbf{a}$ is a vector in the same direction as $\mathbf{a}$, but with twice the magnitude. This generalises to provide a way of **scaling** vectors.

Frame 5.2   Scaled vector

$k > 0 :$ $k\mathbf{v}$ is in direction of $\mathbf{v}$, with magnitude $k|\mathbf{v}|$

$k < 0 :$ $k\mathbf{v}$ reverses direction of $\mathbf{v}$, with magnitude $-k|\mathbf{v}|$

The negative case is consistent with our previous interpretation of $-\mathbf{v}$ as $\mathbf{v}$ with its direction reversed.

Any non-zero vector has one particularly important scale factor associated with it: the scaling that produces a length of one, i.e., a **unit vector**.

Frame 5.3   *Unit vector in direction of* **v**

$$\hat{\mathbf{v}} = \frac{\mathbf{v}}{|\mathbf{v}|} \text{ has direction of } \mathbf{v} \text{ and magnitude } 1$$

The notation used here, $\hat{\mathbf{v}}$, is common, although not a universal one.

This relationship between $k\mathbf{v}$ and $\mathbf{v}$ is very useful in analysing geometrical situations. It delivers a test for lines – interpreted as vectors – being **parallel**:

$$\mathbf{a} = k\mathbf{b} \quad \Rightarrow \quad \mathbf{a} \text{ is parallel to } \mathbf{b}.$$

If we can also show that $\mathbf{a}$ and $\mathbf{b}$ have a point in common, they must lie along the same line, i.e., they are **collinear**.

Example 5.6   Join the mid-points of two sides of a triangle, as in the diagram.

E is the midpoint of OA and F is the mid-point of OB. Then:

$$\overrightarrow{OE} = \tfrac{1}{2}\overrightarrow{OA}, \qquad \overrightarrow{OF} = \tfrac{1}{2}\overrightarrow{OB},$$
$$\overrightarrow{EF} = \overrightarrow{OF} - \overrightarrow{OE}$$
$$= \tfrac{1}{2}\left(\overrightarrow{OB} - \overrightarrow{OA}\right) = \tfrac{1}{2}\overrightarrow{AB}.$$

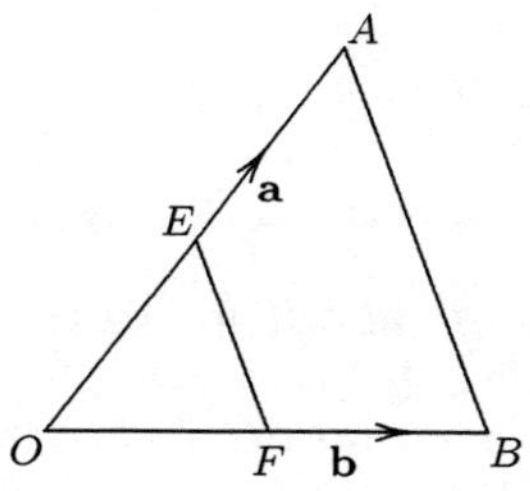

This proves that EF is parallel to AB and is half its length. Note the extensive use of (5.1), a common feature in solving geometrical problems using vector methods.

This argument can also be applied using the simpler notation:

$$\overrightarrow{OE} = \tfrac{1}{2}\mathbf{a}, \quad \overrightarrow{OF} = \tfrac{1}{2}\mathbf{b}, \quad \overrightarrow{EF} = \tfrac{1}{2}(\mathbf{b} - \mathbf{a}) = \tfrac{1}{2}\overrightarrow{AB},$$

and so on.   ∎

Ex 5.6 Let $\mathbf{u}$ be a unit vector in the direction from A to B. What is $|\overrightarrow{AB}|\mathbf{u}$?

Ex 5.7 A triangle has vertices labelled A, B and C. Let P, Q and R be the midpoints of the sides AB, BC and AC. Denote the vectors $\overrightarrow{AB}$ and $\overrightarrow{AC}$ by $\mathbf{b}$ and $\mathbf{c}$, respectively. Draw a labelled diagram.

(a) Express $\overrightarrow{BC}$ in terms of $\mathbf{b}$ and $\mathbf{c}$.

(b) Express $\overrightarrow{BR}$ in terms of $\mathbf{b}$ and $\mathbf{c}$.

(c) Show that $\overrightarrow{PR} = \tfrac{1}{2}\overrightarrow{BC}$ and interpret what this means.

(d) Let M be the midpoint of PR; express $\overrightarrow{MB}$ in terms of $\mathbf{b}$ and $\mathbf{c}$.

5.3 Position Vectors

Vectors become even more powerful when we introduce a numerical representation. This allows geometrical problems to be solved computationally; a prime example is computer graphics.

We obtain a numerical representation by superimposing a **coordinate system**. The link to this is the idea of a **position vector**, which is like the vectors we have been using to date except that one end is fixed, at O: the origin of the coordinate system. The coordinates of the other end of the vector are the numbers we use to represent the vector.

Before looking at the details, we need to be reassured that this can deliver **free** or **displacement vectors**. The method has already been seen in §5.1.

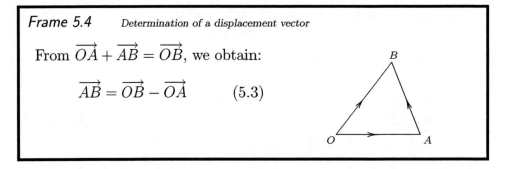

Frame 5.4   *Determination of a displacement vector*

From $\overrightarrow{OA} + \overrightarrow{AB} = \overrightarrow{OB}$, we obtain:

$$\overrightarrow{AB} = \overrightarrow{OB} - \overrightarrow{OA} \qquad (5.3)$$

Think about it like this

Pay particular attention to the order in (5.3): the position vector for the **end** point **minus** that for the **start** point. This is the natural way to measure things; distance: where we finish minus where we start; monthly savings: bank account now minus bank account last month.

We shall concentrate on three-dimensional space; it is straightforward to convert to the easier to visualise two-dimensional plane. There is an issue with such coordinate systems that affects some vector work, but is not relevant in this chapter: is the system left- or right-handed? The one in the diagram on the next page is right-handed (the usual preference) if O is in the "background" of the picture, which most people find easier to visualise. But it is possible to make sense of the diagram by forcing O into the "foreground", when the system is left-handed.

Our target (position) vector is $\overrightarrow{OP}$. Projecting P vertically downwards onto the xy-plane fixes the point Q. Using the parallelogram law, gives

$$\overrightarrow{OQ} = \overrightarrow{OX} + \overrightarrow{OY}.$$

Apply the same law to the vertical parallelogram to find:

$$\mathbf{v} = \overrightarrow{OP} = \overrightarrow{OQ} + \overrightarrow{OZ}$$
$$= \overrightarrow{OX} + \overrightarrow{OY} + \overrightarrow{OZ}.$$

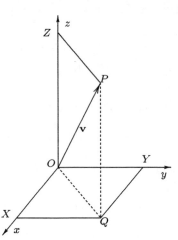

Suppose that P has cartesian coordinates (a, b, c). Then the key points in the diagram are:

$$X : \ (a, 0, 0), \qquad Y : \ (0, b, 0), \qquad Z : \ (0, 0, c).$$

Define $\mathbf{i}$, $\mathbf{j}$ and $\mathbf{k}$ be the **unit** vectors pointing along the x-, y- and z-axes respectively.

Then $\overrightarrow{OX} = a\,\mathbf{i}$, $\overrightarrow{OY} = b\,\mathbf{j}$ and $\overrightarrow{OZ} = c\,\mathbf{k}$ and we obtain the desired expression for our vector:

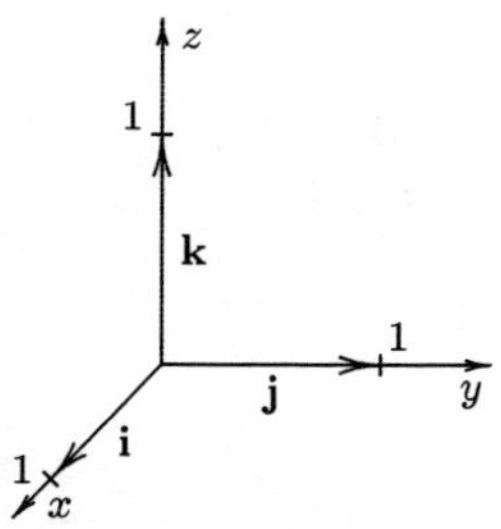

$$\mathbf{v} = \overrightarrow{OP} = a\,\mathbf{i} + b\,\mathbf{j} + c\,\mathbf{k}. \qquad (5.4)$$

a, b and c are the **components** of the vector $\mathbf{v}$. We shall see, in the computational examples that follow, that $\mathbf{i}$, $\mathbf{j}$ and $\mathbf{k}$ are not the only ways to link the vector to its components. The basic job that these three vectors do is to keep the components apart and to label them so that we know which is which. There are other ways of doing this, e.g.,

$$(a, b, c), \quad \text{or} \quad \begin{pmatrix} a \\ b \\ c \end{pmatrix} \quad \text{or} \quad \begin{bmatrix} a \\ b \\ c \end{bmatrix}.$$

We shall make much use of the first of these in vector geometry. It can be read as a shorthand for (5.4), with the unit vectors there, but invisible.

The unit nature of $\mathbf{i}$, $\mathbf{j}$ and $\mathbf{k}$ is essential, to ensure they play a neutral role in the magnitude of $\mathbf{v}$, which we shall see later is fixed by a, b and c.

The arithmetic operations we have introduced are straightforward, using either format.

Example 5.7 Let $\mathbf{a} = 2\mathbf{i} + \mathbf{j} + 4\mathbf{k}$, $\quad \mathbf{b} = \mathbf{i} - 2\mathbf{j} - 3\mathbf{k}$.

$$\mathbf{a} + \mathbf{b} = (2 + 1)\mathbf{i} + (1 - 2)\mathbf{j} + (4 - 3)\mathbf{k} = 3\mathbf{i} - \mathbf{j} + \mathbf{k},$$
$$\mathbf{a} - \mathbf{b} = \big(2 - 1, 1 - (-2), 4 - (-3)\big) = (1, 3, 7).$$

∎

Example 5.8 Let $\mathbf{a} = \mathbf{i} - \mathbf{j}$, $\quad \mathbf{b} = 2\mathbf{j} - \mathbf{k}$.

$$3\mathbf{a} - 2\mathbf{b} = 3\mathbf{i} - 3\mathbf{j} - (2\mathbf{j} - 2\mathbf{k}),$$
$$= 3\mathbf{i} - 5\mathbf{j} + 2\mathbf{k}.$$

∎

Vector algebra of this sort is very powerful in physical situations. The following is a typical calculation.

Example 5.9 Two particles, with masses and velocities

$$m_1 = 3, \quad \mathbf{v}_1 = (2, 0, -1); \qquad m_2 = 2, \quad \mathbf{v}_2 = (-1, 2, 1);$$

collide and stick together, travelling thereafter with velocity $\mathbf{u}$.

Conservation of momentum tells us that the new particle, with mass 5, has the same momentum as the **vector** sum of the individual particles:

$$5\mathbf{u} = 3\mathbf{v}_1 + 2\mathbf{v}_2$$
$$= (6,0,-3) + (-2,4,2) = (4,4,-1),$$

and hence $\mathbf{u} = (4/5, 4/5, -1/5)$. ∎

We can also analyse the various lengths in the diagram displaying the components for $\mathbf{v}$. Use Pythagoras's Theorem:

$$|\overrightarrow{OQ}|^2 = |\overrightarrow{OX}|^2 + |\overrightarrow{OY}|^2 = a^2 + b^2,$$
$$|\overrightarrow{OP}|^2 = |\overrightarrow{OQ}|^2 + |\overrightarrow{OZ}|^2 = a^2 + b^2 + c^2.$$

Frame 5.5   *The magnitude of a vector*

$$|(a,b,c)| = \sqrt{a^2 + b^2 + c^2} \qquad (5.5)$$

Example 5.10   Returning to Example 5.9,

$$|\mathbf{v}_1| = \sqrt{4+0+1} = \sqrt{5} \simeq 2.24$$
$$|\mathbf{v}_2| = \sqrt{1+4+1} = \sqrt{6} \simeq 2.45$$
$$|\mathbf{u}| = \tfrac{1}{5}\sqrt{16+16+1} = \tfrac{1}{5}\sqrt{33} \simeq 1.15$$

Note the way in which the common factor $\frac{1}{5}$ was "taken out of" the square root at the start of the calculation, which made it easier to carry out.

The final velocity is smaller than the initial ones, showing the way the vectors handle the fact that the particles collide at an angle: the magnitudes of the individual momenta (mass times speed) do not add up, which is an illustration of the *triangle inequality*. ∎

Think about it like this

The formula in Frame 5.5 squares all the components and so ensures that all numbers therein are positive or zero. When they are added, cancellation is impossible. That means that the formula is always well-defined – we are never faced with the square root of a negative number – and $|\mathbf{v}| = 0$ only if all components of $\mathbf{v}$ are zero, i.e., $\mathbf{v}$ itself is the zero vector.

The formula for the magnitude allows us to measure the **distance** from A to B, as $|\overrightarrow{AB}|$ or, equivalently, $|\overrightarrow{BA}|$. This is exactly the same as the formula from coordinate geometry for the distance between (a_1, a_2, a_3) and (b_1, b_2, b_3).

Example 5.11   Suppose A and B have position vectors $\mathbf{a} = (1,-3,4)$ and $\mathbf{b} = (3,-2,1)$, respectively. (This is a common notational device: use the equivalent lower case letter for the position vector of a point given by an upper case letter.)

$$\overrightarrow{AB} = \mathbf{b} - \mathbf{a} = (2, 1, -3),$$

$$\text{Distance } A \text{ to } B = |\overrightarrow{AB}| = \sqrt{4 + 1 + 9} = \sqrt{14}.$$

∎

We now have a numerical method for constructing a **unit vector** in a given direction, implementing Frame 5.3.

Example 5.12 First of all, note the consistency of the definition for a vector we already know to be unit:

$$|\mathbf{i}| = \sqrt{1 + 0 + 0} = 1, \qquad (\text{and similarly for } \mathbf{j}, \ \mathbf{k}).$$

Now let $\mathbf{a} = (1, 1, -2)$, so $|\mathbf{a}| = \sqrt{1 + 1 + 4} = \sqrt{6}$. Hence

$$\hat{\mathbf{a}} = \frac{1}{\sqrt{6}} (1, 1, -2) = \left(\frac{1}{\sqrt{6}}, \frac{1}{\sqrt{6}}, -\frac{2}{\sqrt{6}} \right)$$

is a unit vector in the direction of $\mathbf{a}$.

∎

The next example anticipates a calculation related to bonds in chemical compounds.

Example 5.13 A **regular tetrahedron** is a triangular pyramid with all its sides equal: each of its four faces is an equilateral triangle.

Find the point S, lying above the triangle PQR (in the direction of $\mathbf{k}$ or the positive z-axis) so that $PQRS$ is a regular tetrahedron.

This assumes that $\triangle PQR$ is already equilateral, which is readily checked.

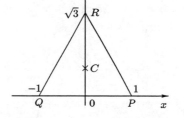

We first find the **centre** or **centroid** of $\triangle PQR$, a sort of "average" of the corners. The precise formula, which will be confirmed in §5.10, is

$$\overrightarrow{OC} = \frac{1}{3} \left(\overrightarrow{OP} + \overrightarrow{OQ} + \overrightarrow{OR} \right)$$

$$= \frac{1}{3} \left(\mathbf{i} - \mathbf{i} + \sqrt{3}\mathbf{j} \right) = \frac{\sqrt{3}}{3}\mathbf{j}.$$

Since S must lie directly above C, due to the symmetry,

$$\overrightarrow{OS} = \overrightarrow{OC} + t\mathbf{k} \quad (\text{for some } t)$$

$$= \frac{\sqrt{3}}{3}\mathbf{j} + t\mathbf{k}.$$

Then one of the sloping sides has vector

$$\overrightarrow{SR} = \overrightarrow{OR} - \overrightarrow{OS} = \sqrt{3}\mathbf{j} - \left(\frac{\sqrt{3}}{3}\mathbf{j} + t\mathbf{k} \right)$$

$$= \frac{2\sqrt{3}}{3}\mathbf{j} - t\mathbf{k},$$

whose length can be found from

$$|\overrightarrow{SR}|^2 = \left(\frac{2\sqrt{3}}{3} \right)^2 + t^2 = \frac{4}{3} + t^2.$$

Now, from the diagram, $|\overrightarrow{PQ}| = 2$ and we require, because of the regularity, $|\overrightarrow{SR}|^2 = |\overrightarrow{PQ}|^2$:

$$\frac{4}{3} + t^2 = 4 \quad \Rightarrow \quad t^2 = \frac{8}{3} = \frac{24}{9} \quad \Rightarrow \quad t = \frac{2\sqrt{6}}{3},$$

where we choose the $+$ sign since we seek the point "above". (There is a second regular tetrahedron, lying below $\triangle PQR$.) Hence the solution is that S is $\left(0, \frac{\sqrt{3}}{3}, \frac{2\sqrt{6}}{3} \right)$.   ∎

Ex 5.8 For the points $A\,(-2, 3, 4)$, $B\,(7, -5, -2)$, $C\,(4, 8, 17)$ with position vectors **a**, **b** and **c** respectively,

(a) verify that $\overrightarrow{AB} + \overrightarrow{BC} = \overrightarrow{AC}$;

(b) evaluate $\mathbf{c} - 2\mathbf{a}$ and $|\mathbf{a} - \mathbf{b}|$;

(c) what is the distance from A to B?

Ex 5.9 Let $\mathbf{a} = (1, 0, 1)$, $\mathbf{b} = (2, 1, 2)$ and $\mathbf{c} = (1, 1, -1)$. Calculate the following:

(a) $\mathbf{a} + \mathbf{b} + \mathbf{c}$ (b) $\mathbf{b} - 2\mathbf{c}$ (c) $\frac{1}{2}(\mathbf{a} + \mathbf{b})$ (d) $|\mathbf{a}|$ (e) $|\mathbf{b}|$ (f) $|\mathbf{b} + \mathbf{c}|$

(g) the distance between **a** and **c**   (h) a unit vector in the direction of **b**

Ex 5.10 Given $\mathbf{p} = 2\mathbf{i} + \alpha\mathbf{j} + \mathbf{k}$ and $\mathbf{q} = \mathbf{i} - \mathbf{k}$, find values of α for which $|\mathbf{p} - \mathbf{q}| = 3$.

5.4 Resolution of Vectors

To take advantage of this numerical representation, we must find a way to calculate the components of a vector when given its magnitude and direction: a process known as **resolution**.

We start in two dimensions. If **v** has magnitude r and is at angle θ to the x-axis, simple trigonometry gives:

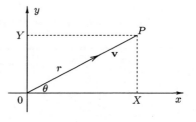

$$\overrightarrow{OX} = (r\cos\theta)\mathbf{i}, \quad \overrightarrow{OY} = (r\sin\theta)\mathbf{j}.$$

These remain true in all quadrants and add to give $\overrightarrow{OP}$.

Frame 5.6   *Components for vector, magnitude r, at θ to x-axis*

$$\mathbf{v} = (r\cos\theta)\,\mathbf{i} + (r\sin\theta)\,\mathbf{j}$$

Example 5.14   A vector **u** has magnitude 6 and is at 30° to the x-axis.

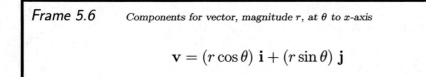

$$\mathbf{u} = (6\cos 30°)\,\mathbf{i} + (6\sin 30°)\,\mathbf{j} = 3\sqrt{3}\mathbf{i} + 3\mathbf{j}$$

■

This process makes straightforward the addition of vectors, initially specified by magnitudes and angles.

Example 5.15   [A continuation of the previous example] Suppose that **v** has magnitude 8 and is at angle $-120°$ to the x-axis.

First, convert $-120°$ to $120°$ by adjusting the sign of $\sin\theta$:

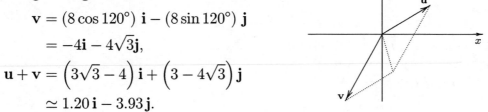

$$\mathbf{v} = (8\cos 120°)\,\mathbf{i} - (8\sin 120°)\,\mathbf{j}$$
$$= -4\mathbf{i} - 4\sqrt{3}\mathbf{j},$$
$$\mathbf{u} + \mathbf{v} = \left(3\sqrt{3} - 4\right)\mathbf{i} + \left(3 - 4\sqrt{3}\right)\mathbf{j}$$
$$\simeq 1.20\,\mathbf{i} - 3.93\,\mathbf{j}.$$

The parallelogram superimposed on the diagram confirms that this is a valid result. ■

To benefit fully from this arithmetical method, we need to be able to reverse the process, i.e., to deduce the magnitude and angle from the components.

Suppose, then, that we have $\mathbf{v} = (a, b)$ and we wish to find its magnitude r and the angle θ it makes with the x-axis. Finding r is straightforward, since the two-dimensional version of (5.5) gives

$$r = \sqrt{a^2 + b^2}.$$

There are three equations that could now give the angle:

$$\cos\theta = \frac{a}{r}, \qquad \sin\theta = \frac{b}{r}, \qquad \tan\theta = \frac{b}{a}.$$

None of these, on its own, will suffice since each gives two possible angles in $(-180°, 180°]$ or, if preferred, $[0°, 360°)$. Since tan has the simplest period, $180°$, the best procedure is as follows:

Frame 5.7   *Determination of magnitude and direction for (a,b)*

(a) $r = +\sqrt{a^2 + b^2}$ $(r > 0)$

(b) Use the signs of $\cos\theta$ (same as that of a) and $\sin\theta$ (same as that of b) to find which quadrant θ is in. (Drawing a sketch, to confirm the quadrant, is recommended.)

(c) Find $\phi = \tan^{-1}\dfrac{b}{a}$

(d) $\theta = \phi$ if the quadrants are the same, else $\theta = \phi \pm 180°$ (according to preference; these two angles are the same)

Think about it like this

This method appears several times: the determination of the **argument** of a **complex number** and the angle in **polar coordinates** require the same steps. Indeed, they are directly equivalent processes. The steps are also similar to those for finding the **phase** for a sinusoid.

Example 5.16   Find the magnitude and direction for $\mathbf{v} = 3\mathbf{i} - 4\mathbf{j}$.

$$r = |\mathbf{v}| = \sqrt{3^2 + (-4)^2} = \sqrt{25} = 5.$$

Since $\cos\theta > 0$ and $\sin\theta < 0$, we know that θ lies in Quadrant 4, as confirmed by the sketch.

Using a calculator,

$$\tan\phi = \frac{-4}{3} = -\frac{4}{3} \quad \Rightarrow \quad \phi = -53.13°.$$

Since this is also in Quadrant 4, $\theta = -53.13°$.

∎

Example 5.17   Find the magnitude and direction for $\mathbf{v} = -4\mathbf{i} + 4\mathbf{j}$.

$$r = |\mathbf{v}| = 4\sqrt{(-1)^2 + 1^2} = 4\sqrt{2} = 4\sqrt{2}.$$

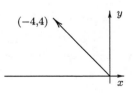

Since $\cos\theta < 0$ and $\sin\theta > 0$, we know that θ lies in Quadrant 2, as confirmed by the sketch.

This time the angle is a simple one:

$$\tan\phi = \frac{4}{-4} = -1 \quad \Rightarrow \quad \phi = -45°.$$

Since this is in Quadrant 4, we must adjust to $\theta = (-45 + 180)° = 135°$. ■

Example 5.18 Returning to Example 5.15, where $\mathbf{u} + \mathbf{v} \simeq 1.20\mathbf{i} - 3.93\mathbf{j}$,

$$|\mathbf{u} + \mathbf{v}| \simeq \sqrt{1.20^2 + 3.93^2} = 4.11,$$
$$\tan\phi \simeq -2.75 \quad \Rightarrow \quad \phi \simeq 70°,$$

which is also θ, since the quadrant is correct ($\cos +$, $\sin -$). ■

There is an alternative way to write the resolution in Frame 5.6. This provides one way to extend the procedure to three dimensions, although we shall return to that in §5.7.

$$\mathbf{v} = (r\cos\theta_x)\,\mathbf{i} + (r\cos\theta_y)\,\mathbf{j},$$

since $\theta_x = 90° - \theta_y$ and hence $\sin\theta_x = \cos\theta_y$, using the **complementary angles** rule.

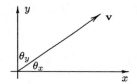

We now pursue this into a third dimension as follows:

$$\mathbf{v} = r\left[\frac{a}{r}\mathbf{i} + \frac{b}{r}\mathbf{j} + \frac{c}{r}\mathbf{k}\right].$$

Each of $d_x = \frac{a}{r}$, $d_y = \frac{b}{r}$, $d_z = \frac{c}{r}$ lies between -1 and 1 and hence there exist angles such that

$$\cos\theta_x = d_x, \qquad \cos\theta_y = d_y, \qquad \cos\theta_z = d_z. \tag{5.6}$$

Using these angles, we have

$$\mathbf{v} = r\,(d_x, d_y, d_z) = r\,[\cos\theta_x\,\mathbf{i} + \cos\theta_y\,\mathbf{j} + \cos\theta_z\,\mathbf{k}]. \tag{5.7}$$

The numbers d_x, d_y and d_z are the **direction cosines (dc)** for the vector **v**. From them we can calculate the angles a vector makes with each axis.

Example 5.19 Let $\mathbf{v} = (9, 2, -6)$, so $|\mathbf{v}| = \sqrt{81 + 4 + 36} = 11$. Then, the direction cosines are $d_x = \frac{9}{11}$, $d_y = \frac{2}{11}$ and $d_z = -\frac{6}{11}$. Using the $\cos^{-1}$ key on a calculator delivers the approximate angles:

$$35° \ (x\text{-axis}), \qquad 80° \ (y\text{-axis}), \qquad 123° \ (z\text{-axis}).$$

■

Ex 5.11 Find the components for the vector with magnitude 2, at 30° to the (positive) x-axis.

Ex 5.12

(a) Find the components for a vector of magnitude 10, making an angle of 45° **to the left of** the positive y-axis.

(b) Find the magnitude and direction of the vector $5\mathbf{i} - 12\mathbf{j}$.

(c) Repeat Exercise 5.5, using components, with $\mathbf{i}$ pointing in the direction of $\mathbf{F}_1$.

Ex 5.13

(a) Find a unit vector in the direction of $\mathbf{r} = 2\mathbf{i} + \mathbf{j} - 2\mathbf{k}$. Find the direction cosines for $\mathbf{r}$ and the angles it makes with each coordinate axis.

(b) Using the position vectors in Exercise 5.9, find the vectors $\overrightarrow{AC}$ and $\overrightarrow{BC}$. What are their direction cosines?

(c) A vector makes an angle 45° with the positive x-axis and an angle 120° with the positive y-axis. What possible angles can it make with the positive z axis?

5.5   The Scalar or "dot" Product

Since vectors contain a direction, determined by angles made with some framework such as a cartesian coordinate system, it is reasonable to assume that they are capable of providing angle measurements. The key to this is one of two standard *products* of two vectors. (The other does not feature in this chapter.)

The product we now consider has three common names: the **scalar, inner** and **dot product**. We shall use the last of these: *scalar* runs the risk of confusion with $\alpha\mathbf{v}$, i.e., multiplication by a scalar, while *inner* is often used in more theoretical contexts. *dot* simply refers to the notation used to show the product of the two vectors and so reminds one that it is different from the other product, written with a *cross* ✕.

Frame 5.8   *The dot product of* $\mathbf{u}$ *and* $\mathbf{v}$

$$\mathbf{u} \bullet \mathbf{v} = (a_1, b_1, c_1) \bullet (a_2, b_2, c_2) = a_1a_2 + b_1b_2 + c_1c_2 \qquad (5.8)$$

This is the three-dimensional form. It can be used in any number of dimensions, through an obvious adjustment, e.g., in two dimensions, we remove the c_1c_2 term.

It is essential to note that the result is a scalar (number). The "cross" product produces a vector, so this is another way to distinguish between the two products.

Example 5.20 Consider various dot products with $\mathbf{u} = (1, -1, 2)$.

$$(1, -1, 2) \bullet (2, 1, 1) = 1 \times 2 - 1 \times 1 + 2 \times 1 = 2 - 1 + 2 = 3$$
$$(1, -1, 2) \bullet (2, 0, -2) = 2 - 0 - 4 = -2$$
$$(1, -1, 2) \bullet (1, -1, -1) = 1 + 1 - 2 = 0$$

This shows the result can be positive, negative, or even zero. ∎

There is a second formula for $\mathbf{u} \bullet \mathbf{v}$, which includes an angle. The fact that the two are identical is proved using the *cosine rule*: see Example 1.29.

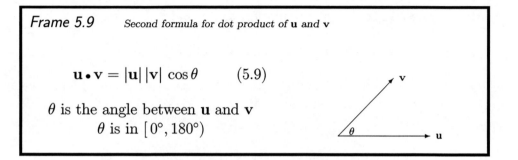

Frame 5.9   *Second formula for dot product of* $\mathbf{u}$ *and* $\mathbf{v}$

$$\mathbf{u} \bullet \mathbf{v} = |\mathbf{u}|\,|\mathbf{v}|\cos\theta \qquad (5.9)$$

θ is the angle between $\mathbf{u}$ and $\mathbf{v}$
θ is in $[0°, 180°)$

In almost all circumstances, the two formulae have different uses:

- (5.8) is used to **calculate** $\mathbf{u} \bullet \mathbf{v}$

- (5.9) is used to **interpret** the result

Suppose that $\mathbf{r} = (a, b, c)$. Then Frame 5.8 gives a very useful link between the dot product and the magnitude:

$$\mathbf{r} \bullet \mathbf{r} = (a, b, c) \bullet (a, b, c) = a^2 + b^2 + c^2 = |\mathbf{r}|^2. \qquad (5.10)$$

This can also be proved using the alternative formula in Frame 5.9:

$$\mathbf{r} \bullet \mathbf{r} = |\mathbf{r}|\,|\mathbf{r}|\cos 0° = |\mathbf{r}|^2.$$

Now consider the link with $\mathbf{i}$, $\mathbf{j}$ and $\mathbf{k}$:

$$\mathbf{r} \bullet \mathbf{i} = (a, b, c) \bullet (1, 0, 0) = a + 0 + 0 = a,$$

while $\mathbf{r} \bullet \mathbf{j} = b$ and $\mathbf{r} \bullet \mathbf{k} = c$. Hence "dotting" a vector with $\mathbf{i}$, $\mathbf{j}$ and $\mathbf{k}$ appears to pick off its coefficients. This proves to be a very useful idea, providing ideas for several later calculations.

As a special case, we have:

$$\mathbf{i} \bullet \mathbf{j} = (1, 0, 0) \bullet (0, 1, 0) = 0 + 0 + 0 = 0,$$

which can also be obtained using (5.9), since these vectors are at right angles to each other and $\cos 90° = 0$. Similarly, $\mathbf{j} \bullet \mathbf{k} = \mathbf{k} \bullet \mathbf{i} = 0$, as are the products in the opposite order, since

$$\mathbf{v} \bullet \mathbf{u} = \mathbf{u} \bullet \mathbf{v}$$

is true in general, as seen from (5.8).

There are other "obvious" general rules. Among the most useful are

$$(k\mathbf{u})\bullet\mathbf{v} = \mathbf{u}\bullet(k\mathbf{v}) = k(\mathbf{u}\bullet\mathbf{v}), \tag{5.11}$$

$$\mathbf{u}\bullet(\mathbf{v}+\mathbf{w}) = \mathbf{u}\bullet\mathbf{v}+\mathbf{u}\bullet\mathbf{w}. \tag{5.12}$$

But note the non-existent rule:

$$\mathbf{a}\bullet\mathbf{u} = \mathbf{b}\bullet\mathbf{u} \quad \text{does } \mathbf{not} \text{ imply} \quad \mathbf{a}=\mathbf{b},$$

illustrated by $\mathbf{i}\bullet\mathbf{j} = \mathbf{i}\bullet\mathbf{k}\,(=0)$, with $\mathbf{j}\neq\mathbf{k}$.

It is a long and technical calculation to expand

$$\mathbf{u}\bullet\mathbf{v} = (a_1\mathbf{i}+b_1\mathbf{j}+c_1\mathbf{k})\bullet(a_2\mathbf{i}+b_2\mathbf{j}+c_2\mathbf{k}),$$

using such rules. The end result, fortunately, is $a_1a_2+b_1b_2+c_1c_2$, using $\mathbf{i}\bullet\mathbf{j}=0$, $\mathbf{i}\bullet\mathbf{i}=|\mathbf{i}|^2=1$ and similar values.

Example 5.21 Expanding in similar style, we find

$$(\mathbf{u}-\mathbf{v})\bullet(\mathbf{u}+\mathbf{v}) = \mathbf{u}\bullet\mathbf{u}+\mathbf{u}\bullet\mathbf{v}-\mathbf{v}\bullet\mathbf{u}-\mathbf{v}\bullet\mathbf{v}$$
$$= \mathbf{u}\bullet\mathbf{u}-\mathbf{v}\bullet\mathbf{v} = |\mathbf{u}|^2-|\mathbf{v}|^2.$$

∎

The most useful application of the two formulae for the dot product is the following rearrangement of (5.9):

$$\cos\theta = \frac{\mathbf{u}\bullet\mathbf{v}}{|\mathbf{u}|\,|\mathbf{v}|}. \tag{5.13}$$

Using (5.8) to find $\mathbf{u}\bullet\mathbf{v}$, we can then calculate θ.

This is straightforward to use for position vectors, when we seek the angle between them at their common end: the origin.

Example 5.22 Find the angle between $\mathbf{u}=(\sqrt{3},1)$ and $\mathbf{v}=(2,2\sqrt{3})$.

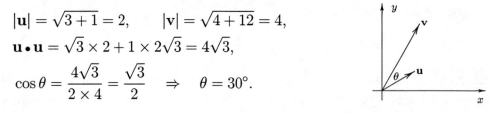

$$|\mathbf{u}|=\sqrt{3+1}=2, \qquad |\mathbf{v}|=\sqrt{4+12}=4,$$
$$\mathbf{u}\bullet\mathbf{u}=\sqrt{3}\times2+1\times2\sqrt{3}=4\sqrt{3},$$
$$\cos\theta=\frac{4\sqrt{3}}{2\times4}=\frac{\sqrt{3}}{2} \quad\Rightarrow\quad \theta=30°.$$

The result can be confirmed by noting that $\mathbf{u}$ makes an angle of 30° with the x-axis, and $\mathbf{v}$ an angle of 60°, a difference of 30°.   ∎

The next example is a two-dimensional one, buried within three dimensions. This time the vectors required are *not* position ones, so they must be constructed before applying (5.13).

Example 5.23 Find the size of $\angle BAC$ in the triangle ABC, where

$$A:\ (1,0,-1), \qquad B:\ (1,2,-2), \qquad C:\ (3,-1,0).$$

We require the angle between $\overrightarrow{AB}$ and $\overrightarrow{AC}$, which we must construct first:

$$\overrightarrow{AB} = \overrightarrow{OB} - \overrightarrow{OA} = (1, 2, -2) - (1, 0, -1) = (0, 2, -1),$$
$$\overrightarrow{AC} = \overrightarrow{OC} - \overrightarrow{OA} = (3, -1, 0) - (1, 0, -1) = (2, -1, 1).$$

Then collect the data:

$$\overrightarrow{AB} \bullet \overrightarrow{AC} = 0 - 2 - 1 = -3, \qquad |\overrightarrow{AB}| = \sqrt{5}, \qquad |\overrightarrow{AC}| = \sqrt{6},$$

and then calculate the angle:

$$\cos \angle BAC = \frac{-3}{\sqrt{5}\sqrt{6}} \quad \Rightarrow \quad \theta \simeq 123°.$$

∎

As a final example, we return to Example 5.13.

Example 5.24 A methane (CH_4) molecule has H atoms at corners of a regular tetrahedron, with the C atom at its centre. What is the angle between the CH bonds?

We shall see, in §5.10, that the centre of the tetrahedron $PQRS$ is the "average" of the position vectors for its corners, similar to the result we used for a triangle, in finding S. Hence, if the centre is K:

$$\overrightarrow{OK} = \frac{1}{4}\left[\overrightarrow{OP} + \overrightarrow{OQ} + \overrightarrow{OR} + \overrightarrow{OS}\right] = \frac{\sqrt{3}}{3}\mathbf{j} + \frac{\sqrt{6}}{6}\mathbf{k}.$$

Then two of the bonds are:

$$\overrightarrow{KP} = \overrightarrow{OP} - \overrightarrow{OK} = \left(1, -\frac{\sqrt{3}}{3}, -\frac{\sqrt{6}}{6}\right),$$
$$\overrightarrow{KQ} = \overrightarrow{OQ} - \overrightarrow{OK} = \left(-1, -\frac{\sqrt{3}}{3}, -\frac{\sqrt{6}}{6}\right),$$

and we find the angle as before:

$$\cos\theta = \frac{-1 + 3/9 + 6/36}{\left(\sqrt{1 + 1/3 + 1/6}\right)^2} = -\frac{1}{3},$$

which gives the angle as $\theta \simeq 109°.$ ∎

An important question to ask about $\mathbf{u} \bullet \mathbf{v}$ is: when is it at an *extreme* value? This has important applications in optimisation problems.

Assume that the vectors have fixed lengths, but the directions could vary. From (5.9), the **maximum** must occur when

$$\cos\theta = 1 \quad \Rightarrow \quad \theta = 0°, \quad \mathbf{u}, \mathbf{v} \text{ are parallel}, \quad \mathbf{u} = k\mathbf{v} \ (k > 0).$$

Similarly, the **minimum** is when

$$\cos\theta = -1 \quad \Rightarrow \quad \theta = 180°, \quad \mathbf{u}, \mathbf{v} \text{ are parallel}, \quad \mathbf{u} = k\mathbf{v} \ (k < 0).$$

Example 5.25   A mountain climber perceives a gradient of $-1/4$ to the East and $1/2$ to the North. What is the steepest ascent direction?

At angle θ N of E, the gradient is

$$\hat{\mathbf{u}} \bullet (-1/4, \ 1/2),$$

where $\hat{\mathbf{u}}$ is a unit vector in that direction. This will be a maximum when $\hat{\mathbf{u}} = k\,(-1/4, \ 1/2)$, for some k (to make it unit).

All that remains is to find the direction, as in Frame 5.7. We have

$$\tan\phi = \frac{1/2}{-1/4} = -2 \quad \Rightarrow \quad \phi = -63°.$$

But we see that θ is in the *second* quadrant, so the correct answer is

$$\theta = -63 + 180 = 117°.$$

The steepest **descent** direction is directly opposite – when the dot product is a minimum – at $-63°$. ∎

The dot product is used in scientific definitions, in multi-dimensional contexts. For example, the **work** done by a force F when it moves its point of application from A to B, in one dimension, is $F \times BA$. But in more dimensions the direction of the force is an important factor. This is accommodated by the definition:

$$W = \mathbf{F} \bullet \overrightarrow{AB}.$$

We now know that the force will do most work when its direction is the same as the direction from A to B, which is not surprising.

Example 5.26   Suppose that A is $(0,0)$ and B is $(1, \sqrt{3})$, where $\mathbf{F}$ has magnitude 10 at angle $30°$. (In the diagram, $\mathbf{F}$ and AB have different scales.)

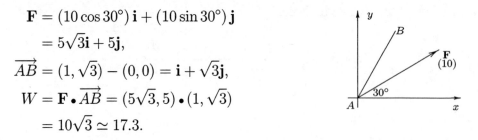

$$\mathbf{F} = (10\cos 30°)\,\mathbf{i} + (10\sin 30°)\,\mathbf{j}$$
$$= 5\sqrt{3}\mathbf{i} + 5\mathbf{j},$$
$$\overrightarrow{AB} = (1, \sqrt{3}) - (0,0) = \mathbf{i} + \sqrt{3}\mathbf{j},$$
$$W = \mathbf{F} \bullet \overrightarrow{AB} = (5\sqrt{3}, 5) \bullet (1, \sqrt{3})$$
$$= 10\sqrt{3} \simeq 17.3.$$

If, however, $\mathbf{F}$ is at $60°$ to the x-axis, $\mathbf{F} = (5, 5\sqrt{3})$ and $W = 5 + 15 = 20$, which is the maximum possible value. ∎

Ex 5.14   Given $\mathbf{u} = 4\mathbf{i} + 7\mathbf{j} + 3\mathbf{k}$ and $\mathbf{v} = 5\mathbf{i} - 2\mathbf{j} + \mathbf{k}$, evaluate $\mathbf{u} \bullet \mathbf{v}$ and calculate the angle between $\mathbf{u}$ and $\mathbf{v}$.

Ex 5.15 Let $\mathbf{a} = (2,0,-1)$, $\mathbf{b} = (1,-1,1)$, $\mathbf{c} = (-1,-2,2)$ and $\mathbf{d} = (0,1,3)$. Calculate the following:

(a) $\mathbf{a} \bullet \mathbf{i}$ (b) $\mathbf{d} \bullet \mathbf{k}$ (c) $\mathbf{a} \bullet \mathbf{b}$ (d) $\mathbf{c} \bullet \mathbf{d}$ (e) $(\mathbf{a} + \mathbf{d}) \bullet \mathbf{c}$

(f) $\hat{\mathbf{c}}$ (unit vector in direction of $\mathbf{c}$)   (g) $(\mathbf{b} \bullet \hat{\mathbf{c}})\hat{\mathbf{c}}$ (h) $\mathbf{b} - (\mathbf{b} \bullet \hat{\mathbf{c}})\hat{\mathbf{c}}$

Ex 5.16 Find the work done by the force $(1,-2,3)$ (magnitude in newtons) as it moves its point of application from $(2,0,-1)$ to $(5,2,-3)$ (in metres).

Ex 5.17 A body of mass 3 kg is to be moved. Gravity acts downwards with magnitude 30 N. To counter this a force $(0,0,30)$ must be applied. Find the work done by this force for each part of the journey: $(0,0,0)$ to $(0,1,2)$ to $(-1,3,2)$ to $(0,0,0)$. What is the total work done?

Now suppose that we realise the z-axis is not vertical, but that gravity acts in the direction $\frac{1}{3}(-2,1,-2)$ and the force is $(20,-10,20)$. Repeat the calculations.

5.6 Orthogonality

Between the maximum and minimum of the possible values of $\mathbf{u} \bullet \mathbf{v}$ lies the most important of all: **zero**.

$$\mathbf{u} \bullet \mathbf{v} = 0 \quad \text{when} \quad \cos\theta = 0, \quad \theta = 90°.$$

In that circumstance we see that the vectors are at right angles to each other. They are said to be **orthogonal** and this is written $\mathbf{u} \perp \mathbf{v}$.

> *Frame 5.10*   *Test of orthogonality of (a_1,b_1,c_1) and (a_2,b_2,c_2)*
>
> $$a_1a_2 + b_1b_2 + c_1c_2 = 0$$

There are many applications of orthogonality. One of the more obvious is finding shortest distances.

Example 5.27 What direction from O gives the shortest distance to AB, where A is $(-1,3)$ and B is $(5,-1)$?

Suppose the gradient of the line from O is m. Then the vector direction is $\overrightarrow{OP} = k(1,m)$ for some k. Also

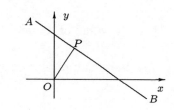

$$\overrightarrow{AB} = \overrightarrow{OB} - \overrightarrow{OA} = (5,-1) - (-1,3) = (6,-4).$$

For the shortest distance, $\overrightarrow{OP} \perp \overrightarrow{AB}$, so

$$0 = \overrightarrow{OP} \bullet \overrightarrow{AB} = k(1,m) \bullet (6,-4) = k(6-4m),$$

giving $m = \frac{3}{2}$. (From this we can find P and hence calculate the shortest distance: see Example 5.33.) ∎

We noted earlier that $\mathbf{i}\bullet\mathbf{j} = \mathbf{j}\bullet\mathbf{k} = \mathbf{k}\bullet\mathbf{i} = 0$, so all three are mutually orthogonal. This, of course, we knew from the cartesian coordinate system. But this is a powerful property – more so in that they are also **unit** vectors – enabling efficient calculations.

A triple of non-zero 3-D vectors such that any two are orthogonal is an **orthogonal set**. If they are also unit, they form an **orthonormal set**. Thus, $\{\mathbf{i}, \mathbf{j}, \mathbf{k}\}$ is an orthonormal set. But there are others.

Example 5.28 It is easy to check that the following form an orthogonal set:

$$\mathbf{u} = (1,1,1), \qquad \mathbf{v} = (1,-1,0), \qquad \mathbf{w} = (1,1,-2).$$

If we now **normalise** them by dividing by their magnitudes, we obtain the **orthonormal set**:

$$\hat{\mathbf{u}} = \frac{1}{\sqrt{3}}(1,1,1), \qquad \hat{\mathbf{v}} = \frac{1}{\sqrt{2}}(1,-1,0), \qquad \hat{\mathbf{w}} = \frac{1}{\sqrt{6}}(1,1,-2).$$

∎

A natural question to ask is whether we could use a different orthonormal set in place of $\{\mathbf{i}, \mathbf{j}, \mathbf{k}\}$, perhaps because they point in more useful directions for a particular application. The answer is "yes", but before showing how to do this, it is time to revisit the idea of **components**.

Ex 5.18 Given $\mathbf{a} = (-6,12,-14)$ and $\mathbf{b} = (t,-8,-9)$, find the value of t for which the vectors $\mathbf{a}$ and $\mathbf{b}$ are perpendicular.

Ex 5.19 Using the vectors defined in Exercise 5.15, $\mathbf{a} = (2,0,-1)$, $\mathbf{b} = (1,-1,1)$, $\mathbf{c} = (-1,-2,2)$ and $\mathbf{d} = (0,1,3)$, find the following:

(a) the angle between $\mathbf{a}$ and $\mathbf{b}$;

(b) the angle between $\mathbf{a}+\mathbf{d}$ and $\mathbf{c}$;

(c) $\angle BAC$, i.e., the angle between $\overrightarrow{AB}$ and $\overrightarrow{AC}$;

(d) the value of α such that $\mathbf{a}+\alpha\mathbf{b}$ is orthogonal to $\mathbf{c}$;

(e) those values of x such that $\mathbf{c}$ is at $45°$ to $(-1,0,x)$.

Ex 5.20 Let C be the circle of radius 1 centred at the origin O. Let A and B be the points where C crosses the positive and negative x-axes, respectively. Suppose X is *any* other point on C.

Express $\overrightarrow{OB}$, $\overrightarrow{XA}$ and $\overrightarrow{XB}$ in terms of $\overrightarrow{OX}$ and $\overrightarrow{OA}$. Noting that $|\overrightarrow{OA}| = |\overrightarrow{OX}| = 1$, prove that $\overrightarrow{XB}$ and $\overrightarrow{XA}$ are orthogonal.

5.7 Components

In §5.3 we defined a, b and c as the **components** of $\mathbf{r} = (a, b, c)$. Some authors insist that a component is a vector and hence they should be $a\mathbf{i}$, $b\mathbf{j}$ and $c\mathbf{k}$. There are circumstances in which one or other definition is more convenient. We shall continue to regard them as numbers, bearing in mind that they are coefficients of unit vectors defining key directions.

Suppose that we prefer to use an orthonormal triple $\mathbf{u}$, $\mathbf{v}$ and $\mathbf{w}$ instead, now dropping the unit vector's 'hat' for the sake of clarity. We therefore wish to find new components α, β and γ so that

$$\mathbf{r} = \alpha\mathbf{u} + \beta\mathbf{v} + \gamma\mathbf{w}. \tag{5.14}$$

There are two ways to proceed. We could write down the three scalar equations implied by (5.14), getting three simultaneous equations for the components. The power of the orthogonality provides a much easier method. Calculate the dot product of both sides of (5.14) with $\mathbf{u}$:

$$\mathbf{r} \bullet \mathbf{u} = \alpha\mathbf{u} \bullet \mathbf{u} + \beta\mathbf{u} \bullet \mathbf{v} + \gamma\mathbf{w} \bullet \mathbf{u}$$
$$= \alpha \times 1 + 0 + 0 = \alpha.$$

We similarly find $\beta = \mathbf{r} \bullet \mathbf{v}$ and $\gamma = \mathbf{r} \bullet \mathbf{w}$. This is similar to the observation we made in §5.5: $\mathbf{r} \bullet \mathbf{i} = a$, etc.

Example 5.29 Returning to the orthonormal set in Example 5.28, find components for $\mathbf{r} = (1, 2, 3)$.

$$\alpha = \frac{1}{\sqrt{3}}(1, 2, 3) \bullet (1, 1, 1) = \frac{6}{\sqrt{3}},$$
$$\beta = \frac{1}{\sqrt{2}}(1, 2, 3) \bullet (1, -1, 0) = -\frac{1}{\sqrt{2}},$$
$$\gamma = \frac{1}{\sqrt{6}}(1, 2, 3) \bullet (1, 1, -2) = -\frac{3}{\sqrt{6}}.$$

Note that

$$\alpha^2 + \beta^2 + \gamma^2 = \frac{36}{3} + \frac{1}{2} + \frac{9}{6} = 14,$$

which happens to be $|\mathbf{r}|^2 = 1 + 4 + 9$. ∎

This last observation about the components is no accident. Expanding

$$\mathbf{r} \bullet \mathbf{r} = (\alpha\mathbf{u} + \beta\mathbf{v} + \gamma\mathbf{w}) \bullet (\alpha\mathbf{u} + \beta\mathbf{v} + \gamma\mathbf{w})$$

and using the orthogonality and unit status of the vectors delivers (eventually) $\alpha^2 + \beta^2 + \gamma^2$. Again this demonstrates how close the structure of the new orthonormal set is to the original one, for which $|\mathbf{r}|^2 = a^2 + b^2 + c^2$.

The components $\mathbf{r} \bullet \mathbf{i} = a$ and $\mathbf{r} \bullet \mathbf{u} = \alpha$ suggest that, for a general **unit vector** $\hat{\mathbf{n}}$,

$$\mathbf{r} \bullet \hat{\mathbf{n}} \text{ measures the } \textbf{component} \text{ of } \mathbf{r} \text{ in direction } \hat{\mathbf{n}}. \tag{5.15}$$

Think about it like this

This relates to expressions such as that for the work done by a force:

$$W = \mathbf{F} \cdot \overrightarrow{AB} = (\text{component of } \mathbf{F} \text{ in direction } A \text{ to } B) \times AB,$$

a scalar version that is a natural adaptation of the one-dimensional version.

Ex 5.21 Verify that $\mathbf{e}_1 = \frac{1}{3}(-1, 2, 2)$, $\mathbf{e}_2 = \frac{1}{3}(2, -1, 2)$, $\mathbf{e}_3 = \frac{1}{3}(2, 2, -1)$ are mutually orthogonal and that each is of unit length.

Hence, find the components of the vector $(1, 2, 3)$ in these three directions.

5.8   Resolution in 3-D

We found, in §5.4, how to **resolve** a vector in two dimensions, to find its components in the $\mathbf{i}$ and $\mathbf{j}$ directions. We also saw how to use **direction cosines** to extend this to three dimensions. The objective in this section is to resolve a vector into two parts: one in a given (general) direction and one at right angles to it.

The dot product gives the **component** in the direction of a vector $\mathbf{u}$ as

$$|\mathbf{r}| \cos \theta = \frac{|\mathbf{r}| \, |\mathbf{u}| \cos \theta}{|\mathbf{u}|} = \frac{\mathbf{r} \cdot \mathbf{u}}{|\mathbf{u}|} = \mathbf{r} \cdot \hat{\mathbf{u}}, \quad (5.16)$$

where $\hat{\mathbf{u}}$ is a **unit** vector in the direction of $\mathbf{u}$, the same expression as (5.15).

This is a number, measuring the size of $\mathbf{r}$ as seen along the direction of $\mathbf{u}$. We can readily turn it into a vector, so that the direction becomes built in:

$$\mathbf{r}_\parallel = (\mathbf{r} \cdot \hat{\mathbf{u}}) \, \hat{\mathbf{u}}, \quad (5.17)$$

is that part of $\mathbf{r}$, **parallel** ($\parallel$) to $\mathbf{u}$. If we define

$$\mathbf{r}_\perp = \mathbf{r} - (\mathbf{r} \cdot \hat{\mathbf{u}}) \, \hat{\mathbf{u}}, \quad (5.18)$$

then

$$\mathbf{r}_\perp \cdot \hat{\mathbf{u}} = \mathbf{r} \cdot \hat{\mathbf{u}} - (\mathbf{r} \cdot \hat{\mathbf{u}})(\hat{\mathbf{u}} \cdot \hat{\mathbf{u}}) = 0,$$

since $\hat{\mathbf{u}}$ is a unit vector. Hence

$$\mathbf{r} = \mathbf{r}_\parallel + \mathbf{r}_\perp \quad (5.19)$$

breaks $\mathbf{r}$ into parts parallel to and perpendicular (orthogonal) to $\mathbf{u}$. The number $|\mathbf{r}_\perp|$ is the **component** of $\mathbf{r}$, **perpendicular** to $\mathbf{u}$.

Example 5.30 Let $\mathbf{r} = (1, -1, 2)$ and $\mathbf{u} = (2, -1, 2)$. Then

$$\hat{\mathbf{u}} = (2/3, -1/3, 2/3), \qquad \mathbf{r} \cdot \hat{\mathbf{u}} = 2/3 + 1/3 + 4/3 = 7/3$$

and the **parallel** part is

$$\mathbf{r}_\parallel = 7/3 \, (2/3, -1/3, 2/3) = 1/9(14, -7, 14),$$

and

$$\mathbf{r}_\perp = (1, -1, 2) - \tfrac{1}{9}(14, -7, 14) = \tfrac{1}{9}(-5, -2, 4).$$

The component parallel to $\mathbf{u}$ is $\mathbf{r} \cdot \hat{\mathbf{u}} = \tfrac{7}{3}$, while that perpendicular is

$$|\mathbf{r}_\perp| = \tfrac{1}{9}\sqrt{25 + 4 + 16} = \frac{\sqrt{45}}{9} = \frac{\sqrt{5}}{3}.$$

Note that $\left(\tfrac{7}{3}\right)^2 + \left(\tfrac{\sqrt{5}}{3}\right)^2 = \tfrac{49}{9} + \tfrac{5}{9} = 6 = |\mathbf{r}|^2.$ ∎

Ex 5.22 Find the components of the force $(4, -3, 2)$ acting parallel and perpendicular to the direction of $(1, 0, -1)$.

Repeat for the force $(3, 1, 3)$, with the same direction.

5.9 Projection

One application of parallel and perpendicular components is **projection**. This is required whenever one or more dimensions are to be lost, e.g., when we try to show a three-dimensional scene in two dimensions, as in computer graphics or in the cinema, where "projection" is a common term.

We shall consider the case of projecting from a plane (two dimensions) to a line (one dimension).

We move points, or a whole line, onto a fixed line, along a path at right angles to it. Thus, the vector $\mathbf{r}$ $(\overrightarrow{OP})$, when projected onto the direction given by the vector $\mathbf{u}$ by drawing a perpendicular from P to X, gives the vector:

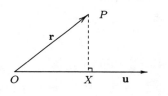

$$\overrightarrow{OX} = \mathbf{r}_\parallel = (\mathbf{r} \cdot \hat{\mathbf{u}})\hat{\mathbf{u}}. \tag{5.20}$$

Example 5.31 Project $(-5, 5)$, $(4, 3)$ and $(3, -4)$ onto $\mathbf{u} = (-6, 8)$.

We first calculate

$$|\mathbf{u}| = 10 \quad \Rightarrow \quad \hat{\mathbf{u}} = (-\tfrac{3}{5}, \tfrac{4}{5}).$$

(1) $\left[(-5, 5) \cdot (-\tfrac{3}{5}, \tfrac{4}{5})\right] \hat{\mathbf{u}} = \tfrac{7}{5}(-3, 4)$

(2) $\left[(4, 3) \cdot (-\tfrac{3}{5}, \tfrac{4}{5})\right] \hat{\mathbf{u}} = \mathbf{0}$

(3) $\left[(3, -4) \cdot (-\tfrac{3}{5}, \tfrac{4}{5})\right] \hat{\mathbf{u}} = -5\hat{\mathbf{u}} = (3, -4)$

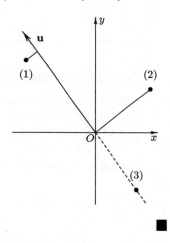

In the third case, the point is already on the line and so is its own projection, as the calculation verifies. ∎

Ex 5.23 Find the projection of the vector $(2, -1)$ onto a vector in direction $(3, 4)$. What is the component of $(2, -1)$ at right angles to this direction?

5.10   Section Formulae

In this final section we consider how to find a point on a line, not by perpendicular projection, but splitting the line in a given ratio, e.g., at the mid-point or one-third of the way from one end.

Consider the diagram below:

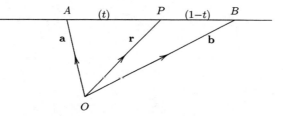

We seek to find a position vector for P, on the line AB, where the proportion $\frac{AP}{AB} = t$. The number t controls the position in the line between A and B, as t moves from 0 to 1:

$$t = 0 \quad \Rightarrow \quad AP = 0 \quad \Rightarrow \quad P = A,$$
$$t = \tfrac{1}{2} \quad \Rightarrow \quad AP = \tfrac{1}{2}AB \quad \Rightarrow \quad P \text{ is mid-point of } AB,$$
$$t = 1 \quad \Rightarrow \quad AP = AB \quad \Rightarrow \quad P = B.$$

The definition of t, interpreted vectorially, gives $\overrightarrow{AP} = t\overrightarrow{AB} = t(\mathbf{b} - \mathbf{a})$ and hence

$$\mathbf{r} = \overrightarrow{OP} = \overrightarrow{OA} + \overrightarrow{AP} = \mathbf{a} + t(\mathbf{b} - \mathbf{a}).$$

Although this form of a **section formula** is useful in more advanced work with vectors and straight lines, a rearranged form is more useful at this stage.

Frame 5.11   Section formula when P divides AB by a fraction t

$$\mathbf{r} = (1 - t)\mathbf{a} + t\mathbf{b}$$

Think about it like this

Note the order of t and $(1-t)$, which may appear perverse until we remember that $t = 0$ places us at A, so we wish a "large" amount of $\mathbf{a}$, i.e., $(1 - 0) \times \mathbf{a}$. Similarly $t = 1$ places us at B and we seek $1 \times \mathbf{b}$.

The most important case of all is $t = \tfrac{1}{2}$, showing that

$$\overrightarrow{OP} = \tfrac{1}{2}(\mathbf{a} + \mathbf{b}) \text{ is the mid-point of } AB. \qquad (5.21)$$

The introduction to this formula suggested that t should be in $[\,0, 1\,]$, but we can let t have *any* value. For the diagram above:

$$t < 0 : P \text{ is to the left of } A; \quad t > 0 : P \text{ is to the right of } B.$$

There is a further version of this formula, where the point P is defined as a **ratio** $\lambda : \mu$ [*lambda : mu*]. This tells us that, if $\lambda + \mu$ represents the length of AB, then λ represents AP, so

$$t = \frac{\lambda}{\lambda + \mu}, \qquad 1 - t = \frac{\mu}{\lambda + \mu}.$$

Frame 5.12   *Section formula when P divides AB in ratio $\lambda : \mu$*

$$\mathbf{r} = \frac{\mu \mathbf{a} + \lambda \mathbf{b}}{\lambda + \mu}$$

Think about it like this

This version is sometimes preferred to that in Frame 5.11 because it is rather more general: we do not need to take the trouble of working out the precise fraction t. Again, the order of λ and μ *appear* perverse at first sight, but bear in mind that a small λ places us near A and so a large multiple of $\mathbf{a}$ is required.

Example 5.32 Suppose P divides the line from $A\,(1, -1, 2)$ to $B\,(4, 2, -1)$ in the ratio $2 : 1$.

$$\mathbf{r} = \frac{1}{2 + 1}\,[1 \times (1, -1, 2) + 2 \times (4, 2, -1)]$$
$$= \frac{1}{3}(9, 3, 0) = (3, 1, 0).$$

$A\,(1,-1,2)$
P
$B\,(4,2,-1)$ ∎

Example 5.33 [Example 5.27: determination of the shortest distance to a line, further calculation]

From before, we know that

$$\overrightarrow{OP} = k(1, {}^3\!/_2) = c(2, 3)$$

using c to clear fractions. From Frame 5.11,

$$\overrightarrow{OP} = (1 - t)(-1, 3) + t(5, -1)$$
$$= (-1 + 6t, 3 - 4t).$$

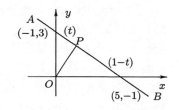

We now have two expressions for the same vector: their components must agree:

$$2c = -1 + 6t \qquad \times 3 \qquad \text{subtract:}$$
$$3c = 3 - 4t \qquad \times 2 \qquad 0 = -9 + 26t$$

Hence $t = {}^9\!/_{26}$, which fixes P as $({}^{14}\!/_{13}, {}^{21}\!/_{13})$ and allows the shortest distance to be evaluated as $|\overrightarrow{OP}| = \frac{7}{\sqrt{13}}$. ∎

This trick, of writing the same vector in two ways, is a powerful one, as we see in the final example. This employs another trick: choose the origin in a convenient place, then adjust the answer at the end, by a translation.

Example 5.34 A **median** of a triangle is a line from a vertex to the mid-point of the opposite side.

Fix the origin O as one vertex of the triangle; let the others be A and B. Draw the medians AL, from A, and BM, from B. Suppose they meet at P. Then extend OP until it meets the opposite side at N. We seek to prove that ON is also a median.

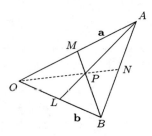

We construct a formula for $\overrightarrow{OP}$, using the fact that it lies somewhere on AL. Using Frame 5.11, with an unknown fraction s, we have:

$$\overrightarrow{OP} = (1-s)\overrightarrow{OA} + s\overrightarrow{OL} = (1-s)\mathbf{a} + \tfrac{1}{2}s\mathbf{b},$$

since L is the mid-point of OB. Similarly, since P lies on BM,

$$\overrightarrow{OP} = t\overrightarrow{OM} + (1-t)\overrightarrow{OB} = \tfrac{1}{2}t\mathbf{a} + (1-t)\mathbf{b}.$$

Since these are the same vector, we have

$$1 - t = \tfrac{1}{2}s \qquad \times 1 \qquad \text{add:}$$
$$\tfrac{1}{2}t = 1 - s \qquad \times 2 \qquad 1 = \tfrac{1}{2}s + 2 - 2s$$

and so $s = t = {}^2\!/_3$, giving $\overrightarrow{OP} = {}^1\!/_3(\mathbf{a} + \mathbf{b})$. Now, the median from O is ${}^1\!/_2(\mathbf{a}+\mathbf{b})$, so $\overrightarrow{OP}$ is parallel to the median. Since they both contain the point O, they must be the same line. Hence all three medians meet at the point P, an important location.

The trouble with this choice of O is that the formula we get for $\overrightarrow{OP}$ is rather too specialised, since it will not directly help with a triangle ABC, say. We can employ the following trick. Let A have position vector $\mathbf{a}$, etc. The vector from O to P can be calculated via A.

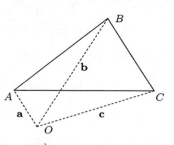

The vector $\mathbf{a}$ in the first calculation is now $\overrightarrow{AB} = \mathbf{b} - \mathbf{a}$, while $\mathbf{b}$ is now $\overrightarrow{AC} = \mathbf{c} - \mathbf{a}$. Hence

$$\overrightarrow{OP} = \overrightarrow{OA} + \overrightarrow{AP} = \mathbf{a} + {}^1\!/_3\left[(\mathbf{b} - \mathbf{a}) + (\mathbf{c} - \mathbf{a})\right]$$
$$= {}^1\!/_3(\mathbf{a} + \mathbf{b} + \mathbf{c}).$$

∎

To sum up, from this example, the medians of a triangle meet at a single point, called the **centroid** (or centre of mass) of the triangle. The centroid divides each median in the ratio 2 : 1. It has the elegant and symmetric formula

$$\overrightarrow{OP} = \tfrac{1}{3}(\mathbf{a} + \mathbf{b} + \mathbf{c}), \tag{5.22}$$

which shows its position vector to be the **average** of those of the vertices.

We used this result in Example 5.13, and then its generalisation to a **tetrahedron** $ABCD$ in 3-D:

$$\overrightarrow{OP} = \tfrac{1}{4}(\mathbf{a} + \mathbf{b} + \mathbf{c} + \mathbf{d}) \tag{5.23}$$

in Example 5.24.

Ex 5.24 Use vectors to find a point on the line joining $A\,(-1,2)$ to $B\,(4,-3)$, 60% of the way from A towards B. Verify that $(0,1)$ lies on this line. Where on the line does it lie?

Ex 5.25 Consider the points $A\,(-1,0,1)$ and $B\,(1,1,-1)$. Let P be positioned between A and B, a fraction t of the distance from A to B. Write down the position vector $\overrightarrow{OP}$; the answer will involve t. Find t such that $\overrightarrow{OP}$ is orthogonal to $\overrightarrow{AB}$. Hence find P and the shortest distance from the origin O to the line AB.

Ex 5.26

(a) Use vectors to show that the diagonals of a **rhombus** meet at right angles. (A rhombus is a parallelogram with all four sides equal.)

(b) Let $ABCD$ be a parallelogram and suppose that M and N are the midpoints of AB and CD respectively. Show that the lines AN and CM trisect the line DB.

5.11   Revision Exercises

Ex 5.27 Let $\mathbf{a} = (1,0,-1)$, $\mathbf{b} = (2,2,-1)$ and $\mathbf{c} = (-1,3,-1)$. Calculate each of the following:

(a) $2\mathbf{a} - \mathbf{b} - \mathbf{c}$;

(b) $(\mathbf{a} + \mathbf{b})\bullet\mathbf{c}$;

(c) the angle between $\mathbf{a}$ and $\mathbf{b}$ (in degrees).

Ex 5.28 Let $\mathbf{u} = (-6,6,-3)$ and $\mathbf{v} = (-3,0,4)$. Calculate each of the following:

(a) $\mathbf{u} - 2\mathbf{v}$;

(b) $\mathbf{u}\bullet\mathbf{v}$;

(c) the angle between $\mathbf{u}$ and $\mathbf{v}$ (in degrees, correct to $2\,\mathrm{dp}$);

(d) a unit vector in the direction of $\mathbf{v}$.

Ex 5.29 Let $\mathbf{u} = (1, 0, -1)$ and $\mathbf{v} = (6, -6, 7)$. Calculate each of the following:

(a) $|2\mathbf{u} + \mathbf{v}|$;

(b) the angle between $\mathbf{u}$ and $\mathbf{v}$ (in degrees, correct to 2 dp);

(c) a **unit vector** in the direction of $\mathbf{v}$.

Ex 5.30 Find a unit vector in the direction of: $\mathbf{u} = (8, -6)$.
Find the projection of $(2, 1)$ in the direction of $\mathbf{u}$.
Find the component of $(2, 1)$ perpendicular to $\mathbf{u}$.

Ex 5.31 Draw the following figure:
OAB is a triangle, with a right angle at A. X the mid-point of OB. Join A to X.
Let $\mathbf{a} = \overrightarrow{OA}$ and $\mathbf{b} = \overrightarrow{OB}$.
Find, in terms of $\mathbf{a}$ and $\mathbf{b}$: $\overrightarrow{AB}$, $\overrightarrow{AX}$.
Write down, using the dot product, a condition that $\angle OAB = 90°$. **Hence** show that $|\overrightarrow{AX}| = |\overrightarrow{OX}|$. (Note that $|\mathbf{u}|^2 = \mathbf{u} \cdot \mathbf{u}$.)

Ex 5.32 Draw the following figure:
OAB is a triangle, with M the mid-point of OA. Extend OB past B to a point E, so that $OE = 2OB$. Join M to E, crossing AB at X.
Let $\mathbf{a} = \overrightarrow{OA}$ and $\mathbf{b} = \overrightarrow{OB}$.
Find, in terms of $\mathbf{a}$ and $\mathbf{b}$: $\overrightarrow{BA}$, $\overrightarrow{OM}$, $\overrightarrow{OE}$, $\overrightarrow{EM}$.
$\overrightarrow{OX}$ can be written as both: $\overrightarrow{OB} + \alpha\overrightarrow{BA}$, $\overrightarrow{OE} + \beta\overrightarrow{EM}$.
Calculate α and β.

Ex 5.33 Draw the following figure:
OAB is a triangle, with M the mid-point of AB and X the mid-point of OM. Let BX meet OA at the point Z.
Let $\mathbf{a} = \overrightarrow{OA}$ and $\mathbf{b} = \overrightarrow{OB}$.
Find, in terms of $\mathbf{a}$ and $\mathbf{b}$: $\overrightarrow{OM}$, $\overrightarrow{OX}$, $\overrightarrow{BX}$.
$\overrightarrow{OZ}$ can be written as both $\overrightarrow{OB} + \alpha\overrightarrow{BX}$ and $\beta\overrightarrow{OA}$.
Calculate α and β.

6 COMPLEX NUMBERS

Consider an attempt to solve $x^2 + 1 = 0$. First write it as $\frac{1}{2}x^2 + \frac{1}{2} = 0$, then apply the formula for the roots of a quadratic, with $a = \frac{1}{2}$, $b = 0$, $c = \frac{1}{2}$:

$$x = \frac{1}{2 \times \frac{1}{2}} \left[0 \pm \sqrt{0 - 4 \times \frac{1}{2} \times \frac{1}{2}} \right] = \pm\sqrt{-1}.$$

There is no real number with a square of -1, which is no surprise: we had labelled this quadratic **irreducible**, since we were unable to factorise it.

Rather than give up at this stage, we follow the ideas that brought negative numbers, fractional numbers and irrational numbers (like $\sqrt{2}$ and π) into our reach, allowing us to use them in calculations. We simply give this quantity – the one with the $+$ sign – a notation and allow it into the system of numbers.

The notation for $\sqrt{-1}$ that is almost universal is i, which is short for *imaginary*, betraying some unease about its existence.

Notation

> The only exceptions to this notation are that some computer systems use I (because of their own conventions) and many engineers use j. That notation originated with electrical engineers, who make particularly heavy use of $\sqrt{-1}$, but use i for *current*, e.g., Ohm's Law: $V = iR$.

6.1 Arithmetic using $\sqrt{-1}$ (i)

The first thing to note, following our decision to allow i into the number system, is that it opens the door to other new numbers, such as $1 + i$ and $2i$. This is no surprise: when we allow use of π we get 2π as well, and $\sqrt{2}$ brings $1 + \sqrt{2}$ with it.

We allow expressions like $3 - 5i$ to be subject to the same arithmetic and algebraic rules as other numbers, except that there is an extra rule: if we encounter i^2, we replace it by -1, since that is forced by the definition of i.

Example 6.1 What are the possible values of i^n?

$$i^3 = i^2 i = (-1) \times i = -i, \quad i^4 = i^2 i^2 = (-1) \times (-1) = 1, \quad i^5 = i^4 i = 1 \times i = i,$$

and we see that this will produce a repeating sequence of just four values; starting with $i^0 = 1$, we build up:

$$[1, \, i, \, -1, \, -i, \, 1, \, i, \, -1, \, -i, \, \ldots].$$

This is also the case for negative powers:

$$i^{-1} = \frac{1}{i} = \frac{i}{i^2} = \frac{i}{-1} = -i, \qquad i^{-2} = \frac{1}{i^2} = \frac{1}{-1} = -1,$$

and so on, generating the same sequence, in reverse. ∎

Example 6.2 Expand $(x-i)(x+i)$.

Using the identity for $(u-v)(u+v)$, we have

$$(x-i)(x+i) = x^2 - i^2 = x^2 - (-1) = x^2 + 1,$$

so we have factorised an **irreducible** quadratic, although the factors involve a non-real number. ∎

It is time for some definitions. The number i and any number of the form αi, with α real, is an **imaginary number**. A number $z = x + iy$, with x and y real, is a **complex number**. The most common variable representing a complex number is, indeed, z with w as a popular reserve. The set of all complex numbers is written as $\mathbb{C}$.

Notation

It is a quirk of mathematical style that i tends to be written after numbers, as in $2i$, but before letters, as in iy. This is of no consequence, since complex numbers obey the same basic arithmetic rules as real numbers, so the order is irrelevant.

Arithmetic using complex numbers is mostly straightforward, provided we remember to use $i^2 = -1$ in multiplications and adopt a "vectorial" approach in addition and subtraction, i.e., we treat the i and non-i parts separately, like individual vector components.

Example 6.3 Calculate the following:

(a) $(3 - 5i) + (1 + 2i) = (3 + 1) + (-5 + 2)i = 4 - 3i$

(b) $(1 - i) - i = 1 - 2i$

(c) $-2(1 - i) = -2 + 2i$

(d) $(1 + i)i = i + i^2 = i - 1$ (or $-1 + i$)

(e) $(1 - 2i)(3 + i) = 3 + i - 6i - 2i^2 = 3 - 5i + 2 = 5 - 5i$

(f) $(1 + i)^2 = 1 + 2i + i^2 = 1 + 2i - 1 = 2i$

(g) $(2 - i)^3 = 2^3 - 3 \cdot 2^2 i + 3 \cdot 2 i^2 - i^3 = 8 - 12i - 6 + i = 2 - 11i$

Case (g) used the Binomial Theorem (3.8) to remove the brackets. ∎

The only elementary arithmetical operation that needs a new approach is **division** by a complex number. To be able to perform any of the other operations on the result, we need to write the result in the $x + iy$ format.

Frame 6.1   Division by $a+bi$

Multiply the term with the division by $\dfrac{a - bi}{a - bi}$

The bottom line becomes the *real* number $a^2 + b^2$

Example 6.4 Calculate the following:

(a) $\dfrac{1}{1+i} = \dfrac{1}{1+i} \times \dfrac{1-i}{1-i} = \dfrac{1-i}{1^2-i^2} = \dfrac{1-i}{2} = \frac{1}{2} - \frac{1}{2}i$

(b) $\dfrac{3-2i}{i} = \dfrac{3-2i}{i} \times \dfrac{-i}{-i} = \dfrac{-i(3-2i)}{-i^2} = \dfrac{-3i+2i^2}{1} = -2-3i$

Alternatively, $\dfrac{3-2i}{i} = \dfrac{3}{i} - 2 = \dfrac{3i}{i^2} - 2 = -3i - 2$

(c) $\dfrac{10+5i}{1-2i} \times \dfrac{1+2i}{1+2i} = \dfrac{(10+5i)(1+2i)}{1+4}$

$\qquad = (2+i)(1+2i) = 2 + 4i + i - 2 = 5i$

∎

We introduced i to deal with $\sqrt{-1}$. What if we encounter square roots of other negative numbers?

Frame 6.2   *Calculation of $\sqrt{-a}$*

$$\sqrt{-a} = \sqrt{a}\sqrt{-1} = \sqrt{a}\,i$$

Example 6.5 $\sqrt{-9} = \sqrt{9}\,i = 3i$. ∎

No $\pm$ has been used in the above. One must always consider whether the context requires its use; see, for example, §6.8.

Complex numbers often occur, or are forcibly introduced, in the middle of a calculation. That generates a need to return to real numbers at the end. There are various ways in which this is done, related to the following key definitions and associated notations.

Frame 6.3   *Numbers associated with $z=x+iy$*

x is the **real part** of z: $\mathrm{Re}(z)$ or $\Re(z)$

y is the **imaginary part** of z: $\mathrm{Im}(z)$ or $\Im(z)$

$\bar{z} = x - iy$ is the **complex conjugate** of z (some use z^*)

Conjugation switches back and fore between z and $\bar{z}$:

$$\bar{\bar{z}} = \overline{x-iy} = x+iy = z$$

$|z| = \sqrt{x^2+y^2}$ is the **modulus** of z; also $|\bar{z}| = |z|$

Since $\mathrm{Re}(z)$, $\mathrm{Im}(z)$ and $|z|$ are all **real numbers**, they help provide ways to regain real arithmetic. The following are the key relationships.

Frame 6.4   *Links between numbers in Frame 6.3*

$$z + \overline{z} = 2x = 2\,\mathrm{Re}(z) \tag{6.1}$$

$$z - \overline{z} = 2iy = 2i\,\mathrm{Im}(z) \tag{6.2}$$

$$z\overline{z} = x^2 - i^2 y^2 = x^2 + y^2 = |z|^2 \tag{6.3}$$

This last result, (6.3), is the basis for the division method:

$$\frac{1}{a+ib} \times \frac{a-ib}{a-ib} = \frac{a-ib}{a^2+b^2},$$

which can be deduced more elegantly from

$$z\overline{z} = |z|^2 \quad \Rightarrow \quad \frac{1}{z} = \frac{\overline{z}}{|z|^2}. \tag{6.4}$$

Think about it like this

All of these calculations with complex numbers can be carried out using pairs of real numbers, effectively the real and imaginary parts x and y. They are, however, much more natural, more elegant and easier to perform using i.

Example 6.6

(a) Let $z = -3 + 4i$, so $\overline{z} = -3 - 4i$. Also,

$$\mathrm{Re}(z) = -3, \qquad \mathrm{Im}(z) = 4 \ \textbf{not}\ 4i,$$
$$|z|^2 = (-3)^2 + 4^2 = 25 \quad \Rightarrow \quad |z| = 5,$$
$$z + \overline{z} = -6 = 2\,\mathrm{Re}(x),$$
$$z\overline{z} = (-3)^2 - (4i)^2 = 9 + 16 = 25 = |z|^2.$$

(b) Let $z = -7$, so $\overline{z} = -7$ also. Further:

$$\mathrm{Re}(z) = -7, \quad \mathrm{Im}(z) = 0, \qquad |z| = +7.$$

The modulus is the same as the absolute value, for real numbers; they are largely unaffected by these new ideas.

(c) Let $z = 2i$, so $\overline{z} = -2i$. Further:

$$\mathrm{Re}(z) = 0, \quad \mathrm{Im}(z) = 2, \qquad |z| = \sqrt{0^2 + 2^2} = 2.$$

■

Ex 6.1 Calculate: $(2-4i)+(-3-i)$, $(1+6i)-(1-6i)$, $(1-i)^2$, $\dfrac{1}{2i}$, $\dfrac{1}{3-i}$.

Ex 6.2

(a) Calculate: $(3+4i)(-3+4i)$, $(3+2i)i+(1-i)^3$, $(2-3i)^2$,

$$\frac{3+2i}{2-i}, \qquad \frac{1}{a-i}+\frac{1}{a+i}, \qquad \frac{b+i}{b-i}, \qquad \frac{(1-3i)^5}{(1+i)^5(2-i)^5}.$$

Here, a and b are **real** numbers; for the last case, think carefully about the order of calculation.

(b) If $z=x+iy$ and $w=u+iv$, with x, y, u and v real, find u and v in terms of x and y for

      i. $w=iz$,   ii. $w=z^3$.

Ex 6.3 For the complex number $z=5-12i$, calculate: $\mathrm{Re}(z)$, $\mathrm{Im}(z)$, $\bar{z}$, $|z|$, $1/z$.

Ex 6.4 Given the complex numbers $z_1=2-3i$ and $z_2=5+i$, calculate their **modulus**, **real** and **imaginary** parts, and **complex conjugate**. Also, find:

      i. $z_1 z_2$,   ii. z_1-z_2,   iii. $\dfrac{1}{z_1}+\dfrac{1}{z_2}$,   iv. iz_2.

6.2   Roots of Polynomials

Our first use of complex numbers was to solve a quadratic equation. This was not an isolated example.

Frame 6.5   *Solution of $az^2+bz+c=0$, with a, b, c real*

$$z = \frac{-b \pm \sqrt{b^2-4ac}}{2a} \tag{6.5}$$

This result now holds for all values of the coefficients, provided we allow z to be complex. It even holds when a, b and c are **complex**, although we need to know how to find the square root of a complex number: see §6.10.

Example 6.7   Let $z^2+2z+5=0$. Then

$$z = \frac{-2 \pm \sqrt{4-20}}{2} = \frac{-2 \pm \sqrt{-16}}{2}$$
$$= \frac{-2 \pm 4i}{2} = -1 \pm 2i,$$

where we used Frame 6.2 to find the square root.

It can often be quicker to use *completing the square* rather than (6.5):

$$(z+1)^2 + 4 = 0 \quad \Rightarrow \quad (z+1)^2 = -4$$
$$\Rightarrow \quad z+1 = \pm\sqrt{4i} = \pm 2i$$
$$\Rightarrow \quad z = -1 \pm 2i$$

■

Example 6.8 Solve $5z^2 - 6z + 5 = 0$. Using $a = 5$, $b = -6$, $c = 5$, (6.5) gives:

$$z = \frac{1}{10}\left[6 \pm \sqrt{36-100}\right] = \frac{1}{10}\left[6 \pm \sqrt{-64}\right]$$
$$= \frac{1}{10}(6 \pm 8i) = {}^3\!/_5 \pm {}^4\!/_5\, i$$

■

The new situation here is where the discriminant $\Delta = b^2 - 4ac < 0$, when we have $\sqrt{\Delta} = \sqrt{4ac - b^2}\, i$. Then the roots are

$$-\frac{b}{2a} \pm \frac{\sqrt{4ac - b^2}}{2a}\, i,$$

showing that they form a **complex conjugate pair** z and $\overline{z}$.

This last fact can prove very useful, as the next example shows. For the next while we shall return to using x as the variable, since the intention is to explore polynomial equations as 'real' entities.

Example 6.9 The quadratic $z^2 + \alpha z + \beta$, with α, β real, has a root $2 + 3i$. Find the quadratic.

Since the coefficients are real, it must also have a root $\overline{2+3i} = 2 - 3i$. Hence we know its factors and can reconstruct it as:

$$[z - (2+3i)][z - (2-3i)]$$
$$= [(z-2) - 3i][(z-2) + 3i]$$
$$= (z-2)^2 + 9 = z^2 - 4z + 13.$$

The initial rearrangements of the internal brackets provides by far the easiest way to expand this.   ■

This calculation can be generalised to provide a formula, although it is just as easy to work it out as in Example 6.9.

Frame 6.6   Quadratic with roots w and $\overline{w}$

$$(z - w)(z - \overline{w}) = z^2 - 2\operatorname{Re}(w)z + |w|^2$$

We noted, in §4.7, that every polynomial with real coefficients can be factorised into linear and (irreducible) quadratic factors. Every linear factor provides one root, while we now see that every quadratic provides two roots. Counting up the number of factors, to match the degree, we conclude that *every polynomial of degree n, with real coefficients, has precisely n roots, real and/or complex conjugate pairs.* (We must count repeated roots by the number of times each occurs.)

This can be extended (without the occurrence of complex conjugate pairs) to the more general **Fundamental Theorem of Algebra**: *Every polynomial of degree n, with coefficients in* $\mathbb{C}$*, has precisely n roots.*

A consequence of this theorem, when applied to the polynomial $x^n - \alpha$, is that the number of nth roots for any number α in $\mathbb{C}$ is precisely n. We shall see how to calculate these in §6.10, but the next example considers one case that illustrates most of the above. (This is not the best way to find roots.)

Example 6.10 Find all *six* values for $\sqrt[6]{1}$.

Two are obvious (± 1), which shows that $x^6 - 1$ has a factor $x^2 - 1$. In fact, by summing a GP (§2.7), we have

$$1 + x^2 + x^4 = \frac{x^6 - 1}{x^2 - 1} \quad \Rightarrow \quad x^6 - 1 = (x^2 - 1)(1 + x^2 + x^4).$$

This last term can also be factorised as two irreducible quadratics. This is not straightforward to do, but it is easy to *verify* that

$$x^6 - 1 = (x - 1)(x + 1)(x^2 - x + 1)(x^2 + x + 1).$$

The roots of $x^6 - 1 = 0$, and hence all the 6th roots of 1, can be found by solving each of the quadratics, using (6.5):

$$x = 1, \quad -1, \quad \tfrac{1}{2}\left(1 \pm \sqrt{3}\,i\right), \quad \tfrac{1}{2}\left(-1 \pm \sqrt{3}\,i\right).$$

∎

Ex 6.5 Find the roots of the equation: $z^2 + 2z + 10 = 0$.

Ex 6.6

(a) Solve $4z^2 - 20z + 41 = 0$.

(b) Construct a quadratic equation with roots $3 \pm i$.

(c) The polynomial $z^3 - 4z^2 - 2z + 20$ has a root $3 + i$. Find all the roots.

6.3   The Argand Diagram

It would be possible to continue in this algebraic manner, doing further calculations with complex numbers, all the time looking out for instances of i^2 to replace by -1. But taking the time to investigate a geometrical/vectorial interpretation opens up useful ways to think about these numbers, ways to apply them and even some simplification in their arithmetic.

We represent the complex number

$$z = x + iy$$

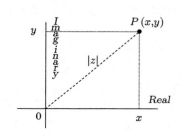

graphically by the point P with cartesian coordinates (x, y). The form $x + iy$ is called the **cartesian form**, to distinguish it from an alternative that we shall soon meet.

There are some new names attached to this **Argand Diagram**. The entire area spanned (to $\pm\infty$ in both directions) is the **complex plane**. The x-axis is referred to as the **real axis** and the y-axis as the **imaginary axis**. In the diagrams that follow, these will not be labelled: the real axis is always horizontal.

It is clear from the diagram above, using Pythagoras' Theorem on one of the triangles, that the modulus, $|z|$, is the distance from the origin to P.

The complex conjugate of z is simply its reflection in the real axis.

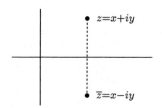

Example 6.11 Plot the points 1, i, $-i$, $1 + i$, $-1 + 2i$, $-2 - i$ in the Argand Diagram.

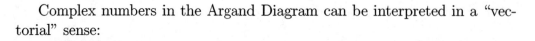

■

Complex numbers in the Argand Diagram can be interpreted in a "vectorial" sense:

$$z = x + iy \qquad \leftrightarrow \qquad x\,\mathbf{i} + y\,\mathbf{j},$$

represented simply by placing an arrowhead on the line from the origin to P in the first diagram. It is unfortunate that the standard notations i and $\mathbf{i}$ clash here; those who use j instead of i receive a bonus at this stage, since the notations agree.

This vectorial interpretation is consistent with the arithmetic.

Example 6.12 Compare the following calculations:

$$(1 - 2i) + (3 + 4i) = 4 + 2i$$
$$(1, -2) + (3, 4) = (4, 2)$$
$$2(1 - i) = 2 - 2i$$
$$2(1, -1) = (2, -2)$$

The details are identical, but there is a hint that, for 2D work, complex numbers offer a slightly more elegant notation. ∎

Now we have this link, we can make use of results in both directions, e.g., the parallelogram law for vectors shows how to add numbers in the complex plane.

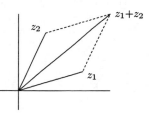

Example 6.13 Add $(1 + i)$ and $-2i$.

Simple complex arithmetic gives

$$(1 + i) + (-2i) = 1 - i$$

This is confirmed by the parallelogram in the diagram.

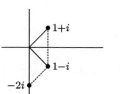

From (5.2) – or the diagram above – we can import the **triangle inequality**,

$$|z_1 + z_2| \leqslant |z_1| + |z_2|, \tag{6.6}$$

which warns of no easy link between $+$ and the modulus.

Interpretation of a complex number as a vector, and its modulus as a length, combine to allow us to measure distances in the Argand Diagram.

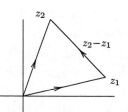

$$D = |z_1 - z_2| = |z_2 - z_1| \tag{6.7}$$

both give the distance between z_1 and z_2.

Example 6.14 Find the distance between $(2 + i)$ and $(1 + 2i)$.

From (6.7),

$$|(1 + 2i) - (2 + i)| = |-1 + i|$$
$$= \sqrt{(-1)^2 + 1^2}$$
$$= \sqrt{2},$$

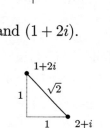

as confirmed by the right-angled triangle in the diagram. ∎

There has been no mention above of multiplication and division. Those operations require a different approach and a new way of writing complex numbers. We shall return to this in §6.5.

Ex 6.7 Find the distance, on the Argand diagram, between $z = 2 + 7i$ and $w = 10 - 8i$.

Ex 6.8

(a) Plot the following points on the Argand Diagram:

$$2, \quad -i, \quad -1 + i, \quad -2 - i, \quad 1 + \sqrt{3}i, \quad 1 - \sqrt{3}i.$$

(b) Calculate $(1+i)^r$ for $r = 0, 1, 2, 3, 4$, and plot them on the Argand Diagram. **Write down** the answers for $r = 5, 6, 7, 8$.

6.4   Loci and Regions

Several applications of complex numbers place conditions on the numbers for which a result is valid. It can be helpful to translate such conditions to lines, curves or regions in the Argand Diagram. In this context, lines and curves are often called **loci**, whose singular **locus** is the Latin word for 'place'.

The following example is typical.

Example 6.15   Using the formula for the sum of a GP, (2.17), gives

$$1 + z + z^2 + z^3 + \cdots + z^n = \frac{1 - z^n}{1 - z}.$$

Previously we used x, assumed real, but there is no reason to prohibit z from being complex.

Suppose we let $n \to \infty$. The infinite series that ensues will **converge** to $1/(1-z)$, provided $|z^n| \to 0$. Since $|z^n| = |z|^n$, this will be the case if $|z| < 1$, the sort of condition on z referred to above.

How does this condition translate to the complex plane? Since $|z|$ is the distance of z from the origin, we require points that lie within 1 unit of the origin, i.e., lie inside the disc, of radius 1, shown in the diagram.

This region is sometimes called the **unit disc** and its boundary the **unit circle**, where "unit" refers to the size of the radius.

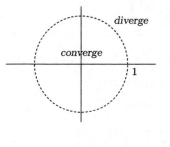

This example shows one of the attractions of using complex numbers for geometry: we can simply write z, rather than the clumsier (x, y) or even $x\mathbf{i} + y\mathbf{j}$. That said, when it comes to straight lines, there is a need to access x and y, usually disguised as $\mathrm{Re}(z)$ and $\mathrm{Im}(z)$, respectively.

Thus,

$$\mathrm{Re}(z) = 0 \text{ is the } y\text{-axis}, \quad x = 0$$
$$\mathrm{Im}(z) = 0 \text{ is the } x\text{-axis}, \quad y = 0$$

The general link is best illustrated by examples.

Example 6.16 Interpret $\mathrm{Re}(z) = -1$, $\mathrm{Im}(z) = 2$, $\mathrm{Re}(z) + \mathrm{Im}(z) = 1$.

Let $z = x + iy$. Then, $\mathrm{Re}(z) = -1$ translates to $x = -1$, a vertical line.

Also, $\mathrm{Im}(z) = 2$ translates to $y = 2$, a horizontal line.

Finally, $\mathrm{Re}(z) + \mathrm{Im}(z) = 1$ translates to $x + y = 1$, a line of gradient -1, as shown in the diagram.

Example 6.17 Interpret $\mathrm{Re}\,[(1 + i)z] + \mathrm{Im}(iz) = 1$.

Write $z = x + iy$, then calculate

$$\mathrm{Re}(x + iy + ix - y) + \mathrm{Im}(xi - y) = (x - y) + x = 2x - y = 1$$

if $y = 2x - 1$, a straight line of gradient 2.

This use of complex numbers comes into its own when **circles** are involved. There are two calculation methods, as we see in the next example.

Example 6.18 Interpret $|z - 1| = 1$.

Again writing $z = x + iy$, we have

$$1^2 = |z - 1|^2 = |(x - 1) + iy|^2 = (x - 1)^2 + y^2 \quad \Rightarrow \quad (x - 1)^2 + y^2 = 1,$$

the equation of a circle, centre $(1, 0)$ and radius 1.

But it is much easier to recall that $|z - w|$ is the distance of z from w, so this locus is the set of points at the constant distance 1 from the complex number 1+0i, i.e., the point $(1, 0)$. That is clearly the circle deduced earlier, but this time no calculation was required.

Example 6.19 Interpret $|z + 2i| = 3$.

This time we use the simple method from the outset. One problem is that the formula for distance uses a minus sign, so we must force one into place:

$$|z - (-2i)| = 3$$

gives points at distance 3 from $-2i$, i.e., $(0, -2)$, a circle centre $-2i$, radius 3.

Using inequalities defines **regions** rather than loci. Two are of particular importance:

$$\mathrm{Im}(z) \geqslant 0 \quad \text{or sometimes} \quad \mathrm{Im}(z) > 0$$

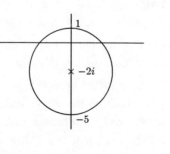

is the **upper half-plane**.

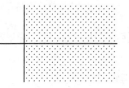

$$\mathrm{Re}(z) \geqslant 0 \quad \text{or sometimes} \quad \mathrm{Re}(z) > 0$$

is the **right half-plane**.

It is often the case that the difference between $<$, $\leqslant$ or $>$, $\geqslant$ is important. A popular convention, similar to the use of $\circ$ and $\bullet$ when drawing graphs, is to use a solid line for $\leqslant$, $\geqslant$ and a dashed line for $<$, $>$.

Example 6.20   Interpret $\mathrm{Im}(z) \geqslant 1$ and $\mathrm{Re}(z) < 1$.

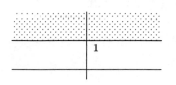

$\mathrm{Im}(z) \geqslant 1$ is similar to the upper half-plane, but lies above $y = 1$. That boundary line is included, because of the $\geqslant$.

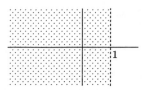

$\mathrm{Re}(z) < 1$ is similar to the left half-plane, but lies to the left of $x = 1$. the boundary line is *not* included, because of the $<$.

Again, the inside and outside of discs are easily handled, much as in Example 6.15.

Example 6.21   Interpret $|2z + 1| \leqslant 1$.

We start by trying to achieve a $|z - w|$ form:

$$|2z + 1| \leqslant 1 \quad \Rightarrow \quad |z + \tfrac{1}{2}| \leqslant \tfrac{1}{2}$$
$$\Rightarrow \quad |z - (-\tfrac{1}{2})| \leqslant \tfrac{1}{2}.$$

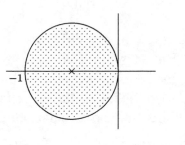

We now know the points are those within a distance of $\tfrac{1}{2}$ from $-\tfrac{1}{2}$, i.e., inside (or on) a circle centre $(-\tfrac{1}{2}, 0)$, radius $\tfrac{1}{2}$.

Example 6.22   Interpret $|z - (1 + i)| > \sqrt{2}$.

This time we can immediately deduce that the points are distant at least $\sqrt{2}$ from $(1+i)$, which means they lie outside a circle centre $(1, 1)$ and radius $\sqrt{2}$.

The circle is not included and so should be drawn with a dashed line. The diagram shows that it must pass through the origin, which is distant $\sqrt{2}$ from $(1, 1)$.

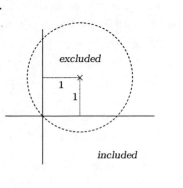

Ex 6.9

(a) Describe the loci given by: $\mathrm{Re}(z) + \mathrm{Im}(z) = 0$, $|z - i| = 1$.

(b) Describe the regions: $\mathrm{Re}(z) > -\tfrac{1}{2}$, $0 < \mathrm{Im}(z) \leqslant 1$.

Ex 6.10

(a) Find, in cartesian form, the following loci:

i. $|z + i| = 1$,   ii. $|z| = |z - 1|$,   iii. $|z| = \sqrt{2}|z - 1|$,   iv. $\mathrm{Re}\left(\dfrac{z + i}{z - i}\right) = 1$.

(b) Sketch the following regions in the Argand Diagram:

$$\mathrm{Re}(z) < 0, \quad 2 \leqslant \mathrm{Im}(z) \leqslant 3, \quad |z + i| < 1, \quad |\mathrm{Re}(z)| + |\mathrm{Im}(z)| \leqslant 1.$$

6.5   Polar Form

The link between the complex number $z = x + iy$ and the vector $x\mathbf{i} + y\mathbf{j}$ invites a different way in which to write z, a way that is strongly linked to the Argand Diagram. This allows straightforward calculations of products, divisions and – most importantly – powers. It underpins virtually all of the remainder of this chapter.

We start by a minor adaptation of a diagram from §5.4. We know that

$$\mathbf{v} = (r \cos \theta)\mathbf{i} + (r \sin \theta)\mathbf{j}.$$

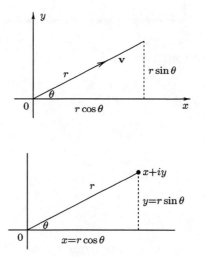

This is easily rewritten in terms of $z = x + iy$:

$$x + iy = r \cos \theta + i(r \sin \theta)$$
$$= r (\cos \theta + i \sin \theta),$$

which is the **polar form** for z.

Notation

> This very important form gets its name because r and θ are called the *polar coordinates* of (x, y), in 'real number' geometry. Note that, in the complex case, it is *always* the practice to write the "i" before the "sin", because of the danger of attaching it to θ.

Frame 6.7   *Polar form for a complex number z*

$$z = r (\cos \theta + i \sin \theta),$$

r is the **modulus** $|z|$, θ is the **argument** arg z

The argument is not unique, since we can add or subtract a multiple of 2π. In most elementary circumstances this is not a serious issue and it is common to stipulate a **principal** argument. There are, however, two common conventions:

$$either \quad \theta \text{ in } (-\pi, \pi],$$
$$or \quad \theta \text{ in } [0, 2\pi).$$

We shall not insist on using one or the other, since each has advantages in different contexts, but the first will be our 'default' choice. Note that the argument is **always** quoted in *radians*, for a reason that will become clear later.

It is necessary to be able to convert between cartesian and polar forms. Polar to cartesian is straightforward.

Frame 6.8 *Conversion from polar to cartesian form*

$$x = r\cos\theta, \qquad y = r\sin\theta$$

Example 6.23 Convert $z = \sqrt{8}\left[\cos\frac{3\pi}{4} + i\sin\frac{3\pi}{4}\right]$ to cartesian form.

We have $r = \sqrt{8}$ and $\theta = 3\pi/4$. Then

$$x = \sqrt{8} \times \left(-\frac{1}{\sqrt{2}}\right) = -\sqrt{4},$$
$$y = \sqrt{8} \times \left(\frac{1}{\sqrt{2}}\right) = \sqrt{4},$$
$$z = -2 + 2i.$$

The diagram provides a check. ∎

Conversion from cartesian to polar is more difficult. The modulus is straightforward, from Frame 6.3, but the argument is more tricky because of the need to determine the correct quadrant. It is entirely analogous to the vector situation. The following is an adaptation of Frame 5.7.

Frame 6.9   *Determination of modulus and argument for $z=a+bi$*

(a) $r = |z| = +\sqrt{a^2 + b^2} \quad (r \geqslant 0)$

(b) Use the signs of $\cos\theta$ (same as that of a) and $\sin\theta$ (same as that of b) to find which quadrant θ is in. (Drawing a sketch, to confirm the quadrant, is recommended.)

(c) Find $\phi = \tan^{-1}\dfrac{b}{a}$

(d) $\arg z = \phi$ if the quadrants are the same, else $\arg z = \phi \pm 180°$ (according to preference; these two angles are the same)

Drawing a rough diagram, as in the following examples, is strongly recommended.

Example 6.24   Convert to polar form each of the following:

(a) $z = \sqrt{3} + i$

We have $r = \sqrt{3+1} = 2$ and

$$r\cos\theta = \sqrt{3}, \quad r\sin\theta = 1.$$

Both are positive, so the argument lies in Quadrant 1.

$$\tan\phi = \frac{1}{\sqrt{3}} \quad \Rightarrow \quad \phi = \frac{\pi}{6},$$

which lies in Quadrant 1, as required. Hence no adjustment is necessary and

$$z = 2\left[\cos\frac{\pi}{6} + i\sin\frac{\pi}{6}\right].$$

(b) $z = -1 - i$

We have $r = \sqrt{(-1)^2 + (-1)^2} = \sqrt{2}$ and

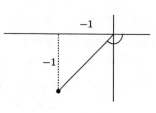

$$r\cos\theta = -1, \quad r\sin\theta = -1.$$

Both are negative, so the argument lies in Quadrant 3.

$$\tan\phi = \frac{-1}{-1} = 1 \quad \Rightarrow \quad \phi = \frac{\pi}{4},$$

which lies in Quadrant 1, which is not correct. Hence adjust by subtracting π: $\arg z = \frac{\pi}{4} - \pi = -\frac{3\pi}{4}$:

$$z = \sqrt{2}\left[\cos\left(-\frac{3\pi}{4}\right) + i\sin\left(-\frac{3\pi}{4}\right)\right].$$

(c) $z = -5$

It is clear from the diagram, as well as
Frame 6.3, that $|z| = +5$. Also, $\arg z = \pi$ and we have:

$$z = 5\left[\cos\pi + i\sin\pi\right].$$

(d) $z = i$

It is clear from the diagram, as well as
Frame 6.3, that $|z| = 1$. Also, $\arg z = \frac{\pi}{2}$
and we have:

$$z = \cos\frac{\pi}{2} + i\sin\frac{\pi}{2}.$$

The argument can also help specify *angular regions* in the Argand Diagram. The following example shows how.

Example 6.25 Find the region defined by $-\frac{\pi}{6} < \arg z \leqslant \frac{\pi}{4}$.

We need all points with arguments between $-30°$ and $+45°$, a region between two lines radiating from the origin. The lower line must be dashed, since we are not allowed points with argument exactly $-\frac{\pi}{6}$.

Ex 6.11 Indicate, on the **Argand diagram**, the position of:

$$\text{(a) } |z| = 4, \ \arg z = \frac{\pi}{3}; \qquad \text{(b) } |z| = 2, \ \arg z = -\frac{\pi}{6}.$$

Convert these polar forms to cartesian form.

Ex 6.12 Plot the point $z = -\sqrt{2} + i\sqrt{2}$ on the Argand Diagram.
Find the polar form of z.

Ex 6.13 Determine the modulus, argument and polar form for each of:
$\sqrt{3} - i, \quad -2 - 2i, \quad -2i$.

Ex 6.14 Sketch the following region in the Argand Diagram: $|\arg z| \leqslant \frac{\pi}{4}$.

6.6 Polar Multiplication and Division

Suppose we have two complex numbers in polar form:

$$z = r\left[\cos\theta + i\sin\theta\right], \qquad w = s\left[\cos\phi + i\sin\phi\right],$$

and we multiply them:

$$zw = rs\left[\cos\theta\cos\phi - \sin\theta\sin\phi + i\left(\cos\theta\sin\phi + \sin\theta\cos\phi\right)\right]$$
$$= rs\left[\cos(\theta + \phi) + i\sin(\theta + \phi)\right].$$

Hence, there is a simple multiplication rule: *multiply the moduli, add the arguments.*

There is a similar rule for division – see later for justification – and for powering (repeated multiplication).

Frame 6.10   *Multiplication/division/powering in polar form*

$$zw = rs\left[\cos(\theta + \phi) + i\sin(\theta + \phi)\right] \tag{6.8}$$

$$\frac{z}{w} = \frac{r}{s}\left[\cos(\theta - \phi) + i\sin(\theta - \phi)\right] \tag{6.9}$$

$$z^n = r^n\left[\cos(n\theta) + i\sin(n\theta)\right] \tag{6.10}$$

where $z = r\left[\cos\theta + i\sin\theta\right],$ $w = s\left[\cos\phi + i\sin\phi\right]$

Example 6.26   Multiply $1 - i$ and $1 + i$:

$$1 + i = \sqrt{2}\left[\cos\tfrac{\pi}{4} + i\sin\tfrac{\pi}{4}\right],$$
$$1 - i = \sqrt{2}\left[\cos\left(-\tfrac{\pi}{4}\right) + i\sin\left(-\tfrac{\pi}{4}\right)\right],$$
$$(1 - i)(1 + i) = 1^2 - i^2 = 1 + 1 = 2,$$
$$\text{or} \; = \sqrt{2} \times \sqrt{2}\left[\cos\left(\tfrac{\pi}{4} - \tfrac{\pi}{4}\right) + i\sin\left(\tfrac{\pi}{4} - \tfrac{\pi}{4}\right)\right]$$
$$= 2\left[\cos 0 + i\sin 0\right] = 2.$$

∎

From (6.4), we have

$$\frac{1}{w} = \frac{\overline{w}}{|w|^2} = \frac{1}{s^2}\,s\left[\cos\phi - i\sin\phi\right]$$
$$= \frac{1}{s}\left[\cos(-\phi) + i\sin(-\phi)\right]. \tag{6.11}$$

Writing $\dfrac{z}{w} = z \times \dfrac{1}{w}$, and using this result, justifies the division rule (6.9). This is also a useful formula in its own right.

Example 6.27   Divide $1 + i$ by i.

$$1 + i = \sqrt{2}\left[\cos\tfrac{\pi}{4} + i\sin\tfrac{\pi}{4}\right],$$
$$i = \left[\cos\tfrac{\pi}{2} + i\sin\tfrac{\pi}{2}\right],$$
$$\frac{1+i}{i} = \frac{1}{i} + 1 = 1 - i,$$
$$or = \frac{\sqrt{2}}{1}\left[\cos\left(\tfrac{\pi}{4} - \tfrac{\pi}{2}\right) + i\sin\left(\tfrac{\pi}{4} - \tfrac{\pi}{2}\right)\right]$$
$$= \sqrt{2}\left[\cos\left(-\tfrac{\pi}{4}\right) + i\sin\left(-\tfrac{\pi}{4}\right)\right]$$
$$= \sqrt{2}\left(\frac{1}{\sqrt{2}} - \frac{1}{\sqrt{2}}i\right) = 1 - i.$$

∎

Example 6.28   Calculate $\cos 15°$ and $\sin 15°$.

We use $15° = \tfrac{\pi}{12} = \tfrac{\pi}{3} - \tfrac{\pi}{4}$. Generate polar forms using these angles and moduli 1. Then perform the division in both polar and cartesian ways. Dividing polar forms with arguments $\tfrac{\pi}{3}$ and $\tfrac{\pi}{4}$ will generate the subtraction.

$$\cos\frac{\pi}{12} + i\sin\frac{\pi}{12} = \frac{\cos\tfrac{\pi}{3} + i\sin\tfrac{\pi}{3}}{\cos\tfrac{\pi}{4} + i\sin\tfrac{\pi}{4}}$$
$$= \frac{\tfrac{1}{2} + \tfrac{\sqrt{3}}{2}i}{\tfrac{1}{\sqrt{2}} + \tfrac{1}{\sqrt{2}}i} = \frac{1}{\sqrt{2}}\frac{1 + \sqrt{3}i}{1 + i} \qquad \left(\times\tfrac{2}{2}\right)$$
$$= \frac{1}{\sqrt{2}}\frac{1}{2}(1 + \sqrt{3}i)(1 - i) \qquad \left(\times\tfrac{1-i}{1-i}\right)$$
$$= \frac{\sqrt{2}}{4}\left[1 + \sqrt{3} + (\sqrt{3} - 1)i\right].$$

Forcing the real and imaginary parts on each side to agree, we find

$$\cos 15° = \frac{\sqrt{2}}{4}\left(1 + \sqrt{3}\right), \qquad \sin 15° = \frac{\sqrt{2}}{4}\left(\sqrt{3} - 1\right).$$

∎

Although these multiplication and division rules are very straightforward, it is not worth converting to polar form just to use them; they are usually reserved for numbers already in that form. The powering rule, (6.10), is different, since it offers huge savings in computation.

Example 6.29   Find some powers of $\sqrt{3} + i$ (see Example 6.24).

Multiply the argument ($\pi/6$) by the powers, and raise the modulus (2) to the same power:

$$z = \sqrt{3} + i = 2\left[\cos\frac{\pi}{6} + i\sin\frac{\pi}{6}\right],$$

$$z^2 = 4\left[\cos\frac{\pi}{3} + i\sin\frac{\pi}{3}\right] = 4\left(\frac{1}{2} + \frac{\sqrt{3}}{2}i\right) = 2 + 2\sqrt{3}i,$$

$$z^3 = 8\left[\cos\frac{\pi}{2} + i\sin\frac{\pi}{2}\right] = 8i,$$

$$z^6 = 64\left[\cos\pi + i\sin\pi\right] = -64,$$

$$z^{-1} = 2^{-1}\left[\cos\left(-\frac{\pi}{6}\right) + i\sin\left(-\frac{\pi}{6}\right)\right] = \frac{1}{4}\left(\sqrt{3} - i\right),$$

$$z^{-3} = 2^{-3}\left[\cos\left(-\frac{\pi}{2}\right) + i\sin\left(-\frac{\pi}{2}\right)\right] = -\frac{1}{8}i.$$

∎

This example has extended (6.10) to allow negative powers. This can be justified. Indeed, (6.11) confirms the w^{-1} case for a general number. We finish with a combined example.

Example 6.30 Calculate z^3/w^4, where z has modulus 4, argument 1.5, and w has modulus 2, argument 0.6.

The modulus of the result is $4^3/2^4 = 4$, while the argument is $3 \times 1.5 - 4 \times 0.6 = 2.1$. The polar and (approximate) cartesian forms are

$$4\left[\cos 2.1 + i\sin 2.1\right] \simeq -2.019 + 3.453\,i.$$

∎

Ex 6.15 Given $z = 2\left(\cos\frac{\pi}{6} + i\sin\frac{\pi}{6}\right)$ and $w = 5\left(\cos\frac{\pi}{3} + i\sin\frac{\pi}{3}\right)$, calculate:

(a) zw,   (b) $\dfrac{w}{z}$,   (c) z^6,   (d) $z - w$.

6.7 Rotation in the Argand Diagram

Consider the effect of multiplying $w = s\left[\cos\phi + i\sin\phi\right]$ by the *unit* complex number

$$z = \cos\alpha + i\sin\alpha.$$

We obtain

$$zw = s\left[\cos(\phi + \alpha) + i\sin(\phi + \alpha)\right],$$

which is precisely the result of **rotating** w about the origin, through angle α.

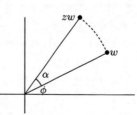

Note that multiplying by z^n rotates the number n times, i.e., it rotates it through $n\alpha$.

There are two particularly important cases. First, when $z = -1$, we have $\alpha = \pi$ and the rotation is through 180°, just as we expect, since this is equivalent to "reversing" a vector.

The other case is $z = i$, where the rotation is through $\alpha = \frac{\pi}{2}$, a right angle.

Example 6.31   Investigate multiplication of $w = 1 + 2i$, by i.

We obtain, by direct calculation,

$$iw = i + 2i^2 = -2 + i, \quad i^2 w = -2i + i^2 = -1 - 2i, \quad i^3 w = -i - 2i^2 = 2 - i.$$

These three points, when plotted on the diagram, show that successive multiplications by i have rotated w through three right angles (clockwise). It is clear that a fourth rotation will bring us back to w; note that $i^4 w = 1 \times w = w$.

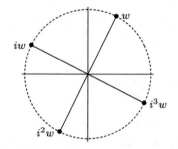

Now consider the unit number with argument $2\pi/n$:

$$z = \cos\frac{2\pi}{n} + i\sin\frac{2\pi}{n}. \tag{6.12}$$

This should rotate points by $2\pi/n$ and multiplying w by z^n should therefore rotate through $n \times 2\pi/n = 2\pi$, bringing w back to its original position. This is consistent with

$$z^n = \cos\left(n \times \frac{2\pi}{n}\right) + i\sin\left(n \times \frac{2\pi}{n}\right) = \cos 2\pi + i\sin 2\pi = 1.$$

For this reason, z is called an nth **root of unity**, i.e., one of the values of $\sqrt[n]{1}$ (other than the more usual value of 1).

This concept of rotation by complex multiplication is useful in several contexts, such as electrical circuits. The idea of rotation through $2\pi/n$ and the associated root of unity will prove helpful when we consider general roots in §6.8 and §6.10.

Ex 6.16   If $z = \sqrt[3]{1}$, then $z^3 - 1 = 0$, for which we would expect to find three roots. Hence, when complex numbers are allowed, we expect a number to have three cube roots.

Use the factorisation $z^3 - 1 = (z - 1)(z^2 + z + 1)$ to find all three cube roots of 1.

Show that these can be written as 1, ω, ω^2 for some ω.

Plot these numbers in the Argand diagram.

6.8 de Moivre's Theorem

The powering result in Frame 6.10, when applied to a unit complex number, delivers a well-known result:

Frame 6.11   *de Moivre's Theorem*

$$(\cos\theta + i\sin\theta)^n = \cos n\theta + i\sin n\theta \qquad (6.13)$$

(Some authors do not insist on a unit number and so will have an r inside the bracket on the left, and r^n on the right. The above version is the more common.)

A standard application of this theorem is a speedy and general way to express sin and cos for multiple angles, i.e., an extension of the well-known

$$\sin 2\theta = 2\sin\theta\cos\theta, \qquad \cos 2\theta = 2\cos^2\theta - 1.$$

This can be done by a real number method, requiring lengthy technical use of the addition formulae. The following method, illustrated by an example, is typical of the way that complex numbers can be introduced and then removed when they have done their job.

Example 6.32   Find an expression for $\cos 4\theta$.

We expand the formula in Frame 6.11, using the binomial theorem:

$$\begin{aligned}
\cos 4\theta + i\sin 4\theta &= (\cos\theta + i\sin\theta)^4 \\
&= \cos^4\theta + \binom{4}{1}\cos^3\theta(i\sin\theta) + \binom{4}{2}\cos^2\theta(i\sin\theta)^2 \\
&\quad + \binom{4}{3}\cos\theta(i\sin\theta)^3 + (i\sin\theta)^4 \\
&= \left(\cos^4\theta - 6\cos^2\theta\sin^2\theta + \sin^4\theta\right) \\
&\quad + i\left(4\cos^3\theta\sin\theta - 4\cos\theta\sin^3\theta\right).
\end{aligned}$$

Now match the real parts on each side:

$$\cos 4\theta = \cos^4\theta - 6\cos^2\theta\sin^2\theta + \sin^4\theta.$$

(Matching the imaginary parts will give an expression for $\sin 4\theta$.)

If we wish to have a result involving only cos, we can continue:

$$\begin{aligned}
\cos 4\theta &= \cos^4\theta - 6\cos^2\theta(1-\cos^2\theta) + (1-\cos^2\theta)^2 \\
&= 8\cos^4\theta - 8\cos^2\theta + 1.
\end{aligned}$$

■

As we noted in §6.6, de Moivre's theorem holds for negative values of n. Our particular use for it here exploits the fact that it also holds for *fractional* values. This suggests a method for finding roots of complex numbers.

Example 6.33 Find $\sqrt{-1}$.

Using the polar form for -1:

$$\sqrt{-1} = (-1)^{1/2} = \left[\cos \pi + i \sin \pi\right]^{1/2}$$
$$= \cos \frac{\pi}{2} + i \sin \frac{\pi}{2} = i.$$

Is there not a second square root? We might hazard a guess that the usual $\pm$ applies, so it is $-i$. Alternatively, we can calculate it directly using a different argument for -1: the argument $-\pi \ (= \pi - 2\pi)$ provides $-i$ using the method above. ∎

The $\pm$ idea is well-founded: it relies on $\left(-\sqrt{-1}\right)^2 = (-1)^2 \left(\sqrt{-1}\right)^2 = -1$. In the general case, we can use our root of unity.

Suppose that w is a value of $z^{1/n}$, so that $w^n = z$. Using (6.12), let $\delta \ [delta] = \cos \frac{2\pi}{n} + i \sin \frac{2\pi}{n}$. We have

$$(\delta w)^n = \delta^n w^n = 1 \times z = z, \qquad \left(\delta^2 w\right)^n = \delta^{2n} w^n = 1 \times z = z,$$

and so on. The full set of roots is

$$\{w, \ \delta w, \ \delta^2 w, \ \ldots, \ \delta^{n-1} w\}.$$

Hence there are n values, lying on a circle containing w, spaced around the circle by the angular distance $2\pi/n$.

This approach provides one way for finding the roots of a complex number.

(a) Find the polar form: $z = r\left[\cos\theta + i\sin\theta\right]$.

(b) Apply de Moivre's theorem, taking the root of r as the one and only positive real value:

$$w = r^{1/n}\left[\cos\frac{\theta}{n} + i\sin\frac{\theta}{n}\right].$$

(c) Calculate $\delta w, \ \ldots, \ \delta^{n-1}w$, or plot the points on a circle in the Argand Diagram, spaced by angle $2\pi/n$.

Example 6.34 Find the cube roots of $-8i$.

The polar form is $-8i = 8\left[\cos\left(-\frac{\pi}{2}\right) + i\sin\left(-\frac{\pi}{2}\right)\right]$. Hence one root is

$$w = \sqrt[3]{8}\left[\cos\left(-\frac{\pi}{2 \times 3}\right) + i\sin\left(-\frac{\pi}{2 \times 3}\right)\right]$$
$$= 2\left[\cos\left(-\frac{\pi}{6}\right) + i\sin\left(-\frac{\pi}{6}\right)\right]$$
$$= 2\left[\frac{\sqrt{3}}{2} - \frac{1}{2}i\right] = \sqrt{3} - i.$$

The other two roots are δw and $\delta^2 w$, where

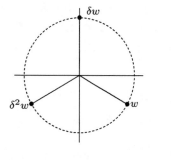

$$\delta = \cos\frac{2\pi}{3} + i\sin\frac{2\pi}{3} = -\frac{1}{2} + \frac{\sqrt{3}}{2}\,i.$$

These values, $2i$ and $-\sqrt{3}-i$, are shown on the diagram.

∎

We shall not pursue this further at the moment, since there is a better way to set out the (identical) calculation.

Ex 6.17 Plot the point $z = 1 + i\sqrt{3}$ on the Argand diagram.

Find the polar form of z.

Use the polar form to calculate $1/z$ and z^2, plotting the results on the same diagram.

Find one square root for z, plotting it on the diagram. Plot the second square root.

Ex 6.18 Expand $(\cos\theta + i\sin\theta)^2$ and then use de Moivre's Theorem to find expressions for $\cos 2\theta$ and $\sin 2\theta$.

Ex 6.19 Use de Moivre's Theorem to find $\cos 3\theta$ and $\sin 3\theta$ in terms of $\cos\theta$ and $\sin\theta$, respectively.

6.9 Euler's Formula

We have held back from introducing a short notation for the polar form, although they do exist. There are two reasons:

- Why introduce an artificial notation when there is a *natural* representation that is just as neat? We shall derive this below.

- Using artificial notations means that the key results in Frame 6.10 have to be translated, e.g., $r\angle\theta \cdot s\angle\phi = rs\angle(\theta + \phi)$. These results are an *automatic* consequence of the natural representation below.

Notation

Common alternatives are $r\angle\theta$ and $r\,\mathrm{cis}\,\theta$, where "cis" is short for "cos/i/sin".

Let $z(\theta) = \cos\theta + i\sin\theta$ and differentiate it with respect to θ:

$$\frac{dz}{d\theta} = -\sin\theta + i\cos\theta$$
$$= i\left[\cos\theta + i\sin\theta\right]$$
$$= iz.$$

It is known that the only solutions of this *differential equation* have the form $z(\theta) = Ce^{i\theta}$, for a constant C. (The fact that this fits the equation can be verified by differentiation.) Also,

$$z(0) = \cos 0 + i\sin 0 = 1 \quad\Rightarrow\quad 1 = Ce^0 \quad\Rightarrow\quad C = 1.$$

This gives us a simple formula for $z(\theta)$, known as **Euler's Formula**, and hence a neat way of writing the polar form. The use of differentiation explains why radian measure is essential.

Frame 6.12   *Polar form using Euler's Formula*

$$z = r\left[\cos\theta + i\sin\theta\right] = re^{i\theta} = |z|e^{i\theta}$$

Example 6.35   Rewrite the polar forms for the numbers in Example 6.24.

$$\sqrt{3} + i = 2e^{\pi i/6}, \qquad -1 - i = \sqrt{2}e^{-3\pi i/4}, \qquad -5 = 5e^{\pi i}, \qquad i = e^{\pi i/2}$$

∎

The results for multiplication, division and powering are now simple consequences of the properties of the exponential function, e.g.,

$$re^{i\theta}se^{i\phi} = rse^{i(\theta+\phi)},$$

and so need no artificial formulae to represent them.

Frame 6.13   *Properties of the polar form*

$$zw = rse^{i(\theta+\phi)} \qquad\qquad (6.14)$$

$$\frac{z}{w} = \frac{r}{s}e^{i(\theta-\phi)} \qquad\qquad (6.15)$$

$$z^n = r^n e^{in\theta} \qquad\qquad (6.16)$$

where $z = re^{i\theta}, \qquad w = se^{i\phi}$

The last of these, with $r = 1$, proves de Moivre's Theorem and, because of the properties of the exponential function, confirms that it true for all types of number n.

There are two particularly intriguing special values:

$$\theta = \pi \quad \Rightarrow \quad e^{i\pi} = -1 \quad \left[\cos\pi + i\sin\pi\right]$$
$$\Rightarrow \quad e^{i\pi} + 1 = 0,$$

which is an astonishing equation: it links the five most important numbers in mathematics, e, π, i, 0 and 1.

The other is

$$\theta = 2\pi \quad \Rightarrow \quad e^{2i\pi} = 1 \quad \left[\cos 2\pi + i\sin 2\pi\right],$$

which allows us to change the angle in the polar form, without changing the value, e.g.,

$$z = re^{i\theta} = re^{i\theta}e^{2i\pi} = re^{i(\theta + 2\pi)} = \cdots = re^{i(\theta + 2k\pi)},$$

where k is any integer (in $\mathbb{Z}$).

Using this new version of the polar form, we can calculate **one** value for any power of a complex number, positive, negative, fractional or, indeed, any real number, simply by using the index laws in §1.5.

Example 6.36 Find a value for $\left(16 - 16\sqrt{3}\,i\right)^{-2/5}$.

The argument for $16 - 16\sqrt{3}\,i$ is $-\pi/3$ and hence the polar form is $z = 32e^{-i\pi/3}$. A possible value is then

$$32^{-2/5}\exp\left[\left(-\frac{i\pi}{3}\right)\left(-\frac{2}{5}\right)\right] = \frac{1}{4}\exp\left(\frac{2\pi i}{15}\right)$$
$$= \frac{1}{4}\left[\cos\frac{2\pi}{15} + i\sin\frac{2\pi}{15}\right]$$
$$\simeq 0.2284 + 0.1017\,i.$$

(Here we have used the notation $\exp(z) = e^z$ because of the complicated argument.) ∎

There are four other values for the number in this example, since it is related to a fifth root. We shall see how to track them down in the next section.

Ex 6.20 Verify that $e^{\pi i/2} = i$.

Hence find **one** of the values for each of $\sqrt[3]{i}$ and $i^{2/3}$.

6.10   Roots of Numbers

We can also write the nth **root of unity** we encountered in (6.12), using Euler's Formula:

$$\delta = e^{2i\pi/n} \quad \Rightarrow \quad \delta^n = e^{2i\pi} = 1.$$

Then the set:

$$\{1,\ \delta,\ \delta^2,\ \ldots,\ \delta^{n-1}\} \qquad (6.17)$$

are all different and each satisfies $z^n = 1$.

To find all n of the nth roots of any other complex number, simply find **one** root, e.g., use the calculation in the previous section, then multiply the result by each of the numbers in (6.17).

As observed before, these multiplications will result in rotating the original value through the angle $2\pi/n$, and repeating the rotations until we return to that original value.

Note: the use of δ here is not universal. The most common symbol used is ω [*omega*], but that has been avoided here since it is too similar to w.

Example 6.37   Find all cube roots of 8.

The polar form is $8 = 8\left[\cos 0 + i\sin 0\right] = 8e^{0i}$. Hence one root is

$$w = 8^{1/3}e^{0i/3} = 2,$$

as we expect.

The other two roots are 2δ and $2\delta^2$,
where

$$\delta = \cos\frac{2\pi}{3} + i\sin\frac{2\pi}{3} = -\frac{1}{2} + \frac{\sqrt{3}}{2}i.$$

These values, $-1 + \sqrt{3}\,i$ and $-1 - \sqrt{3}\,i$,
are shown in the diagram.

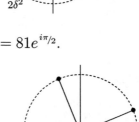

Example 6.38   Find all solutions for $z^4 = 81i = 81e^{i\pi/2}$.

The simplest solution is:

$$z = 81^{1/4}e^{i\pi/2 \times 1/4} = 3e^{i\pi/8}.$$

The other three roots are δz, $\delta^2 z$ and
$\delta^3 z$, where

$$\delta = \cos\frac{2\pi}{4} + i\sin\frac{2\pi}{4} = i.$$

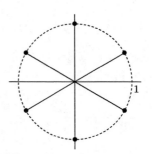

These values are shown in the diagram, as the vertices of a square, since
the rotations caused by the multiplications by $\delta = i$ are through a right
angle.   ■

Example 6.39   Find all values for $(-1)^{1/6}$. Note that $-1 = e^{i\pi}$.

The simplest solution is:

$$z = e^{i\pi/6} = \cos\frac{\pi}{6} + i\sin\frac{\pi}{6} = \sqrt{3}/2 + 1/2\,i.$$

The other five roots are of the form $\delta^k z$,
where

$$\delta = \cos\frac{2\pi}{6} + i\sin\frac{2\pi}{6} = 1/2 + \sqrt{3}/2\,i.$$

These values are shown on the diagram, as the vertices of a hexagon,
since the rotations caused by the multiplications by δ are through $60°$.   ■

To find all fractional powers of the general form m/n, first ensure that
m and n have no common factors. Then proceed as above. Thus, find one
answer as in the previous section: $\left(re^{i\theta}\right)^{m/n}$, then multiply repeatedly by δ^m,
where $\delta = e^{i\pi/n}$. (In fact, provided that common factors have been cancelled
from m and n, multiplying by simple powers of δ will suffice: see the example
below.)

Example 6.40 Find all values for $(2+2i)^{4/3}$.

The polar form for $2+2i$ is

$$z = \sqrt{8}\left[\cos\frac{\pi}{4} + i\sin\frac{\pi}{4}\right] = \sqrt{8}e^{\pi i/4},$$

from which we find

$$(2+2i)^{4/3} = \left(2^{3/2}\right)^{4/3}\left(e^{\pi i/4}\right)^{4/3}$$
$$= 4e^{\pi i/3}$$
$$= 4\left[\cos\frac{\pi}{3} + i\sin\frac{\pi}{3}\right] = 2 + 2\sqrt{3}\,i.$$

To find the other two values, multiply by $\delta^4 = \delta^3\delta = \delta$ (since $\delta^3 = 1$), and $\left(\delta^4\right)^2 = \delta^8 = \delta^6\delta^2 = \delta^2$. Thus we need only the simple powers δ and δ^2, as suggested above. Here $\delta = -\sqrt{3}/2 + 1/2\,i$. ∎

Ex 6.21 From the identity $x^4 - 1 = (x-1)(x+1)(x^2+1)$, find all four fourth roots of 1. Verify that these are also e^0, $e^{\pi i/2}$, $e^{\pi i}$, $e^{3\pi i/2}$.

Plot these roots on the Argand diagram. Hence explain why they can be written as 1, $i1$, i^21, i^31.

Ex 6.22 Express each of the bracketed numbers in the following expressions in the form $re^{i\theta}$. Hence calculate, in cartesian form, **one** value for each power or root:

(a) $\sqrt{(-9i)}$,　(b) $(-1)^{5/6}$,　(c) $\sqrt[3]{(-2+2i)}$,　(d) $\left(-4\sqrt{2} + 4\sqrt{2}i\right)^{2/3}$.

Ex 6.23 Find **all** the values for the following:

(a) $(27i)^{1/3}$,　(b) $(2-2i)^{-2/3}$,　(c) $(-16)^{3/4}$,　(d) $\left(-2-2\sqrt{3}i\right)^{3/2}$.

6.11　Exponential and Trigonometric Functions

Euler's Formula not only delivers a convenient notation and a simple method for finding these complicated powers, but it opens up the possibility of evaluating the exponential function and all trigonometric functions for all numbers in $\mathbb{C}$. (It also allows us to evaluate logs, but that will not be covered here.)

Suppose that $z = x + iy$. Then

$$e^z = e^{x+iy} = e^x e^{iy},$$

which, together with Frame 6.12, gives the following formula for e^z.

Frame 6.14　*The value of the exponential function*

$$e^{x+iy} = e^x\left(\cos y + i\sin y\right) \tag{6.18}$$

Example 6.41   Calculate e^i, $e^{-1-i\pi/2}$.

$$e^i = e^0 \left(\cos 1 + i \sin 1\right) \simeq 0.5403 + 0.8415\,i,$$

$$e^{-1-i\pi/2} = e^{-1}\left[\cos\left(-\frac{\pi}{2}\right) + i\sin\left(-\frac{\pi}{2}\right)\right] = -e^{-1}i.$$

∎

We know, from §6.9, that

$$\cos\theta + i\sin\theta = e^{i\theta},$$
$$\cos\theta - i\sin\theta = e^{-i\theta}.$$

Add these and divide by 2, to obtain $\cos\theta$; subtract and divide by $2i$ to obtain $\sin\theta$. Then change θ to z, since there is no reason to assume that θ must be real. We obtain a pair of formulae, also due to Euler.

Frame 6.15   *Euler's formulae for $\cos z$ and $\sin z$*

$$\cos z = \frac{1}{2}\left[e^{iz} + e^{-iz}\right] \qquad\qquad (6.19)$$

$$\sin z = \frac{1}{2i}\left[e^{iz} - e^{-iz}\right] \qquad\qquad (6.20)$$

The exponential values are calculated using Frame 6.14.

Example 6.42   Evaluate $\cos\frac{i}{4}$ and $\sin(1-i)$.

$$\cos\frac{i}{4} = \frac{1}{2}\left[e^{i^2/4} + e^{-i^2/4}\right]$$

$$= \frac{1}{2}\left[e^{-0.25} + e^{0.25}\right] \simeq 1.0314,$$

$$\sin(1-i) = \frac{1}{2i}\left[e^{i-i^2} - e^{-i+i^2}\right]$$

$$= \frac{1}{2i}\left[e^1(\cos 1 + i\sin 1) - e^{-1}(\cos(-1) + i\sin(-1))\right]$$

$$= -\frac{1}{2}i\left[\left(e - e^{-1}\right)\cos 1 + i\left(e + e^{-1}\right)\sin 1\right]$$

$$\simeq 1.2985 - 0.6350\,i$$

∎

The most important conclusion from these last two sections is that the set of complex numbers is remarkably *complete*, in the sense that we have managed to find answers within it for *every* calculation we have tried. Compare this with the real numbers, where $\sqrt{-1}$ fails, as well as calculations such as $\ln(-1)$ and $\sin^{-1}(2)$. (Those two quantities also have a value in $\mathbb{C}$.)

Ex 6.24   Evaluate $e^{2-\pi i}$ and $\cos i\pi$.

Ex 6.25   Evaluate $e^{1-i\pi/6}$, $\sin\left(\dfrac{i\pi}{2}\right)$, $\cos(\pi(1+i))$.

6.12 Revision Exercises

Ex 6.26 Let $z = 2 + i$ and $w = 1 + 3i$. Find the following:

(a) $2z + w$;

(b) $|z - w|$;

(c) $\dfrac{z}{w}$.

Ex 6.27 Let $z = 1 - 2i$ and $w = 3 - i$. Calculate:

(a) $2z - 3w$;

(b) $|z + w|$;

(c) $\dfrac{1}{z}$;

(d) w^2.

Ex 6.28 Let $z = 12 - 5i$. Find the following:

$$|z|, \quad \bar{z}, \quad \frac{1}{z}, \quad z^2, \quad \text{polar form of } z.$$

(Quote the argument of the polar form, in radians, correct to 3 dp.)

Ex 6.29 Solve $4z^2 - 12z + 25 = 0$.

Ex 6.30

(a) Find the roots of the quadratic $z^2 + 8z + 65 = 0$.

(b) Find a quadratic with integer coefficients, whose roots are $\frac{1}{2} \pm \frac{3}{2}i$.

Ex 6.31 Find the polar form for $z = -1 + \sqrt{3}i$.
Plot both z and z^2 on the Argand Diagram.

Ex 6.32 The complex number z has polar form $4\left[\cos\left(-\dfrac{2\pi}{3}\right) + i\sin\left(-\dfrac{2\pi}{3}\right)\right]$.
Use this form to calculate z^3, converting the answer to cartesian form.
Write z in the form $re^{i\theta}$ and use this to find **one** fourth root of z, leaving the answer in exponential form. (Any of the four roots will suffice.)

Ex 6.33 A complex number is written in the form $z = \sqrt{8}\,e^{3\pi i/4}$.

(a) Calculate its cartesian form, i.e., $z = a + bi$, with a, b real.

(b) Find *one* cube root for z, in both (exponential) polar and cartesian form.

(c) Plot this cube root in the Argand Diagram. Mark, on the same diagram, the other two cube roots.

MATHEMATICAL

METHODS

1

1 FUNCTIONS AND GRAPHS

Einstein's famous equation $E = mc^2$ brought to the public's attention the fact that physical science involves **formulae**. Indeed, this had been the case for centuries and textbooks are still awash with useful formulae such as

$$i = \frac{V}{R}, \qquad T = 2\pi\sqrt{\frac{l}{g}}, \qquad p = \frac{RT}{v}.$$

About two hundred years ago, Fourier made one of the most significant advances in the application of mathematics to science and engineering, a side effect of which was to reveal that we need more than a simple 'formula'; we need the concept of a **function**, introduced in §1.1. Although the two ideas are similar, a problem had arisen due to a failure to grasp that more than one formula may be required to describe some feature. A function can have many formulae associated with it, provided they do not interfere with each other. This is investigated in §1.4.

1.1 Definition of a Function

A function describes mathematically the way in which one quantity is related to others. It allows us to provide a precise description – a *model* – of a process such as an experiment, a production line or a natural phenomenon. The relation is not two-way: some quantities are deemed more fundamental in that their values determine those of another quantity: they lead and the other must follow. In this way it is like a formula, with the determined quantity its **subject**. But functions may exist when there is no single formula or even no formula at all.

The formal definition of a function involves two sets X and Y and a rule that relates to each member of X a single member of Y.

A method for visualising this, which is particularly helpful in science and engineering, is to think of it as a **process**, with an **input** (in X) and an **output** (in Y). The 'rule' is the process itself. The input 'drives' the output, which is uniquely determined by that input. This interpretation can be represented pictorially as in the diagram below. Pay particular attention to the arrows leading from the input x to the output y.

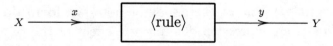

$$X \xrightarrow{\quad x \quad} \boxed{\langle\text{rule}\rangle} \xrightarrow{\quad y \quad} Y$$

We shall initially consider only functions linking two quantities, i.e., we shall assume X and Y are sets of **numbers**.

The six items that follow are often used in connection with a function, although not every one is equally important or even essential. We shall exemplify them using a typical function, one that everyone is familiar with. (The name used is not a standard one.)

Example 1.1   Consider the function that squares numbers, which we shall call SQ in this example.

input	1	2	3	0	½	−2	etc.
output	1	4	9	0	¼	4	etc.

1. (**essential**) We must specify the set X in which all inputs are to be found; it is called the **domain**. For SQ we would normally choose the domain to be all the real numbers ($\mathbb{R}$). We may, for some reason, choose to make the domain smaller than this, to restrict the action of the function. For some functions, we may have to restrict the domain to avoid certain 'illegal' inputs, e.g., those that lead to division by zero.

2. (**essential**) The function must have a **rule**. In other words, if we choose an input from the domain, it must be possible – in theory – to determine the corresponding output. For SQ, the rule is: *multiply the input by itself*. It is possible for us to be aware that there is a rule, but not to know what it is.

3. (**essential**) The input must determine the output **uniquely**, just as we would expect in a mechanical process. For SQ, once we are given the input, we have no choice but to square it, delivering a well-determined number. This does not necessarily hold in reverse: the output may not determine the input that gives rise to it. For SQ, we obtain output 4 from two possible inputs, 2 and −2. This is the reason why the direction arrows in the diagram are essential.

4. (**not important**) The strict definition requires us to specify the set Y, called the **codomain**. Since one can always be found from the domain and the rule – at least in theory – by calculating all possible outputs, it is not as important as those and will rarely concern us. For SQ, we can state that the codomain is $\mathbb{R}$, but a sharper answer is $\{x \text{ in } \mathbb{R} : x \geqslant 0\}$.

5. (**not essential**) A function is usually given a **name**, e.g., SQ. For most theoretical work we use single letters, such as f and g. There are standard functions that are used so frequently that they have their own multi-letter names, e.g., sin and log. In scientific work, there are several standard conventions, such as v for velocity and E for electric field.

6. (**not essential**) Finally, there may be a known **formula** for the function. This is an expression defining the effect of the rule using mathematical notation rather than words. We give the input a symbolic name, often x for space models or t for time models, and find a formula for the output using that symbol. For SQ, the formula is $x \times x$ or x^2. We often give the output the symbol y and then describe the rule as in $y = x^2$.

∎

We can now draw these threads together to set up the sort of notation we shall use. For a function with **name** f and **domain** X we write its **formula** as $f(x)$ or $y = f(x)$. A precise notation for the effect of f translates the diagram into:

$$f : x \rightarrow f(x) \quad (x \text{ in } X), \tag{1.1}$$

where x is the input and $(y =) f(x)$ is the output. For example,

$$SQ : x \rightarrow x^2 \quad (x \text{ in } \mathbb{R}). \tag{1.2}$$

There are many advantages to a notation, as in (1.2), which reflects so well the process model, but it is cumbersome for practical work, where we often talk of the function $y = x^2$ or even just x^2.

Notation

> Many people allow themselves to refer to the function x^2, using the formula as a name. This is, strictly speaking, improper but has been used in practice for a very long time and persists because it is so succinct. The version $y = x^2$ is almost as succinct and clearly shows the input and output.

In item 6 above, we chose x to stand for a representative input from the domain. It is called the **independent** variable. It is a 'variable' because we need not fix its value in advance of using it. It is 'independent' since there are no restrictions on it, other than belonging to X. Once x has been chosen, y is determined by the function rule and is called the **dependent** variable. It inherits the status of 'variable' from x, to which it is tied, or 'dependent'.

Example 1.2   Suggest a suitable domain for the function with formula:

$$f(x) = \sqrt{x^2 - 1}.$$

The square root is defined only when its input is $\geqslant 0$, i.e., when $x^2 - 1 \geqslant 0$. Hence we require $x \geqslant 1$ or $x \leqslant -1$, i.e., $|x| \geqslant 1$, using the notation for the **size** of x, covered in §1.4. The largest possible domain is thus

$$\{x \text{ in } \mathbb{R} : |x| \geqslant 1\}.$$

∎

Quantities fixed in advance, whether written as explicit numbers or represented by symbols, are *constants*. It is normal practice to use letters near the start of the Roman or Greek alphabets to represent constants and ones near the end to represent variables.

Notation

> In the notation $y = f(x)$, the brackets are very important since they delineate the input unambiguously, a matter we shall return to in §1.5. But there are several common exceptions. In particular, unusual or even no brackets may be used, for example:
>
> $$y = \sqrt{x}, \qquad y = |x|, \qquad y = \sin x.$$

In the square root function, the horizontal bar that covers the input is a case of a rather old-fashioned convention whereby such a bar acts as a bracket, as in $a + \overline{b + c}$, equivalent to $a + (b + c)$. All these functions have computer programming counterparts where the conventional bracketed form is essential: $\mathtt{SQRT}(x)$, $\mathtt{ABS}(x)$ and $\mathtt{SIN}(x)$, respectively.

A function $f(x)$ is considered a *unary operator* on x and, as such, usually has higher priority than $+$, $\times$, etc. When brackets are used, as in $f(x)$ or $|x|$, this is clear since the brackets will enforce early evaluation. Care is needed for other situations: $\sin x + y$ will be evaluated as $(\sin x) + y$, since sin has higher priority than $+$; explicit brackets must be used to obtain $\sin(x + y)$.

Ex 1.1 Which of the following are functions? For each that is a function, specify its domain and discuss whether it has a formula.

(a) The square root of a number x.

(b) The non-negative square root of a number x.

(c) The circumference of a circle of radius r.

(d) The height above sea level at a point with longitude x and latitude y.

(e) The temperature at the point in (d).

(f) The temperature at the point in (d) at time t.

(g) The number x or y that is the larger.

(h) The number x or y that has the larger *size*.

Ex 1.2 For the formula $g(x) = 1/\sqrt{1 - x}$, find a domain set that is as large as possible. Then find a range set that is as small as possible. (This maximises the number of valid 'inputs' while avoiding impossible 'outputs'.)

1.2   Graphs

Many of a function's properties are best illustrated by its **graph**, which is a set of points (x, y), with x and y linked via the function: $y = f(x)$, for all the x in the domain.

Think about it like this

Draw two perpendicular lines (*axes*), the x-axis horizontal and the y-axis vertical, and fix a scale on them. Place marks at points (a, b), where $b = f(a)$ and $a \in A$ (the domain of f), situated a units along the x-axis and b units along the y-axis. If the domain consists of an interval on the real line then these marks will often join up to give a continuous line. For a function known to be well-behaved it is usually safe to guess its behaviour between the plotted points.

Example 1.3 Draw the graph of the function SQ.

The data from Example 1.1 gives points

$$(0,0), \ (1,1), \ (2,4), \ (\tfrac{1}{2}, \tfrac{1}{4}),$$

as well as others with negative x co-ordinates. Mark each with • and join them up.

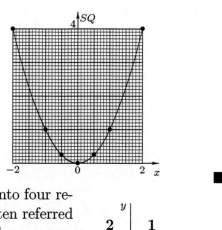

■

The axes in a graph divide the plane into four regions known as **quadrants**. These are often referred to when discussing a function, and are always numbered as shown on the right. In particular, the counting is done in **anticlockwise** order, which is *always* chosen as the 'positive' sense.

1.3 Linear Functions and Straight Lines

A simple but extremely important function is $f(x) = mx + c$, where m and c are constants. The graph is a straight line and hence $f(x)$ is called a **linear** function.

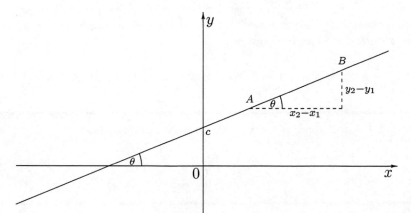

The constant m measures the slope or **gradient** of the line, while c measures the **intercept** on the y-axis, i.e., the value of y, or $f(x)$, when $x = 0$. The gradient is also $\tan\theta$, where θ [*theta*] is the angle the line makes with the positive x-axis.

Example 1.4   The line $y = x - 1$ has $m = 1$ and $c = -1$.

The gradient of the line is 1 and it crosses the y-axis at $(0, -1)$. This allows us to draw it, as shown on the right.

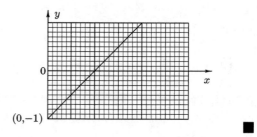

A line is fixed in position when we know two points on it, so the graph can be drawn by choosing two different x values and computing the corresponding y values.

Conversely, choosing two points on the line, perhaps measured from its graph, we can proceed as follows. Suppose the points are $A = (x_1, y_1)$ and $B = (x_2, y_2)$. Calculate the gradient:

$$m = \frac{y_2 - y_1}{x_2 - x_1}. \qquad (1.3)$$

Think about it like this

The concept of gradient pervades all calculus and it is necessary to ensure its definition is firmly understood. In particular, you must not confuse the top and bottom of the fraction in (1.3). This is a precise measure of an everyday idea: a road or hill is said to have a large gradient if its height increases quickly as we move in a horizontal direction, i.e., the y change is large in comparison with the x change. This means the y difference is on the top and the x difference is on the bottom.

Once the gradient is known, the equation of the line is readily found.

Frame 1.1   Equation of a straight line, gradient m, through (a,b)

$$y - b = m(x - a) \qquad (1.4)$$

It is sometimes necessary to find a line perpendicular to a given line, usually called the **normal** (line). If the given line has gradient m then the normal has gradient n given by

$$mn = -1. \qquad (1.5)$$

Knowing a point on the normal allows us to find its equation from (1.4), with m replaced by n, calculated using (1.5).

Example 1.5   A line passes through $(1, 2)$ and $(-1, 6)$. Find its equation.

Also, find the equation of the line normal to this, also passing through $(1, 2)$.

The gradient is $\dfrac{6-2}{-1-1} = -2$. Use Frame 1.1 with either point as (a, b); we use $a = 1$, $b = 2$:

$$y - 2 = -2(x - 1) \quad \Rightarrow \quad y = -2x + 4.$$

Assume the normal has gradient n. Then $-2n = -1$ and $n = \frac{1}{2}$. The normal is thus

$$y - 2 = \tfrac{1}{2}(x - 1) \quad \Rightarrow \quad y = \tfrac{1}{2}x + \tfrac{3}{2}.$$

∎

Ex 1.3

(a) What is the gradient of the line through $A\,(-1, 1)$ and $B\,(2, 7)$?

(b) Find the equation of the line through $A\,(-1, 1)$ and $B\,(2, 7)$.

(c) Find the equation of the normal to the line in (a), through the point A.

Ex 1.4 In each of the following cases the cartesian equations of two lines are given. Do these lines intersect? If they do, find the coordinates of the common point.

(a) $y = 2x - 1$, $\quad y + x = 2$;

(b) $x + 2y = 3$, $\quad 4x - 6y = 5$;

(c) $y = 2x - 1$, $\quad y = 2x + 1$.

1.4 Piecewise Functions

A function and its formula must not be confused. It is not always possible to devise a formula: the height of a plant (h) is a function of time (t) but it is unlikely that this could be precisely described by a formula $h = f(t)$.

Also, it may not be possible to find a *single* formula to define a function throughout its entire domain. We may have to break the domain into pieces and specify a different formula in each piece. Such functions are called **piecewise**.

We start with two important examples. The **absolute value** function $y = |x|$ measures the size of a number x and the **sign** or **signum** function $y = \operatorname{sgn} x$ gives its sign. In each case there are different formulae for $x < 0$, $x = 0$ and $x > 0$ (or $x \geqslant 0$). (A point where two pieces of a function are joined together is sometimes called a **knot**; both these functions have a knot at $x = 0$.) Their definitions are as follows.

$$|x| = \begin{cases} -x, & \text{if } x < 0; \\ x, & \text{if } x \geqslant 0. \end{cases} \qquad \operatorname{sgn} x = \begin{cases} -1, & \text{if } x < 0; \\ 0, & \text{if } x = 0, \\ 1, & \text{if } x > 0. \end{cases} \qquad (1.6)$$

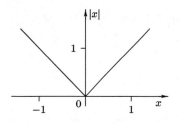

Example 1.6 Draw the graph of $f(x) = \begin{cases} 2x, & \text{if } 0 \leqslant x < 1; \\ \frac{5}{2} - \frac{1}{2}x, & \text{if } 1 \leqslant x < 3; \\ 4 - x, & \text{if } 3 \leqslant x \leqslant 4. \end{cases}$

Each piece is linear, so find the end-points and join them:

$$\begin{aligned} 2x &: & (0,0) &\text{ to } (1,2), \\ \tfrac{5}{2} - \tfrac{1}{2}x &: & (1,2) &\text{ to } (3,1), \\ 4 - x &: & (3,1) &\text{ to } (4,0). \end{aligned}$$

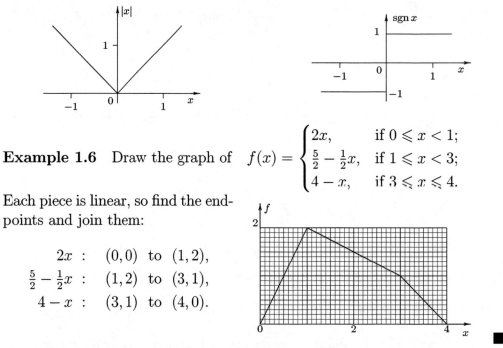

∎

Think about it like this

Working with a piecewise function is like filling out a form where different boxes have to be chosen according to one's status. For each x we work out which subformula ('box') is relevant and calculate the value. That subformula has no validity outside the part of the domain for which it is defined. Thus, for the example above, there is no meaning whatever to the value of $4 - x$ at $x = 0$, since $4 - x$ applies only in the interval $[3,4]$. The fact that it could be evaluated outside this interval is irrelevant. The case of the non-included end-point, such as 3 in $[1,3)$, is rather different. It can be included in the evaluation, but only to help draw that part of the graph.

Example 1.7 The gravitational attraction by the earth at distance r from its centre is quantified by the following function:

$$F(r) = \begin{cases} \dfrac{mg}{R}r, & \text{if } 0 \leqslant r < R; \\ \dfrac{mgR^2}{r^2}, & \text{if } R \leqslant r. \end{cases}$$

Here m is the mass of the object studied, r is its distance from the centre of the earth, R is the radius of the earth and g is the acceleration due to gravity at its surface.

The value at the knot comes from the second piece:

$$F(R) = \frac{mgR^2}{R^2} = mg.$$

But this value is also given by the first piece if we let $r = R$, even although it is not in its domain. Hence the two agree, as we would expect from physical considerations. The graph also shows this.

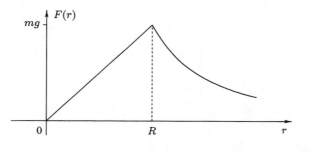

This shows the concept of a piecewise function to be quite natural. Such functions often occur when, for example, we measure some quantity that changes property as we cross a boundary between two materials.

The function sgn x effectively models a 'switch', changing its output from -1 to 1 as we cross $x = 0$. There is another function that fulfils this task more neatly, the **Heaviside** function. Changing to independent variable t, to represent 'time', it is written $H(t)$ and defined by

$$H(t) = \begin{cases} 0, & \text{if } t < 0; \\ 1, & \text{if } t \geqslant 0. \end{cases} \qquad (1.7)$$

It is shown pictorially in the diagram below, where the axes have been omitted so as not to obscure some useful conventions.

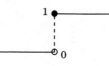

Notation

The two pieces for $H(t)$ (like those for sgn x) do not join together, so there is a need to indicate which value we should use at the 'jump'. That value is marked as '•'. A point on the graph that is *not* a value is marked 'o'. Strictly speaking, the gap at this point should be left empty since there is no value of the function 'in between' the o and •; recall that a function can take only one value for any given input. It is a common convention to use a broken line to help the eye follow the graph. Note that the graph for the function sgn x ought to have 'o' at $(0, -1)$ and $(0, 1)$, and a '•' at $(0, 0)$.

$H(t)$ models a process with output 0 until $t = 0$, when a switch is thrown and the output becomes 1. More complex models are readily created:

$$F(t) = H(t)f(t) \qquad (1.8)$$

gives an output 0 until $t = 0$, followed by $f(t)$.

This shows that discontinuous functions can play a useful role. Indeed, examples can be found in everyday life.

Example 1.8 A bank pays interest of 2% for deposits less than £500 and 5% for £500 or more.

Let the deposit be x and the interest paid $I(x)$. Then:

$$I(x) = \begin{cases} 0.02x, & \text{if } 0 \leqslant x < 500; \\ 0.05x, & \text{if } 500 \leqslant x. \end{cases}$$

Draw the lines $I = 0.02x$ and $I = 0.05x$, but restricted to their own parts of the domain, as shown in the definition above. Note the position of the •, since £500 earns the higher rate of interest.

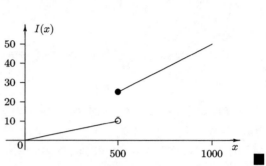

Ex 1.5 Sketch the graphs of the functions with the formulae:

(a) $f(x) = \begin{cases} -1-x, & \text{if } -2 \leqslant x < 0; \\ -1+x, & \text{if } 0 \leqslant x \leqslant 2; \end{cases}$

(b) $g(x) = \begin{cases} -(2+x), & \text{if } -4 \leqslant x < -2; \\ 0, & \text{if } -2 \leqslant x < 2; \\ 2-x, & \text{if } 2 \leqslant x \leqslant 4. \end{cases}$

Ex 1.6 Find $f + g$ when f and g are given by:

$$f(x) = \begin{cases} x^2, & \text{if } x \leqslant 1; \\ 2x-1, & \text{if } x > 1; \end{cases} \qquad g(x) = \begin{cases} 5x+3, & \text{if } x \leqslant 0; \\ x^4+3, & \text{if } x > 0. \end{cases}$$

1.5   Arguments of Functions

Consider the contents of the brackets in function notation: the x part in $f(x)$. We deem x to be a variable and so it can be replaced by anything we wish, in the domain of f, e.g., a number, a constant, another variable name, an expression involving numbers and arithmetic operators, another function of x and so on. Whatever replaces the x in '$f(x)$' is called the **argument** of the function. In the notation $y = f(x)$, x can be viewed as a 'marker', indicating in the formula where the actual value is to be inserted. The argument is then copied in place of every x in the formula.

When we replace x by an argument, it is good practice initially to wrap this expression inside brackets before replacing each x by it, then remove them if that tidies up the answer. Brackets form a key defence against unintended side-effects, as well as playing a useful defensive role, as the next example shows.

Example 1.9   Use the argument $a + 1$ in the function $f(x) = 1 - x$.

When replacing x by $a + 1$, insert it in brackets:

$$f(a+1) = 1 - (a+1) = 1 - a - 1 = -a.$$

A careless replacement by $1 - a + 1$ leads to the wrong final expression. ∎

Think about it like this

> In normal function notation, $f(x)$, there are three purposes for the brackets. One is to tell the process f how much of what follows is its input.
>
> A second purpose is to protect that input from contamination by other parts of the expression. For the function $x\sin(x)$, the two instances of x must be kept apart, since this is very different from $\sin(x^2)$. In fact, one is the *output* of x and the other the *input* of $\sin(x)$. This point may seem obvious as set out in the previous sentence, but particular care is needed when using exceptional notations such as $\sin x$ or $\sqrt{x}$. There is a serious danger in writing $\sin x\, x$, since someone may read it as $\sin x^2$; one should always write $x\sin x$ if that is what is intended.
>
> A third purpose is to force evaluation of their contents before use of the function rule, just as they override the rules of precedence in arithmetic. When reading the next example, note how we have to add 9 and 16 *before* applying the square root: an attempt to defer that addition gives the wrong answer.

Example 1.10 Consider the function $f(x) = \sqrt{x}$.

The following exemplify a variety of different arguments:

$$f(9) = \sqrt{9} = 3,$$
$$f(4k) = \sqrt{4k} = 2\sqrt{k}, \quad \text{since } \sqrt{xy} = \sqrt{x}\sqrt{y},$$
$$f(\theta - 1) = \sqrt{\theta - 1}, \quad \text{which does not simplify,}$$
$$f(9 + 16) = \sqrt{9 + 16} = \sqrt{25} = 5,$$
$$\mathbf{not}\ \sqrt{9} + \sqrt{16} = 3 + 4 = 7,$$
$$f(a^2) = \sqrt{a^2} = |a|.$$

Note the use of the absolute value in the last case. The square root is never negative, although a may well be. It is safe to use $|a|$ since $a^2 = (-a)^2$. ∎

Think about it like this

> People often make errors by applying a function rule to parts of its argument separately. It is tempting to misuse the similarity between the following:
>
> | | | |
> |---|---|---|
> | $a(x + y) = ax + ay$ | (where a is a number) | ALWAYS TRUE, |
> | $f(x + y) = f(x) + f(y)$ | (where f is a function) | RARELY TRUE. |
>
> Here f is a shorthand for something much more complicated than a number.
>
> In some cases, we can find ways to rewrite $f(x + y)$ and $f(xy)$, but usually not in an obvious way. For example, $\sqrt{x + y}$, $\frac{1}{x+y}$ and $\log(x + y)$ have *no* useful alternatives, while $\sin(x + y)$ and $(x + y)^2$ do, but not as simple as $\sin x + \sin y$ or $x^2 + y^2$.
>
> Similarly, there is no useful alternative for $\sin(xy)$, although there is for $\log(xy)$. Also, $\sqrt{xy}$, $\frac{1}{xy}$ and $(xy)^2$ *can* be rewritten in an 'obvious' way.

We now concentrate on the special case where the argument is a **linear** function $ax + b$, with a and b constants, which leads to the function formula $f(ax + b)$. This can also be regarded as the composition $f \circ g$ of f and the function $g(x) = ax + b$. (See §5.3.)

This function may appear to be quite different from $f(x)$, but the change is equivalent to moving the origin along the x-axis and rescaling that axis, together with a reflection in the y-axis if $a < 0$. Hence it leaves the fundamental shape of the graph unchanged, and means that $f(ax + b)$ has many similar properties to $f(x)$.

Rather than study this in general, examine the graphs that follow. These show a random $f(x)$, followed by $f(-x)$, $f(x + 1)$, $f(2x)$. Since f has no special formula, no scales have been given, except for a single fixed reference point on each axis to help appreciate how the shape has changed.

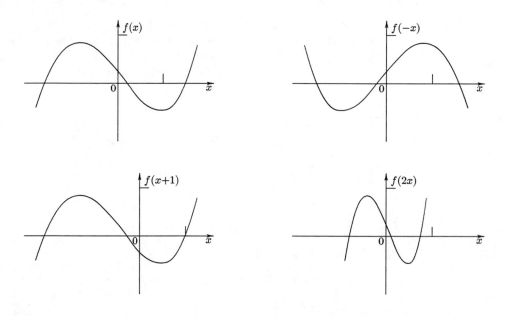

The case $f(x + \alpha)$ is similar to $f(x + 1)$, unless $\alpha < 0$, in which case the function's graph is translated to the right. The case $f(\beta x)$ (with $\beta > 0$) is similar to $f(2x)$, unless $0 < \beta < 1$, in which case the graph expands rather than contracts; if $\beta < 0$ there is also a reflection like that for $f(-x)$. More complicated arguments can be treated by combining these fundamental cases.

Think about it like this

These results may seem counter-intuitive in that *adding* something to the argument shifts the graph in the *negative* direction; also, multiplying the argument by a *large* scale factor *shrinks* the graph. This apparent strangeness should be noted and used as a trigger to your memory.

It is, in fact, all we could expect. Suppose that $f(x)$ has some recognisable feature, such as a maximum, at $x = X$. Then $f(x + 1)$ will have that feature when $x + 1 = X$, i.e., $x = X - 1$, which is one unit earlier in the graph.

Example 1.11 Let $f(x) = x^2$, whose graph is shown in Example 1.3. Sketch the graphs of:

$$f(x - 1), \qquad f(x + 1), \qquad f(2x), \qquad f(\sqrt{x}).$$

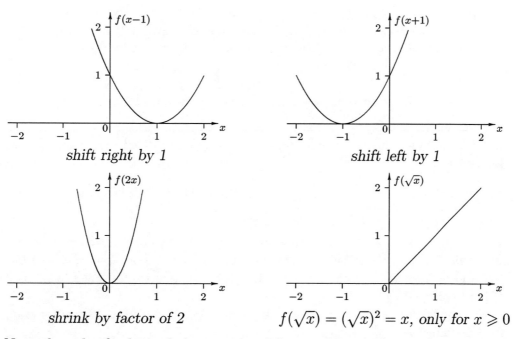

shift right by 1

shift left by 1

shrink by factor of 2

$f(\sqrt{x}) = (\sqrt{x})^2 = x$, only for $x \geqslant 0$

Note that the final graph has a very different shape: *the argument is not linear.* ■

These changes have involved the argument (or input) and the x-axis. Changes to the *output* of a function involve changes along the y-axis. For these we use expressions such as $f(x)+\alpha$, $\beta f(x)$, etc., which are quite different from the earlier expressions. Here the argument is *always* 'x'. The following graphs exemplify this situation; the last combines both ideas, with reflections in both axes.

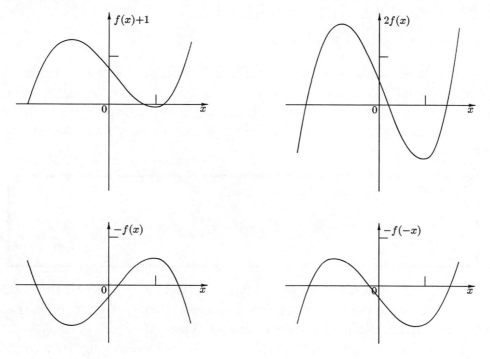

Think about it like this

> This time the results seem more in line with intuition: adding to the output shifts the graph up the y-axis; multiplying by a large number expands the graph (in the y direction).
>
> Thinking of the function with the prominent feature, $f(x) + 1$ will still have it at $x = X$, but it will have moved one unit up the y-axis.

Ex 1.7 A function has formula $f(x) = 1 - x^2$. Write down expressions for the following:

$$f(2a), \quad f(z^2), \quad f(\sqrt{x}), \quad f(1 - h), \quad xf(x), \quad f(1/x), \quad f(1/x)x^2, \quad f(x + y).$$

Ex 1.8 The *integer part* or *floor* function is very convenient in certain calculations, particularly if they are to be programmed for a computer. For input x, it is written $\lfloor x \rfloor$ and defined as the largest integer less than or equal to x. Hence $\lfloor 3.75 \rfloor = 3$, $\lfloor 5 \rfloor = 5$ and $\lfloor -1.8 \rfloor = -2$.

Specify this function in piecewise notation for $0 \leqslant x < 3$ and draw its graph for that interval.

Hence draw the graph of $\lfloor x + 0.5 \rfloor$ and describe what useful purpose this function fulfils.

Ex 1.9 The Heaviside function, $H(t)$, is defined as $H(t) = \begin{cases} 0, & \text{if } t < 0; \\ 1, & \text{if } t \geqslant 0. \end{cases}$

Here t represents time.

Draw graphs of the following functions:

   (a) $H(t - 1)$,   (b) $H(t) - H(t - 1)$,   (c) $H(-t)$,   (d) $tH(t)$.

1.6   Functions with Symmetries

1.6.1   Oddness and Evenness

An **even function** is one whose graph is symmetric about the y-axis: the portion to the left is an exact mirror image of that to the right. Thus, $f(-2) = f(2)$, $f(-1) = f(1)$, etc. This means that its graph is unaffected by changing the argument from 'x' to '$-x$'. Hence a test for an even function is the following **identity**.

Frame 1.2   *Condition for an even function*

$$f(-x) = f(x) \quad \text{(for all } x\text{)}$$

An **odd function** has a graph that is 'antisymmetric' about the y-axis, meaning that the portion to the left is an exact copy of that to the right after *two* mirror reflections, one in each axis. Thus, $f(-2) = -f(2)$, $f(-1) = -f(1)$, etc. This means that its graph is unaffected by changing the argument from 'x' to '$-x$' and simultaneously changing the sign of the output. Hence the test for an odd function is the following.

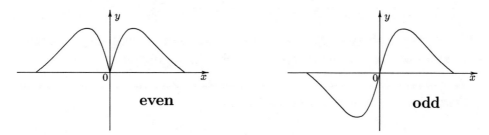

Frame 1.3   *Condition for an odd function*

$$f(-x) = -f(x) \quad \text{(for all } x\text{)}$$

These properties are illustrated in the diagrams below.

even   **odd**

Example 1.12   Classify the following functions as even, odd or neither:

$$x^2, \qquad x^3, \qquad |x|, \qquad \operatorname{sgn} x.$$

x^2: we have $(-x)^2 = x^2$ and so this is **even**. See Example 1.3 for a confirmatory graph.

x^3: we have $(-x)^3 = -x^3$ and so this is **odd**. This is confirmed by the graph on the right.

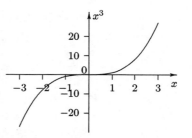

Note that 2 is even and 3 is odd. In general, x^n is even/odd corresponding to n being even/odd.

$|x|$: we have $|-x| = |x|$, since any minus sign will be removed by the absolute value. Hence this is **even**. See the graph in §1.4 for confirmation.

$\operatorname{sgn} x$: the graph in §1.4 shows this to be **odd**. Note that the value at $x = 0$ is defined to be zero, fitting in with $f(-0) = -f(0)$, since both are 0.

Further examples, as we see in the next chapter, are $\cos x$, which is even, and $\sin x$, which is odd. ∎

Think about it like this

> Master the terms *even* and *odd*. They both refer to symmetries of a 'mirror' type. The graph of an even function for negative x is just what a mirror placed along the y-axis would show as a reflection of the positive part. An odd function requires two reflections, the second being in the x-axis. You may like to think of 'odd' as having a rather more 'peculiar' graph. Alternatively, think of the simple parabola $y = x^2$ with its *even* power and symmetric shape to remember which property is 'even'.

1.6.2   Periodicity

If the graph of a function (defined for all x) remains unchanged after being moved through some distance P in one or other direction along the x-axis, then every portion of length P must fall into the exact place left vacant by the portion to the left or right. Hence the graph must consist of repeated copies of a pattern of length P.

The following function is typical of the sort of graph involved.

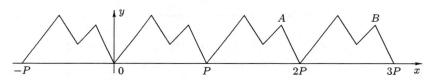

Moving a graph through a distance P is achieved by using the argument $x + P$ or $x - P$, which motivates the following definition.

Frame 1.4   *Definition of a periodic function*

$$f(x + P) = f(x) \qquad \text{(for all } x\text{)} \qquad (1.9)$$

The number P is the **period** of the function. (Strictly speaking, we ought to stipulate that P is the *smallest* number with this property.)

The pattern of width P can be *any* part of the graph. For the graph above, the part of the domain between 0 and P would seem the obvious one to choose, to generate the whole graph, and many would regard this as the **natural** or **defining** interval or period. But it could also be generated by making copies of the portion between A and B.

Note that the 'natural' interval $[0, P)$ is closed on the left and open on the right; we could use the opposite if we prefer. It is possible that the value at the start may not be the same at the finish, which will generate a clash when one period stops and the next starts. It is not allowed to have two values at one point, so a 'jump' is the usual way to resolve this, giving priority (a • on the graph) at the closed end of the interval. This is not an issue for the example above.

The most familiar (and important) examples of periodic functions are $\cos x$ and $\sin x$, each of which has period $360°$ or 2π radians. This property will be much used in the next chapter. There are, however, two 'natural' periods in common use: $[0, 360°)$ and $(-180°, 180°]$.

Using Frame 1.4 repeatedly shows that

$$f(x) = f(x \pm nP) \quad \text{(all } x\text{, all } n \text{ in } \mathbb{N}\text{)}. \qquad (1.10)$$

This allows the calculation of $f(x)$ for large or small x to be converted into a calculation in the defining interval, which can be readily carried out.

We can also ask reverse questions, e.g., for which values of x is $f(x) = \alpha$? Assuming there is such a value in the defining interval, β say, we can find others by adding or subtracting multiples of P, as $x = \beta \pm nP$.

Example 1.13   A function $f(x)$ has period 4 and formula for one period:

$$f(x) = 16x - x^3, \qquad (0 \leqslant x < 4).$$

Its graph is shown below.

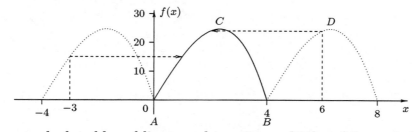

Values are calculated by adding or subtracting multiples of the period 4 until the argument is in the interval $[0, 4)$ at which point the formula may be used. The results for the first two cases have been illustrated on the graph above.

$$f(6) = f(6 - 4) = f(2) = 16 \times 2 - 2^3 = 24$$

$$f(-3) = f(-3 + 4) = f(1) = 16 \times 1 - 1^3 = 15$$

$$f(11) = f(11 - 2 \times 4) = f(3) = 16 \times 3 - 3^3 = 21$$

$$f(65) = f(65 - 16 \times 4) = f(1) = 15$$

$$f(-29) = f(-29 + 8 \times 4) = f(3) = 21$$

$$f(36) = f(36 - 9 \times 4) = f(0) = 0$$

When is $f(x) = 0$? The only such value in $[0, 4)$ is $x = 0$. All others are given by $x = 0 \pm 4n$.

Knowing the graph on *any* patch of width 4 is sufficient to construct it everywhere. One may think it most natural to use repeated copies of the portion between A and B to do this, but it is just as acceptable to use the portion between C and D. ∎

Think about it like this

The concept of a *period* is both important and useful. Once we know the graph or the formula for a periodic function over *any* period, we know it everywhere. Suppose we know the graph over the interval $[a, a + P)$, where P is the period. Then draw this graph on a piece of tracing paper and repeatedly copy it (without any rotation or reflection) placing the left end at $a + P$, $a + 2P$, ..., $a - P$, $a - 2P$, ..., and you will have the full graph.

There is a danger here. We are very accustomed to writing from left to right. Hence copying the period starting at $a + P$, $a + 2P$, etc. is straightforward. Many people find it hard to switch to drawing from right to left and if they start from a in that direction they may inadvertently flip the template over. Hence it is safer to complete the left hand portion by drawing from left to right, either one period at a time or by starting at the extreme left: $a - nP$ for some suitable n.

There are many natural periodic functions. The following are important in electronics.

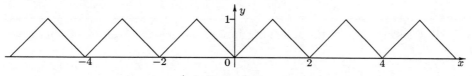

A triangular wave

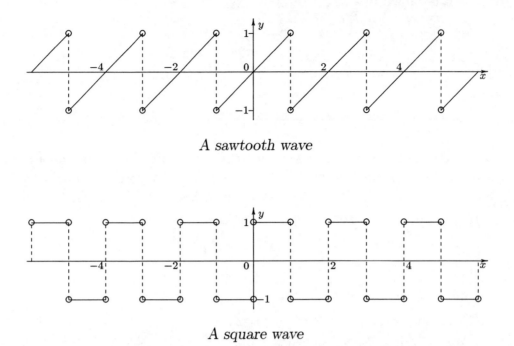

A sawtooth wave

A square wave

For the cases illustrated here, the **triangular wave** is *even*, the **sawtooth wave** and **square wave** are *odd*.

Think about it like this

> Look carefully at these graphs to ensure you see that they could be built up by copying different shapes, all with the width of one period, but starting at different places: any patch of width one period is a possible generating template.

These can be adapted in several ways, changing their period, the position relative to the x-axis and the y-axis, and the maximum value. The most important adaptation is to the **period** itself. The 'shrinking' property seen in §1.5 provides the answer.

Frame 1.5   *Changing the period of a periodic function*

$$\text{If } f(x) \text{ has period } P, \text{ then } f(\alpha x) \text{ has period } \frac{P}{\alpha}$$

This receives heavy use when working with the trigonometric functions $\sin x$ and $\cos x$; it will be illustrated in that context, in the next chapter.

Ex 1.10 Classify each of the following functions as even, odd, or neither even nor odd:

$$x^3\sqrt{|x|}, \qquad x^3 + x^4, \qquad x^2 + x^4.$$

Ex 1.11 Deduce whether each of the following is even or odd. [Hint: use the algebraic definitions, based on examining $f(-x)$.]

$$\sqrt{x^2+1}, \qquad x-x^3, \qquad (10^x-10^{-x})/2, \qquad x^{2/3}.$$

Ex 1.12 A function f is defined as periodic with period 6 and is given on the interval $(-3,3\,]$ by

$$f(x) = \begin{cases} -6-2x, & \text{if } -3 < x < -2; \\ x, & \text{if } -2 \leqslant x < 2; \\ 6-2x, & \text{if } 2 \leqslant x \leqslant 3. \end{cases}$$

Find each of the following values:
$$f(-{}^3\!/_2), \quad f(8), \quad f(-6), \quad f(5), \quad f(25), \quad f(-49), \quad f(45).$$

Ex 1.13 A function f is periodic with period 5 and is given in $[0,5)$ by

$$f(x) = x^2 - 5x \quad (0 \leqslant x < 5).$$

Find $f(21)$ and $f(-8)$. Find a formula for $f(x)$ in $[5,10)$. Draw the graph of $f(x)$ over $[-5,10]$.

1.7 Revision Exercises

Ex 1.14 Plot the following data, with f on the horizontal axis, and draw a line through it. Use this graph to estimate the gradient of the line.

Frequency (f)	0.69	0.74	0.82	0.96	1.18
Potential (V)	0.55	0.73	1.09	1.67	2.57

This data was reported by Millikan in 1916, for the element lithium. It provided corroboration of Einstein's theory of the *photelectric effect* and an extremely accurate measurement for Planck's constant h. (Millikan won the Nobel Prize in 1923 for this work.)

The model suggested by Einstein's theory is:

$$V = \frac{h}{e}f - \frac{\phi}{e},$$

where $e = 1.602 \times 10^{-19}\,\mathrm{C}$ is the charge on the electron. V is measured in volts and f in units of $10^{15}\,\mathrm{Hz}$. Use your value for the gradient to find an estimate for h (which will be in units Js: joule-sec).

ϕ is the *work function* for the material, a measure of the energy needed to release an electron. Estimate the work function for lithium, in terms of the unit eV (*electron-volt*), which is defined as 1 volt $\times\, e$, so you require to compute a value for ϕ/e.

Ex 1.15 Sketch graphs for: $f(x+1)$, $f(\tfrac{1}{2}x)$, $f(-x)$, $-f(-x)$, for the function below.

The graph to the right is that of the piecewise function

$$f(x) = \begin{cases} x^2, & \text{if } 0 \leqslant x < 1; \\ 2 - x, & \text{if } 1 \leqslant x \leqslant 2. \end{cases}$$

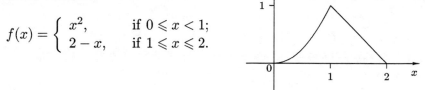

Ex 1.16 The concentration C involved in a certain chemical reaction is described by the formula $C = 5/(8t + 5)$, where t is measured in minutes. Find a formula linking C and T, where T is measured in seconds.

Ex 1.17 Classify each of the following functions as even, odd, or neither even nor odd:

$$x^4 \cos x, \ \ x^3 \sin x, \ \ x^5 + x^6, \ \ \sqrt{|x|}, \ \ (\sin x)^3, \ \ \sin x + \cos x, \ \ x - \sin x, \ \ \frac{x}{1 + x^2}.$$

Ex 1.18 A function f is periodic with period π. It is given in $[0, \pi)$ by

$$f(x) = 2 \sin x \quad (0 \leqslant x < \pi).$$

Find $f\left(\tfrac{3\pi}{2}\right)$. Find a formula for $f(x)$ in $[\pi, 2\pi)$.

Ex 1.19 A function $f(x)$ has **period** 5 and is defined in the interval $[0, 5)$ by

$$f(x) = \begin{cases} \dfrac{1}{x+1}, & \text{if } 0 \leqslant x < 3; \\[2ex] 2 - \tfrac{1}{2}x, & \text{if } 3 \leqslant x < 5. \end{cases}$$

Calculate the values of $f(46)$, $f(-30)$, $f(-21)$ and $f(38)$.

Ex 1.20 A function $f(x)$ has **period** 6 and is defined on part of its domain (a full period) by

$$f(x) = \begin{cases} x^2, & \text{if } 0 \leqslant x \leqslant 2; \\ 6 - x, & \text{if } 2 < x < 6. \end{cases}$$

Draw the graph of $f(x)$ for $-12 \leqslant x \leqslant 12$.

Evaluate $f(33)$ and $f(-22)$.

2 TRIGONOMETRIC FUNCTIONS

Trigonometry was first used to solve *static* 'mensuration' problems, e.g., the measurement of angles, distances and areas, related to what we now regard as 'surveying'. The quantities involved, $\sin\theta$, $\cos\theta$, $\tan\theta$, etc., are functions, since they depend in a well-defined way on the value of the 'input' θ.

Later, these quantities were found to describe important oscillatory phenomena, such as vibrations and waves. This is related to the way that $\sin\omega t$ and $\cos\omega t$ describe the coordinates of a rotating point, following the circumference of a circle. In this more *dynamic* context, they are often entitled **circular functions**.

Vibrations are *periodic* phenomena; at the end of the previous chapter it was noted that $\cos x$ and $\sin x$ were good examples of even/odd and periodic functions. We can put these observations to use in analysing these trigonometric functions.

2.1 Trigonometric Ratios

The basic definitions are those of the **trigonometric ratios**, sine, cosine and tangent. They are related to the triangle shown in the diagram below, and are usually written in abbreviated form.

$$\sin\theta = \frac{\text{opposite}}{\text{hypotenuse}}$$

$$\cos\theta = \frac{\text{adjacent}}{\text{hypotenuse}}$$

$$\tan\theta = \frac{\text{opposite}}{\text{adjacent}} = \frac{\sin\theta}{\cos\theta}$$

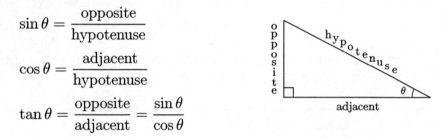

There are two special triangles that generate well-known values:

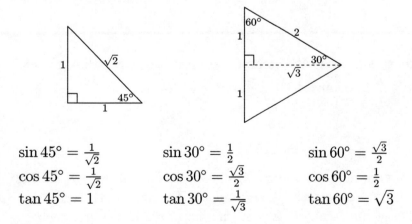

$$\sin 45° = \tfrac{1}{\sqrt 2} \qquad \sin 30° = \tfrac{1}{2} \qquad \sin 60° = \tfrac{\sqrt 3}{2}$$
$$\cos 45° = \tfrac{1}{\sqrt 2} \qquad \cos 30° = \tfrac{\sqrt 3}{2} \qquad \cos 60° = \tfrac{1}{2}$$
$$\tan 45° = 1 \qquad \tan 30° = \tfrac{1}{\sqrt 3} \qquad \tan 60° = \sqrt 3$$

This 'static' context disguises the fact that sin, cos, etc. are *functions*. Although we have defined them using a fixed triangle we can draw such a triangle with any chosen angle, at least between 0° and 90°. Hence we think of sin, cos and tan as functions with angles as input. (We ignore the 'domain' at the moment since we shall soon be able to get round this apparent restriction to acute angles.)

Notation

> There are some anomalies in the notations used for these functions, mostly due to conventions set out above, which were established a long time before the development of modern function notation. In particular, note the lack of brackets for the function argument. In complicated cases, or cases where there is possible ambiguity, brackets are often used. They are compulsory in computer programming, where $\texttt{SIN}(x)$, etc., are used.

2.2   The Relation to a Circle

The cos and sin functions also lie at the heart of many *dynamic* phenomena, especially those that are 'periodic' in nature, such as mechanical vibration and electrical oscillation. The 'dynamic' nature of these functions originates from rotational motion. It is normal practice in this context to use **radian** measure.

Thus: 1 **radian** is the angle whose arc in a unit circle (radius 1) has length 1. Since the circumference of the unit circle is 2π, the full angle at its centre must be 2π radians, equivalent to $360°$.

Frame 2.1   Radian-degree conversion

$$1 \text{ rad} = \frac{180°}{\pi}, \qquad 1° = \frac{\pi}{180} \text{ rad}$$

Here we have used the common abbreviation for radian(s): **rad**.

Example 2.1   Convert $60°$, $\frac{5\pi}{4}$ rad.

$$60° = 60 \times \frac{\pi}{180} = \frac{\pi}{3} \text{ rad},$$

$$\frac{5\pi}{4} \text{ rad} = \frac{5\pi}{4} \times \frac{180}{\pi} = 225°. \qquad \blacksquare$$

For the more general circle (radius r) shown above, we find arc-lengths and areas by proportionality arguments. The arc-length AB is $s = r\theta$. Also, the full circle has area πr^2 and so the sector OAB has area $\pi r^2 \times \frac{\theta}{2\pi} = \frac{1}{2}r^2\theta$.

Notation

> It is now an appropriate time to change our notation from the use of θ as variable to x or t, to fit better with our usual function notation. We shall often use t, representing *time*, reflecting the dynamical applications.

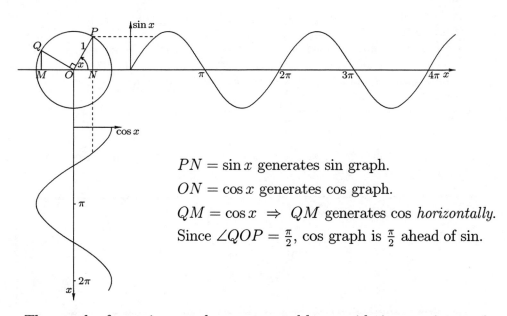

$PN = \sin x$ generates sin graph.

$ON = \cos x$ generates cos graph.

$QM = \cos x \Rightarrow QM$ generates cos *horizontally*.

Since $\angle QOP = \frac{\pi}{2}$, cos graph is $\frac{\pi}{2}$ ahead of sin.

The graph of $y = \sin x$ can be constructed by considering a point moving along the circumference of a unit circle, as shown above, and recording its *height*. The same device can be used to produce the graph of $y = \cos x$, where this time the *horizontal* displacement is projected downwards, to a graph rotated through 90°. The key quantities PN and ON are seen to be $\sin x$ and $\cos x$ respectively, from the right-angled triangle ONP. The great advantage in this way of generating the functions is the lack of restriction placed on the input angle: we can even use negative angles by rotating in the negative (clockwise) direction.

This shows that the graph of $\cos x$ is identical to that of $\sin x$ except that we start 90° or $\frac{\pi}{2}$ further on. This means that

$$\sin\left(\tfrac{1}{2}\pi + x\right) = \cos x \qquad \text{(for all } x\text{)}$$

and many other sin/cos relationships can be read off the graphs.

Periodicity

The main diagram above is unchanged after a rotation through 2π, which shows both sine and cosine have period 2π.

> **Frame 2.2**   *Periodicity of sin/cos*
>
> $$\sin(x + 2\pi k) = \sin x \qquad\qquad (2.1)$$
> $$\cos(x + 2\pi k) = \cos x \qquad\qquad (2.2)$$
> $$(k \text{ in } \mathbb{Z})$$

By adding or subtracting a suitable multiple of 2π (360°) from our angle, we can find a new angle between $-\pi$ and $+\pi$, whose sin and cos are the same.

Notation

In some cases it is useful to identify a 'natural' or 'standard' period for these functions. Normally, this is taken as $(-\pi, \pi]$ or $(-180°, 180°]$, i.e., $-\pi$ $(-180°)$ is not included, while π $(180°)$ is. This is the convention we generally adopt, but there are situations where $[0, 2\pi)$ or $[0°, 360°)$ is more appropriate. The best policy is to be prepared to use either, according to what suits the context.

Oddness/Evenness

The graphs of sin and cos show that sine is an **odd** function and cosine is an **even** one.

Frame 2.3   *Even/odd properties of cos/sin*

$$\sin(-x) = -\sin x \qquad (2.3)$$
$$\cos(-x) = \cos x \qquad (2.4)$$

Using these results, we can change the problem of evaluating a sin or cos of a negative angle x into one for a positive angle $-x$. In the sin case we must record that the sign changes.

Supplementary Angles

The graphs of sin and cos also show the following identities to be true. They relate angles that add up to π $(180°)$, which are called **supplementary**.

Frame 2.4   *Supplementary angle rules*

$$\sin(\pi - x) = \sin x \qquad (2.5)$$
$$\cos(\pi - x) = -\cos x \qquad (2.6)$$

Using these results, we can change the problem of evaluating a sin or cos of an angle x between $\frac{\pi}{2}$ and π into one for an angle $\pi - x$ between 0 and $\frac{\pi}{2}$. In the cos case we must record that the sign changes.

Complementary Angles

The triangle in the diagram at the start of this chapter shows the following identities to be true for acute angles (in fact they are true for all angles). They relate angles that add up to $\frac{\pi}{2}$ $(90°)$, which are called **complementary**.

Frame 2.5   *Complementary angle rules*

$$\sin\left(\tfrac{\pi}{2} - x\right) = \cos x \qquad (2.7)$$
$$\cos\left(\tfrac{\pi}{2} - x\right) = \sin x \qquad (2.8)$$

Using these results, we can choose whether to express evaluation for an angle between 0 and $\frac{\pi}{2}$ as a sin or a cos calculation.

Example 2.2 Evaluate $\sin\frac{8\pi}{3}$.

Move into $(-\pi, \pi]$ by subtracting 2π: $\quad \frac{8\pi}{3} - 2\pi = \frac{2\pi}{3}$.

We are already in $[0, \pi]$: no need to use oddness.

Move into $[0, \frac{\pi}{2})$ by subtracting from π: $\quad \pi - \frac{2\pi}{3} = \frac{\pi}{3}$, with no sign change (sin involved).

Hence the value is $\sin\frac{\pi}{3}$ or $\sin 60°$, which is $\frac{\sqrt{3}}{2}$.

■

Example 2.3 Evaluate $\sin(-390°)$.

Move into $(-180°, 180°]$ by adding $360°$: $\quad -390 + 360 = -30$.

Move into $[0, 180°]$ using oddness: $-30°$ is replaced by $30°$, and we record the need to change the sign of the result.

We are already in $[0, 90°]$: no need to use supplementary angle.

Hence the value is $-\sin 30° = -\frac{1}{2}$.

■

Example 2.4 Simplify $\cos(\frac{\pi}{2} + x)$.

Try the supplementary angle:

$$\cos\left(\tfrac{\pi}{2} + x\right) = -\cos\left(\pi - \left(\tfrac{\pi}{2} + x\right)\right) = -\cos\left(\tfrac{\pi}{2} - x\right)$$
$$= -\sin x \quad \text{(complementary angle)}.$$

■

There is a quick method for finding the *sign* of the trigonometric functions: the 'ASTC' rule tells us which of the three principal circular functions is positive in each quadrant, in turn.

A is *all*,
S is *sin*,
T is *tan*,
C is *cos*.

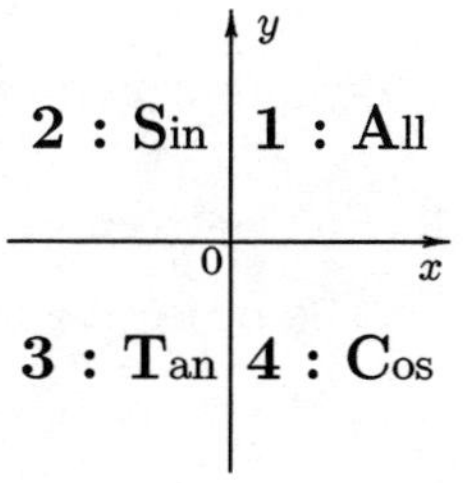

2 : Sin | 1 : All

3 : Tan | 4 : Cos

The graphs of sin/cos give further special values that regularly occur:

$$\sin 0 = 0, \ \cos 0 = 1, \qquad \sin\tfrac{\pi}{2} = 1, \ \cos\tfrac{\pi}{2} = 0, \qquad \sin\pi = 0, \ \cos\pi = -1,$$

$$\sin\left(-\tfrac{\pi}{2}\right) = -1, \ \cos\left(-\tfrac{\pi}{2}\right) = 0, \qquad \sin(-\pi) = 0, \ \cos(-\pi) = -1.$$

The graph of $y = \tan x$ can be constructed from those of $\sin x$ and $\cos x$ and is shown below. There are 'infinite' jumps at *odd* multiples of $\frac{\pi}{2}$ (when its denominator, $\cos x$, is zero). These points are excluded from the domain. $\tan x$ is also an *odd* function and *periodic*, but its period is π, not 2π.

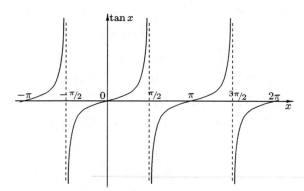

We occasionally encounter the reciprocals of sin, cos and tan. Their full names are **secant**, **cosecant** and **cotangent**; their definitions and abbreviations are as follows.

Frame 2.6   *Other trigonometric ratios*

$$\sec x = \frac{1}{\cos x}, \qquad \operatorname{cosec} x = \csc x = \frac{1}{\sin x}, \qquad \cot x = \frac{1}{\tan x} = \frac{\cos x}{\sin x}$$

Their properties can be deduced from those of $\sin x$ and $\cos x$. In particular, their signs in the various quadrants may be deduced from the ASTC diagram.

Ex 2.1

(a) Convert to radians: $135°$, $330°$.

(b) Convert to degrees: $\frac{2\pi}{3}$, $\frac{7\pi}{6}$.

(c) Calculate *exactly* each of: $\sin\frac{2\pi}{3}$, $\tan\frac{7\pi}{6}$, $\cos\frac{11\pi}{6}$.

Ex 2.2 Find in terms of $s = \sin\theta$: $\sin\left(5\pi + \theta\right)$, $\cos\left(\frac{3\pi}{2} + \theta\right)$, $\sin\left(4\pi - \theta\right)$.

Ex 2.3 The objective is to graph

$$f(x) = \frac{\sin x}{2 - \sqrt{3}\cos x}$$

for $-3\pi \leqslant x \leqslant 3\pi$.

(a) Tabulate $f(x)$ for $x = 0$ to π, in intervals of $\frac{\pi}{6}$, using 4 dp. Then complete the portion of the graph for $0 \leqslant x \leqslant \pi$.

(b) Show that $f(x)$ is odd, i.e., $f(-x) = -f(x)$. Hence complete the graph for $-\pi \leqslant x < 0$.

(c) Show that $f(x)$ has period 2π, i.e., $f(x + 2\pi) = f(x)$. Hence complete the full graph.

2.3   Trigonometric Identities

Note the distinction between an **equation** (true for only certain values of the variables involved) and an **identity** (true for all such values). It is identities that help us use algebraic calculations to rearrange formulae.

The fact that there are clear connections between the behaviour of sin and cos, not to mention that tan is defined in terms of them, means that this topic is rich in identities. Before examining these, note the following unusual notational convention, which is universally used in this context :

$$\sin^2 x = (\sin x)^2.$$

Notation

This is a special notation for the square of the *output* of the sin function – and for other trigonometric ratios – used because the squares occur so frequently. It helps avoid confusion with the rarely required $\sin(x^2)$, where the *input* is squared. It ought more logically to be written $\sin(x)^2$, but this is impossible when the bracketless version is used, since it would appear as $\sin x^2$, the same as $\sin(x^2)$.

It is an unusual notation, especially in elementary mathematics, and should not normally be extended to other functions.

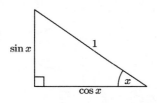

The Theorem of Pythagoras, applied to the right-angled triangle in the diagram, gives

$$\sin^2 x + \cos^2 x = 1 \quad \text{(for all } x\text{)}.$$

Also, dividing this result by $\cos^2 x$ gives

$$\frac{\sin^2 x}{\cos^2 x} + 1 = \frac{1}{\cos^2 x} \quad \Rightarrow \quad \tan^2 x + 1 = \sec^2 x.$$

There is a third such identity, found similarly.

Frame 2.7   *Pythagorean identities*

$$\sin^2 x + \cos^2 x = 1 \tag{2.9}$$
$$\tan^2 x + 1 = \sec^2 x \tag{2.10}$$
$$\operatorname{cosec}^2 x = 1 + \cot^2 x \tag{2.11}$$

These three results mean that, given the value of any one of the six functions, we can (almost) deduce the values of all the others. At some stage we need to take a square root and may not know which sign to choose unless we know some extra information, such as the quadrant in which the angle lies. Thus, given $\sin\theta$, we can calculate $\cos\theta$ as $\pm\sqrt{1-\sin^2\theta}$, but the square root offers us two signs and we do not know which one to choose unless we are told the quadrant involved.

There is an alternative way to solve such problems and it is the one we shall use in the examples that follow. Draw a right-angled triangle and label one of the acute angles as x. Then attribute lengths to two sides to be consistent with the trigonometric ratio whose value we know, ignoring any minus sign. For example, given $\cos x = -\frac{1}{3}$, use length 1 for 'adjacent' and length 3 for 'hypotenuse'. (Any scale can be used.) Use Pythagoras to complete the triangle. All other ratios can then be read off, except for their signs. The signs can be deduced using any extra information given and the 'ASTC' rule.

Example 2.5

(a) Given that $\sin\theta = {}^5/_{13}$ and $90° \leqslant \theta \leqslant 180°$, compute $\cos\theta$.

Construct the triangle shown, with 'opposite' 5 and 'hypotenuse' 13: $d^2 + 25 = 169$, so $d = 12$. Then $\cos\theta = \pm{}^{12}/_{13}$ and we choose $-{}^{12}/_{13}$ because θ lies in the second quadrant.

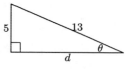

(b) Given that $\cos\phi = \dfrac{x}{\sqrt{1+x^2}}$, where ϕ lies in the first quadrant, find a formula for $\sin\phi$.

Construct the triangle shown, with 'adjacent' x and 'hypotenuse' $\sqrt{1+x^2}$: $d^2 + x^2 = 1 + x^2$, so $d = 1$. This time choose $+\dfrac{1}{\sqrt{1+x^2}}$ for $\sin\phi$ because ϕ lies in the first quadrant.

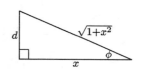

■

All the other identities we require follow from the so-called **addition rules**. These can be derived by a geometrical calculation based on trigonometric ratios.

Frame 2.8   *Addition rules for sin/cos*

$$\sin(x+y) = \sin x \cos y + \cos x \sin y \qquad (2.12)$$
$$\sin(x-y) = \sin x \cos y - \cos x \sin y \qquad (2.13)$$
$$\cos(x+y) = \cos x \cos y - \sin x \sin y \qquad (2.14)$$
$$\cos(x-y) = \cos x \cos y + \sin x \sin y \qquad (2.15)$$

Dividing the first and third of these gives an analogous formula for tan:

$$\tan(x+y) = \frac{\tan x + \tan y}{1 - \tan x \tan y}. \tag{2.16}$$

Example 2.6   Rework Example 2.4: simplify $\cos\left(\frac{\pi}{2} + x\right)$.
    Use (2.14):

$$\cos\left(\tfrac{\pi}{2} + x\right) = \cos\tfrac{\pi}{2}\cos x - \sin\tfrac{\pi}{2}\sin x$$
$$= 0 \times \cos x - 1 \times \sin x = -\sin x.$$

∎

Setting $x = y$ in (2.12) and (2.14) gives the (heavily-used) **double-angle formulae**.

Frame 2.9   *Double-angle formulae*

$$\sin 2x = 2\sin x \cos x \tag{2.17}$$
$$\cos 2x = \cos^2 x - \sin^2 x = 2\cos^2 x - 1 = 1 - 2\sin^2 x \tag{2.18}$$

The identity $\sin^2 x + \cos^2 x = 1$ is used to derive the last two versions for $\cos 2x$.

Example 2.7   Suppose $\cos x = 1/2$.
    Then, $\cos 2x = 2 \times (1/2)^2 - 1 = -1/2$, values that are consistent with $x = \pi/3$. ∎

Example 2.8   Find an expression for $\sin 3x$ in terms of $\sin x$ only.
    Write $3x = 2x + x$, use (2.12), then the two double-angle formulae, choosing the sin version for $\cos 2x$:

$$\sin 3x = \sin 2x \cos x + \cos 2x \sin x$$
$$= 2\sin x \cos x \cos x + (1 - 2\sin^2 x)\sin x$$
$$= 2\sin x \cos^2 x + \sin x - 2\sin^3 x$$
$$= 2\sin x(1 - \sin^2 x) + \sin x - 2\sin^3 x$$
$$= 3\sin x - 4\sin^3 x,$$

on using the 'Pythagoras' identity to write $\cos^2 x$ in terms of $\sin x$. ∎

There are alternative versions of these results – the **half-angle formulae** – obtained by replacing every x by $\frac{x}{2}$. The double-angle and half-angle formulae are precisely the same, but are used in different applications.

Example 2.9   Prove that

$$\frac{1 - \cos x}{\sin x} = \frac{\sin x}{1 + \cos x}$$

and simplify both these expressions.

$$\sin^2 x = 1 - \cos^2 x = (1 - \cos x)(1 + \cos x).$$

Divide both sides by $\sin x(1 + \cos x)$ to obtain the required formula.

Consider the left-hand side, using half-angle formulae:

$$1 - \cos x = 1 - \left(1 - 2\sin^2 \tfrac{1}{2}x\right) = 2\sin^2 \tfrac{1}{2}x,$$
$$\sin x = 2\sin \tfrac{1}{2}x \cos \tfrac{1}{2}x.$$

Divide these:

$$\frac{1 - \cos x}{\sin x} = \frac{2\sin^2 \tfrac{1}{2}x}{2\sin \tfrac{1}{2}x \cos \tfrac{1}{2}x} = \tan \tfrac{1}{2}x.$$

The right-hand side must also equal this, since it equals the left.   ∎

Finally, the addition rules can be manipulated to allow interchange between sums and products of sin and cos. Adding and subtracting the results in (2.12)–(2.15) produces the following.

Frame 2.10   *Products of sin/cos expressed as sums*

$$2\sin x \cos y = \sin(x + y) + \sin(x - y) \tag{2.19}$$
$$2\cos x \sin y = \sin(x + y) - \sin(x - y) \tag{2.20}$$
$$2\cos x \cos y = \cos(x + y) + \cos(x - y) \tag{2.21}$$
$$2\sin x \sin y = \cos(x - y) - \cos(x + y) \tag{2.22}$$

These results can be reversed to give sums of sin/cos in terms of their products but these are rarely required in calculus.

Example 2.10   A **standing wave** is similar to the motion of a guitar string when plucked in its middle, in the absence of friction. Each point oscillates perpendicular to the initial line. Certain waves of this type have their height at position x and time t expressed by

$$z(x, t) = A\sin kx \sin \omega t.$$

Express this as the difference of two cosines.

Using (2.22),

$$z(x, t) = \tfrac{1}{2}A\left[\cos(kx - \omega t) - \cos(kx + \omega t)\right].$$

This is an important calculation since the first term represents a **travelling wave** moving to the right at speed $\frac{\omega}{k}$. The second term represents a wave travelling to the left at the same speed. Their difference gives the standing wave.   ∎

Ex 2.4 Given that $\cos x = -\frac{4}{5}$, and that $180° < x < 270°$, calculate the value of $\sin x$.

Ex 2.5 The angle x lies in the **third quadrant** and $\operatorname{cosec} x = -2$. Find the values of the other five trigonometric ratios without finding x itself.

Ex 2.6 Given that $\sin x = \frac{2}{3}$, calculate $\cos 2x$.

Ex 2.7 Use half-angles to simplify $\sqrt{2 - 2\cos x}$, $\dfrac{1 - \cos x}{1 + \cos x}$.

Ex 2.8 Write the following as the sum or difference of sin/cos terms:
   (a) $2\sin 7x \cos 2x$,   (b) $\sin 5x \sin 3x$.

2.4   Amplitude, Period and Phase

The sine curve is the basis for many oscillatory functions. To be fully useful we must be able to 'tune' the sine function to achieve any specified period, range of values and starting point.

We consider only symmetrical oscillation about the value zero. With this restriction the general oscillation or **sinusoidal** function is as follows. (We change the variable to t, since this formula is almost always encountered in time-related problems.)

Frame 2.11   *Sinusoidal oscillation*

$$y = A\sin(\omega t + \phi) \tag{2.23}$$

A is **amplitude** ω is **circular** or **angular frequency**
$T = 2\pi/\omega$ is **period** $\nu = \frac{1}{T}$ is **frequency**
ϕ is **phase:** $\phi > 0$ is a **lead**, $\phi < 0$ is a **lag**

Notation

These Greek letters are almost universally used in this context: ω [*omega*] for angular frequency, ν [*nu*] for frequency, ϕ [*phi*] for phase. The last of these is natural since ϕ represents the 'ph' sound.

Think about it like this

These terms apply to all periodic phenomena, not just pure 'sinusoids' as above.

The **amplitude** measures the size of the oscillation: y must oscillate between $\pm A$ since the sin term takes maximum and minimum values ± 1. The **period** is simply the period of the function y as we defined it in the previous chapter.

The **phase** tells us where the graph of y starts, in relation to that of $\sin \omega t$; it usually lies in a range from $-\pi$ to $+\pi$. Recall that adding ϕ will move the curve to the left, so that it appears to start earlier, which is why we refer to the $\phi > 0$ case as a **lead**.

Note the formula for the period: $T = \frac{2\pi}{\omega}$, which is consistent with the result in Frame 1.5, adapting the period 2π of $\sin t$.

Example 2.11   A very important sinusoidal oscillation in everyday life! Describe $230\sqrt{2}\sin(100\pi t + \phi)$.

This oscillates between $-230\sqrt{2}$ and $+230\sqrt{2}$, an **amplitude** of $230\sqrt{2}$.

The **period** is $\frac{2\pi}{100\pi} = \frac{1}{50}$, giving a **frequency** of 50 cycles per second. There is a **phase lead** of ϕ.

This is the form of U.K. mains voltage. The amplitude that is usually quoted is the **rms** value $\frac{230\sqrt{2}}{\sqrt{2}}$, i.e., 230 V. (The meaning of 'rms' will be given in §8.3: it requires some calculus.) ∎

This expression for y can be expanded using the addition rule (2.12) to find a version with no explicit phase:

$$A\sin(\omega t + \phi) = [A\sin\phi]\cos\omega t + [A\cos\phi]\sin\omega t. \qquad (2.24)$$

The form in (2.23), however, is normally more useful in that it immediately tells us the amplitude; the only complicating feature is the phase, which may not be of importance. It is also the more natural form, e.g., a digital spectral analyser will return a value for A, not separate coefficients for sin and cos. For this reason it is often necessary to reverse this calculation, i.e., to go from (2.24) to (2.23).

Our aim, therefore, is to find the amplitude A and phase ϕ so that

$$a\cos\omega t + b\sin\omega t = A\sin(\omega t + \phi), \qquad (2.25)$$

for a given a and b.

Compare (2.25) with (2.24): we must satisfy

$$a\cos\omega t + b\sin\omega t = [A\sin\phi]\cos\omega t + [A\cos\phi]\sin\omega t,$$

for *all* t. The easiest way to force this is to match the pattern on the two sides:

$$a = A\sin\phi, \qquad b = A\cos\phi. \qquad (2.26)$$

Think about it like this
>The alternative is to argue that this expression must be true for all t. Setting, in turn, $t = 0$ and $t = \frac{\pi}{2\omega}$ gives the same equations.

These must be solved to find A and ϕ. It is easy to find the amplitude A, but care is needed to find which of two possible values of ϕ is correct. This is best shown by means of examples.

Example 2.12   Express as a single sin function: $4\sin t - 3\cos t$.
   We have

$$4\sin t - 3\cos t = A\sin(t + \phi) = A\sin t\cos\phi + A\cos t\sin\phi$$

if $A\cos\phi = 4$ and $A\sin\phi = -3$. Then, using (2.9),

$$A^2 = (A\cos\phi)^2 + (A\sin\phi)^2 = 4^2 + (-3)^2 = 25 \quad \Rightarrow \quad A = 5.$$

Also,

$$\tan\phi = \frac{A\sin\phi}{A\cos\phi} = \frac{-3}{4} \quad\Rightarrow\quad \phi = -0.6435 \text{ or } -0.6435 + \pi,$$

using the fact that $\tan x$ has period π. Since $\sin\phi < 0$ and $\cos\phi > 0$, ϕ lies in the fourth quadrant. Hence the correct value for the phase is $\phi = -0.6435$.

Answer: $5\sin(t - 0.6435)$.

■

Think about it like this

The problem of having to select the correct angle from the two possible ones also occurs in a fundamental calculation involving vectors and a similar one for complex numbers. Precisely the same approach – noting the signs of sin and cos and hence deciding on the correct quadrant using 'ASTC' – solves the problem.

Example 2.13 Express as a single sin function: $\cos t - \sin t$.
  This time we have $A\cos\phi = -1$ and $A\sin\phi = 1$. Then

$$A^2 = (-1)^2 + (1)^2 = 2 \quad\Rightarrow\quad A = \sqrt{2}.$$

Also,

$$\tan\phi = \frac{A\sin\phi}{A\cos\phi} = \frac{1}{-1} = -1 \quad\Rightarrow\quad \phi = -\tfrac{\pi}{4} \text{ or } -\tfrac{\pi}{4} + \pi.$$

Since $\sin\phi > 0$ and $\cos\phi < 0$, ϕ lies in the second quadrant, so the correct value for the phase is the second one, $\phi = \frac{3\pi}{4}$.

Answer: $\sqrt{2}\sin\left(t + \frac{3\pi}{4}\right)$.

■

There is a similar version based on the expression $A\cos(t - \beta)$, popular with some people. The method is a straightforward adaptation of that above.
  Finally, one useful application for this form is to determine t such that $a\cos\omega t + b\sin\omega t = K$, for some given K. This is easily done when the version with amplitude and phase is used. Finding zero, maximum and minimum values are the most common situations. This makes use of

$$\sin x = 0 : \quad x = 0,\ \pi,\ 2\pi,\ \ldots,\ -\pi,\ -2\pi,\ \ldots,$$
$$\sin x = \pm 1 : \quad x = \tfrac{\pi}{2},\ \tfrac{3\pi}{2},\ \tfrac{5\pi}{2},\ \ldots,\ -\tfrac{\pi}{2},\ -\tfrac{3\pi}{2},\ \ldots.$$

Example 2.14 Find the first positive value of t for which $\cos\pi t - \sin\pi t$ is a maximum.
  Using Example 2.13, with πt replacing t,

$$\cos\pi t - \sin\pi t = \sqrt{2}\sin\left(\pi t + \tfrac{3\pi}{4}\right).$$

This has value $\sqrt{2}$ when the argument of sin is $\frac{\pi}{2}$. This gives, however, $t = -1/4$, which is not positive.

The next maximum value of $\sqrt{2}$ occurs at argument $\frac{5\pi}{2}$, giving

$$\pi t + \tfrac{3\pi}{4} = \tfrac{5\pi}{2} \quad \Rightarrow \quad t = 7/4.$$

There is a minimum value of $-\sqrt{2}$ at argument $\frac{3\pi}{4}$, i.e., $t = 3/4$ and the first zero is at $t = 1/4$. ∎

Ex 2.9 Find the amplitude and the period of the function

$$f(t) = 2\sin(\pi t) + 5\cos(\pi t).$$

Ex 2.10 Express each of the following in the form $r\sin(\omega t + \alpha)$:
  (a) $\sin t - \cos t$,   (b) $12\cos 2t - 5\sin 2t$.

2.5   Revision Exercises

Ex 2.11 Simplify: $\sin(x + \pi)$, $\sin(x - \pi)$, $\cos(x + \pi)$, $\cos(x - \pi)$.

Ex 2.12 Use an appropriate addition rule, with angles $45°$ and $30°$, to show that

$$\tan 15° = \frac{\sqrt{3} - 1}{\sqrt{3} + 1}.$$

Ex 2.13 Find a, b and ω such that $\cos^2 4x = a + b\cos\omega x$.

Ex 2.14 Write, in simpler form:

  (a) $\cos^4 x - \sin^4 x$,   (b) $\tan x + \cot x$,   (c) $\sqrt{2\cos x + 2}$.

Ex 2.15 Write the following as the sum or difference of sin/cos terms:
  (a) $\cos 6x \sin x$,   (b) $2\cos 7x \cos 3x$.

Ex 2.16 Find the amplitude and the period of the function

$$f(t) = 6\cos(2\pi t) - 8\sin(2\pi t).$$

Ex 2.17 Find the amplitude and the period of the function

$$f(t) = 8\cos\left(\tfrac{1}{2}t\right) - 15\sin\left(\tfrac{1}{2}t\right).$$

Ex 2.18 Write $f(t) = 3\cos(\pi t) + 4\sin(\pi t)$ in the form $A\sin(\omega t + \phi)$. (Give exact values for A and ω; give ϕ in radians to 2 dp.) What is the period of f? Solve $f(t) = 0$.

3   EXPONENTIAL & LOGARITHMIC FUNCTIONS

Many physical phenomena are **multiplicative** or 'compound' rather than **additive** or 'simple'. The difference is illustrated by interest on money, where *compound interest* grows in proportion to the current investment, whereas *simple interest* is the same amount each time. These compound phenomena are often modelled as **exponential** processes, examples being biological population growth and radioactive decay.

Calculations using exponential functions can be difficult because the key factor is in a 'powering' position. There is, however, a very useful tool to make these calculations easier: the **logarithm**. Not only can it transfer this factor into an easier position, but it converts **exponential** models into **linear** ones.

3.1   Exponential Functions

An **exponential function** has the following form.

Frame 3.1   An exponential function

$$y = a^x \qquad (a \text{ constant}) \qquad\qquad (3.1)$$

Here a is a fixed number (the **base**) and x is the (input) variable, in this case called the **exponent**. We are currently able to evaluate y for several, though not all, values of x.

Example 3.1   Consider the case $a = 4$, so that the function is $f(x) = 4^x$.
We can easily calculate the following:

$$f(1) = 4^1 = 4, \qquad\qquad f(2) = 4^2 = 16,$$
$$f(-1) = 4^{-1} = 1/4 = 0.25, \qquad f(\tfrac{1}{2}) = 4^{1/2} = \sqrt{4} = 2,$$

not forgetting $f(0) = 4^0 = 1$.

Positive integers are easy – we evaluate simple powers of 4 – and negative integers are just their reciprocals. We can evaluate $f(x)$ for any rational number $x = \frac{m}{n}$, at least in principle. For example:

$$f(\tfrac{2}{3}) = 4^{2/3} = (4^2)^{1/3} = \sqrt[3]{16} = 2.5198\cdots.$$

We encounter problems with inputs such as $x = \sqrt{2}$, although these can eventually be overcome using logarithms. ∎

If we set out to draw a graph of $y = a^x$, we are able to plot so many points that we can effectively draw the line for the graph without the need for any of these tricky values.

We shall restrict much of our attention to a single important choice for a. This apparently clumsy number delivers calculus formulae that are much neater than those for any other value. This important number is:

$$e = 2.71828\ 18284\ 59045\ 2\ldots. \tag{3.2}$$

We called any function of the form $y = a^x$ **an** *exponential function*. The special case $y = e^x$ is called **the** *exponential function*, since it is by far the most important. We shall see later that all exponential functions are similar to e^x: their graphs have the same shape and they are closely linked computationally.

Notation

Often the exponent can be complicated, e.g., if e^x is composed with another function. This can make the superscript notation clumsy. There is an alternative notation that avoids this: we write $\exp(x)$, resembling $\mathtt{EXP}(x)$, which is used in most computer implementations. Whichever notation is used, 'x' is a genuine exponent. Thus

$$e^2 = e \times e, \quad \exp(\tfrac{1}{2}) = e^{1/2} = \sqrt{e}, \quad \exp(-1) = e^{-1} = \tfrac{1}{e}, \quad \text{etc.}$$

A particularly common example is $\exp(-x^2) = e^{-x^2}$.

The graph of e^x is shown below, together with its reflection in the y-axis, which is $y = e^{-x}$. The first is the standard model for *exponential growth*; the second is that for *exponential decay*. Note from the graph that the domain is $\mathbb{R}$ and that all its (output) values are positive numbers. This last observation is important; in particular, e^x is never zero. (Note that the graph shows $e^0 = 1$, $e^1 = 2.718\cdots$.)

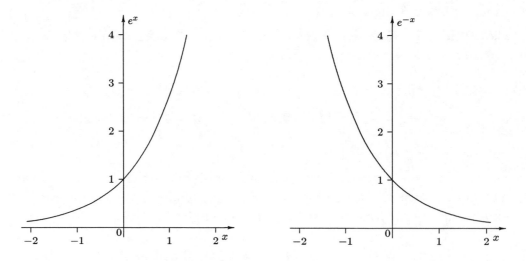

There are practical problems associated with exponential functions. They are not as easy to work with as linear functions and calculations using them are complicated by the fact that the inputs sit in a superscript or 'powering' position. The **logarithm** is the answer to these problems: it converts exponential processes to linear ones. To define it we must first investigate the general idea of an **inverse function**.

Ex 3.1 Simplify: $\dfrac{e^{5x}}{e^{3x}}$, $\dfrac{16^{\frac{x}{2}}}{4^{\frac{x}{2}}}$.

Ex 3.2 Solve the equation $5^x + 5^{-x} = 2$. [**Hint**: Set $y = 5^x$.]

3.2   The Inverse Function

Suppose we have a function $y = f(x)$ and we wish to know the value of the input x that will output a given value of y, in other words we wish to *reverse* the process of the function, reading the input from the output. This can be done if f has an **inverse function**.

Assume, for the moment, that f does have an inverse function. We give it the name f^{-1} and the roles of x and y reverse: if x as input gives y as output for f, then the same y as input gives the same x as output for f^{-1}. Thus, a value of y determines a value for x; y has become the independent variable and x the dependent variable. This leads to the following definition.

Frame 3.2   *The inverse function for f*

$$y = f(x) \quad \Leftrightarrow \quad x = f^{-1}(y) \qquad\qquad (3.3)$$

This construction is illustrated by the 'process' diagram below.

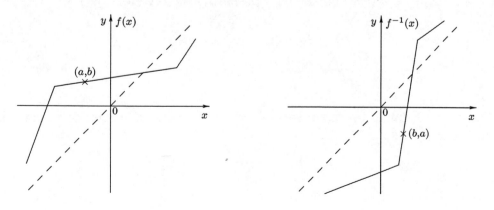

The graph of the inverse of f is easily found from that of f, since the same x-y correspondences apply. If (x, y) is a point on the graph of f, then (y, x) is a point on the graph of f^{-1}. The new graph can be found by the simple device of exchanging the labels on the x and y axes. This, however, leaves the axes in an unconventional order so some adjustment is needed to allow us to appreciate the new graph. We can swap the axes by reflecting the graph in the line $y = x$ (dashed in the diagram below).

In some cases we can construct a formula for f^{-1} using algebraic methods, based on (3.3). We solve the equation $y = f(x)$ to find x in terms of y, as $x = g(y)$, say. Then the formula for g is the required formula for f^{-1}. (We often swap the variable symbols at the end, to use the normal input symbol x, but this is not essential.)

Notation

Note that the superscript used in f^{-1} has *nothing whatever* to do with a similar notation used in reciprocation, as in $x^{-1} = \frac{1}{x}$. Thus

$$f^{-1}(x) \neq \frac{1}{f(x)}.$$

Example 3.2   Find the inverse function for $f(x) = 3x - 1$.

Write y for $f(x)$, then use simple algebra to find x in terms of y:

$$y = 3x - 1 \quad \Rightarrow \quad x = \frac{1}{3}(y + 1),$$

giving $f^{-1}(y) = \frac{1}{3}(y + 1)$. It is common to swap y for x, to quote the result using the normal input variable:

$$f^{-1}(x) = \frac{1}{3}(x + 1),$$

although the x here should not be confused with the x in $f(x)$.   ■

Example 3.3   Find the inverse function for

$$f(x) = \frac{1}{x - 2} \qquad (x \neq 2).$$

Let $y = \dfrac{1}{x - 2}$ and clear fractions:

$$(x - 2)y = 1 \quad \Rightarrow \quad xy - 2y = 1.$$

Retain only the x term on the left (preparing to solve for x):

$$xy = 2y + 1,$$
$$x = \frac{2y + 1}{y} \qquad \text{(provided } y \neq 0\text{)}.$$

This is the formula for the inverse function. Reverse the roles of x and y in the answer:

$$f^{-1}(x) = \frac{2x + 1}{x} \qquad (x \neq 0).$$

■

There are cases in which we cannot do such a calculation and f^{-1} is effectively a 'new' type of function. This is one of the reasons why the inverse function is important, as we see in the next section.

There is one other issue, which we shall leave as a pointer to the future. Reversing a function is not always straightforward. An example is the reversal of the 'square' function $y = x^2$. There are **two** inputs, $+2$ and -2, that give $y = +4$, which means that reversing the input-output roles, as we did above, does not lead to a properly defined function: there would be two possible values for some inputs. Such difficulties do not arise if the function is **one-one**, i.e., each output arises from only one input. Exponential functions are one-one, so we can safely invert them.

Ex 3.3 In each of the following cases find the inverse of the given function. Express your answers in the form $f^{-1}(x) = \cdots$. In each case find the domain of the inverse function f^{-1}.

$$f(x) = 5x + 3, \qquad f(x) = \frac{x-1}{x+1}.$$

3.3 Definition and Properties of Logarithms

We define the **logarithmic function** or **logarithm** or **log**, with **base** a, to be the inverse of the exponential function a^x. It is written with name **log** and the base a is shown as a (fixed) subscript. We have:

$$y = a^x \quad \Leftrightarrow \quad x = \log_a(y).$$

It is more usual to see this relationship written in the opposite order, with x and y swapped round. In words we have the following, which is well worth committing to memory since it is a direct definition of the logarithm.

Frame 3.3   *Definition of logarithm*

The **logarithm** of a number to a given **base** is the power (y) to which the base (a) must be raised to give the number (x):

$$y = \log_a(x) \quad \Leftrightarrow \quad a^y = x \qquad (3.4)$$

One special version of the logarithm, popular in pre-calculator days, is the **common log**, which has base 10. This persists in use because of scientific definitions introduced at that time, such as pH. Also, it is used in the design of the *slide rule*, once regularly used by engineers.

Frame 3.4   *Common logarithms*

$$y = \log_{10}(x) \quad \Leftrightarrow \quad 10^y = x \qquad\qquad (3.5)$$

Notation

The 'bracketless' function notation is very common for logarithms. We shall therefore write $\ln x$, etc., from now on, although computer implementations are usually $\mathtt{LN}(x)$ or $\mathtt{LOG}(x)$. This sloppy convention necessitates care when using complicated arguments. The best advice is to insert brackets if in doubt. It is never wrong to do so and is essential when using computer languages and other software.

Example 3.4   Evaluate the following common logs:

$$\log_{10} 100, \quad \log_{10} 0.1, \quad \log_{10} 1, \quad \log_{10} \sqrt{10}.$$

$$10^2 = 100 \quad \Rightarrow \quad \log 100 = 2$$
$$10^{-1} = 0.1 \quad \Rightarrow \quad \log 0.1 = -1$$
$$10^0 = 1 \quad \Rightarrow \quad \log 1 = 0$$
$$10^{1/2} = \sqrt{10} \quad \Rightarrow \quad \log \sqrt{10} = 1/2$$

∎

The key logs, however, are those that invert **the** exponential function, i.e., those with base e. These are the **natural** (or **Napierian**) logarithms. They are most commonly written as $\ln x$, where 'ln' stands for **l**n **n**atural.

Notation

The common logarithm is normally written $\log_{10} x$. Textbooks use a variety of notations for the natural logarithm; most use 'ln' but some use 'log'. Those that use 'ln' tend to reserve 'log' for a general logarithm to an unspecified base. What is certain is that 'ln' is never used for anything except the natural logarithm.

We now know that e^x and $\ln x$ are function–inverse function pairs and it is worth repeating (3.4) for this special case.

Frame 3.5   *The natural logarithm / exponential function link*

$$y = \ln x \quad \Leftrightarrow \quad e^y = x \qquad\qquad (3.6)$$

Think about it like this

> You can think of this as an algebraic step, where "ln" is 'cancelled' from the left and replaced by "e to the power of", on the right, or vice versa. See the next example.

We learned in the previous section how to graph the inverse function. This technique allows us to find the graph of $y = \ln x$, derived from that of $y = e^x$ and shown below.

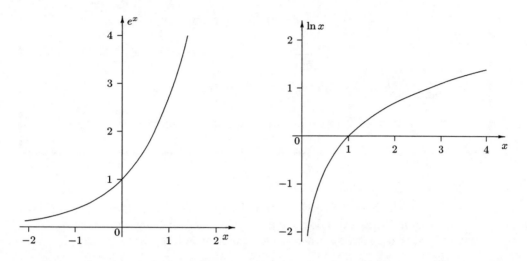

Note that $\ln x$ (and any other log) is not defined for $x \leqslant 0$, in other words, the **domain** of logarithmic functions is $\{x \ : \ x > 0\}$.

There are two essential aspects of logs that must be mastered. One is the content of (3.4), i.e., how to use the definition to search for a value and how to find a number given its log. Calculators help do this numerically, as we see in the next example, but not every piece of mathematics involves numbers. The numerical examples illustrate:

$$\ln x = c \quad \text{has solution} \quad x = e^c,$$
$$e^x = C \quad \text{has solution} \quad x = \ln C.$$

Example 3.5 Solve

(a) $\ln x = -0.75$, (b) $\log_{10} x = 0.33$, (c) $e^{0.25x} = 3.4$, (d) $\exp(-10t) = 0.075$.

Each of these can be done using a key on a standard scientific calculator, although they differ in where the keys are placed and, sometimes, on how they are labelled. Typical labels are: ln, log (for common log), e^x and 10^x.

(a) $x = e^{-0.75} = 0.4723\ldots$,

(b) $x = 10^{0.33} = 2.1379\ldots$,

(c) $0.25x = \ln 3.4 \quad \Rightarrow \quad x = 4\ln 3.4 = 4.895\ldots$,

(d) $-10t = \ln 0.075 \quad \Rightarrow \quad t = -\frac{1}{10}\ln 0.075 = 0.259\ldots$.

The second aspect is the set of **rules of logarithms**, the four formulae that allow us to perform algebra using them.

Frame 3.6   *Rule of logarithms*

$$\log(1) = 0 \tag{3.7}$$
$$\log(x_1 \times x_2) = \log(x_1) + \log(x_2) \tag{3.8}$$
$$\log\left(\frac{x_1}{x_2}\right) = \log(x_1) - \log(x_2) \tag{3.9}$$
$$\log(x^n) = n\log(x) \tag{3.10}$$

x_1, x_2, $x > 0$; n is **any** number, not necessarily an integer

---

Think about it like this

The key results here are the $\log(ab)$ and $\log a^c$ rules. Note that there is no rule for simplifying either $\log(a+b)$ or $(\log a)(\log b)$; being aware of where the $+$ and $\times$ occur in the rules is very important for accurate work.

These show that the log has converted multiplication into addition; it also converts division into subtraction and powering into multiplication. These properties are what makes a slide rule work: the scales are logarithmic and distances are added/subtracted to replicate multiplication/division.

Indeed, the formulae are derived by using inverse function methods to reverse the **index laws**, where *multiplication* of powers leads to *addition* of indexes.

Example 3.6   Without using a calculator, find x where

$$\log x = 3\log 2 + \tfrac{1}{3}\log 27 - \log 12.$$

Use, in order, (3.10), (3.8), (3.9):

$$\begin{aligned}
\log x &= \log 2^3 + \log \sqrt[3]{27} - \log 12 \\
&= \log 8 + \log 3 - \log 12 \\
&= \log(8 \times 3) - \log 12 \\
&= \log \frac{24}{12} = \log 2,
\end{aligned}$$

and hence $x = 2$. (This is true for **any** base, but can be verified on a calculator using either the 'log' or 'ln' key.) ∎

Example 3.7   Show that $\log\dfrac{1}{x} = -\log x$ for all x and any base.

Either use (3.9),

$$\log\frac{1}{x} = \log 1 - \log x = -\log x, \quad \text{since } \log 1 = 0,$$

or (3.10),

$$\log \frac{1}{x} = \log x^{-1} = -1 \times \log x.$$

∎

Notation

This result is frequently used at the end of a calculation, to convert from one of these forms to another. This is purely cosmetic, reflecting a preference by some authors to avoid minus signs and others to avoid fractions.

Example 3.8   Evaluate $\log_3 5 - \log_3 15$.
(3.9) and Example 3.7 give:

$$\log_3 5 - \log_3 15 = \log_3 \frac{5}{15} = \log_3 \frac{1}{3} = -\log_3 3 = -1.$$

∎

There is a fundamental property of functions and their inverses that is very useful in this context. Since the inverse of a function reverses the action of the function, the inverse of the inverse must take us back to the original function: if the function processes x to obtain y, the inverse processes y to obtain x, and *its* inverse must process x to obtain y.

Example 3.9   Find the inverse of the inverse of $f(x) = 3x - 1$, as found in Example 3.2.
That example gave $f^{-1}(x) = \frac{1}{3}(x+1)$. Let $y = \frac{1}{3}(x+1)$. Then $3y = x+1$ and $x = 3y - 1$, the original function. ∎

This observation leads to the following (which are also true for any base):

$$x = e^{\ln x} \quad (x > 0), \tag{3.11}$$
$$x = \ln(e^x) \quad (x \text{ in } \mathbb{R}). \tag{3.12}$$

We shall make extensive use of (3.11) in what follows, while (3.12) has a role to play in the next section.
Apply (3.11) with $x = a$ to find $a = e^{\ln a}$, which then gives

$$y = a^x = \left(e^{\ln a}\right)^x = e^{x \ln a}. \tag{3.13}$$

This shows that *any* exponential function a^x is just *the* exponential function with its argument changed from x to $(\ln a)x$. This result is particularly useful for a time variable.

Frame 3.7   *General exponential in terms of e*

$$a^t = e^{kt}, \quad (k = \ln a, \ |k| \text{ is the } \textbf{rate constant})$$

Example 3.10 Express e^{-kt} as an exponential function with base 2. Start from Frame 3.7:

$$2^t = e^{(\ln 2)t} \quad \Rightarrow \quad 2^{\alpha t} = e^{\alpha(\ln 2)t},$$

for any α. We now choose α so that $\alpha(\ln 2) = -k$, giving

$$e^{-kt} = 2^{-kt/\ln 2}.$$

The advantage of this form is that we know that 2^{-x} halves in value when x increases by 1: $2^{-(x+1)} = 2^{-1}2^{-x} = \frac{1}{2}2^{-x}$. Hence, e^{-kt} halves in value when $\frac{k}{\ln 2}t$ increases by 1, i.e., when t increases by $\frac{\ln 2}{k}$. ∎

The importance of this calculation is that it shows $\frac{\ln 2}{k}$ to be the **half-life**, the *constant* time taken for an exponential function to halve its current value, *no matter when we start measuring it*. This quantity is greatly favoured in science, since it is so easy to use, so much so that it is a standard measurement for how fast a radioactive substance decays. Typical of its use is to state immediately that the quantity will quarter in two half-lifes (½ of ½ is ¼), become an eighth of its size in three half-lifes, etc.

Think about it like this

> The fact that all exponential functions are related to each other leads to the advice: aim to use **the** exponential function. It has much simpler calculus properties, as we shall see later.

> The approach used here is typical of a manoeuvre that allows us to to introduce the key exponential function into expressions. This may seem an unlikely aim, but we shall see that there are occasions when replacing x by $e^{\ln x}$ allows us to make more progress than using x on its own.

Having noted that all exponential functions are closely related, the same fact holds for all logarithms: they are all simple multiples of each other.

Let $y = \log_a x$, so that, swapping over x and y in (3.13),

$$x = a^y = \left(e^{\ln a}\right)^y = e^{y \ln a}.$$

The natural log of x is the power of e that gives x, so this tells us that $\ln x = y \ln a$. In other words, we have the following.

Frame 3.8   *General logarithms in terms of natural logarithms*

$$y = \log_a x = \frac{\ln x}{\ln a} = \left(\frac{1}{\ln a}\right) \ln x \qquad (3.14)$$

Think about it like this

> This result allows us to compute any logarithm provided we have a method for computing natural logarithms, and that is always available on scientific calculators.

All logarithms basically do the same job, being multiples of one another. The natural log, however, has much simpler calculus properties. Deciding to use common logs rather than natural logs is like using inches instead of metres in scientific calculations: it is possible to make progress, but rather perverse. Stick with natural logs – except for quantities like pH and decibels – and convert to another log at the end, if you really must.

Example 3.11 Calculate $\log_{10} 2$ and $\log_2 16$, using only the 'ln' key.

First, we have $\log_{10} 2 = \ln 2 / \ln 10 = 0.3010\cdots$, exactly as given directly by the 'log' key.

Second, we have $\log_2 16 = \ln 16 / \ln 2 = 4$, exactly as it should be, since $2^4 = 16$. ∎

Think about it like this

The results in Frames 3.7 and 3.8 can also be linked by the graphical interpretation of the inverse function. The graph of a^x is that of $\log_a x$ with the axes reversed. The rescaling of the y-axis by $1/\ln a$ to deduce $y = \log_a x$ from $y = \ln x$ translates into a rescaling of the x-axis to deduce $y = a^x$ from $y = e^x$. §1.5 tells us this is equivalent to using an argument $(\ln a)x$ instead of x.

Ex 3.4

(a) Binary logs use base 2, e.g. $\log_2 8 = 3$, since $2^3 = 8$. Calculate the following:

$$\log_2 2, \qquad \log_2 4, \qquad \log_2 16, \qquad \log_2 1.$$

(b) Logs can be fractional, e.g. $\log_{16} 4 = \frac{1}{2}$ since $16^{\frac{1}{2}} = \sqrt{16} = 4$. Calculate the following:

$$\log_{16} 2, \qquad \log_8 4, \qquad \log_9 27.$$

Ex 3.5 Use a calculator to solve (to 4 dp) each of the following equations for x.

(a) $e^x = 2$ (b) $e^{-3x} = 10$ (c) $5e^{0.2x} = 26$
(d) $\ln x = -2$ (e) $\ln x^2 = 10$ $(x > 0)$

Ex 3.6

(a) Simplify $\exp\left(\dfrac{\ln 5^x}{x}\right)$.

(b) Solve the equation $5^x - 5^{-x} = \dfrac{3}{2}$. (Note the similarity to Exercise 3.2.)

Ex 3.7 Solve the following equations for x:

(a) $\log(x + 1) - \log x = \log 5$;

(b) $2 \ln x + \ln 3 = \ln 4$.

Ex 3.8

(a) Find the exact value of x where

$$\ln x - 3 \ln 2 + \ln 7 = 1.$$

(b) Find the base a of the logarithm $\log_a$ for which

$$\log_a 16 - \log_a 2 = 3.$$

3.4   Applications of Logarithms

In addition to occurring frequently in calculus, logarithms are heavily used in the measurement of quantities that naturally grow **geometrically** rather than **arithmetically**. By this we mean quantities whose change over a period (usually a time period) is given by $x \to ax$ rather than $x \to x + a$.

Example 3.12   Two contrasting growth profiles. Compare the following quantities:

    (a) The total output of a factory that produces d items per day.

    (b) The total value of an investment that pays interest at $i\%$ per year.

  (a) Let the amount produced prior to the start of the month be A and the total produce by the end of day n be u_n. Then

$$u_0 = A, \qquad u_{n+1} = u_n + d, \qquad u_n = A + nd.$$

    This is an **arithmetic** progression and u_n is a **linear** function of n.

  (b) Let the amount at the end of year n be v_n and $v_0 = P$. Then

$$v_{n+1} = \left(1 + \tfrac{i}{100}\right) v_n, \qquad v_n = P\left(1 + \tfrac{i}{100}\right)^n.$$

    This is a **geometric** progression. It can be converted to a much simpler **linear** function by using a log:

$$\ln v_n = \ln P + n \ln\left(1 + \tfrac{i}{100}\right).$$

    (This has form $\ln v = C + nD$, remembering that P and i are constants.)

                                                                        ■

Think about it like this

    As a further example, write the quantity x in scientific notation and examine its common log:

$$x = a \times 10^n \quad \Rightarrow \quad \log_{10} x = \log_{10} a + \log_{10} 10^n = \log_{10} a + n.$$

    We see that **multiplying** x by 10 **adds** 1 to its (common) log.

Examine (3.12). The log has 'pulled down' the exponent x onto the main line of the calculation. Logs allow us to access exponents, quantities in the powering position and therefore usually difficult to work with. This is implemented using a technique summed up by: *take the log of both sides.*

Example 3.13   An amount of £1000 is deposited at an interest rate of 5% per annum. How many years does it take before the balance in the account becomes at least £2000?

From Example 3.12(b) we find that the amount at the end of year n is $v_n = 1000 \times (1.05)^n$.

We require $v_n \geqslant 2000$, so

$$1000 \times (1.05)^n \geqslant 2000, \qquad \text{i.e.,} \quad (1.05)^n \geqslant 2.$$

To access this exponent n, use a log on both sides of the inequality (any base will do). For example

$$n \ln 1.05 \geqslant \ln 2, \qquad n \geqslant \frac{\ln 2}{\ln 1.05} = 14.207.$$

Since n must be a whole number, choose 15 years. ∎

Think about it like this

(3.12) is an equation, but the idea of taking the logs of both sides also applies to inequalities, since the graph of $\log x$ shows it increases as x increases, so inequalities in x are preserved in $\log x$.

You do, however, need to take care not to apply the method to *negative* numbers, for which the log is not defined.

Logarithms will moderate the progression of an exponential growth or decay, turning it into a more easily managed **linear** process, as we saw in Example 3.12(b):

$$y = Ae^{kt} \quad \Rightarrow \quad \ln y = \ln A + kt,$$

using (3.12). (Compare $y = a + bt$.)

Because logarithms make exponential processes much easier to manipulate, they are often used to define measuring scales for such processes, scales that make them easier to comprehend. They are used for this purpose in measuring pH, sound intensity and electronic signals.

This connection also helps interpret experimental results, especially where an exponential process is anticipated. This application deserves a section of its own.

Ex 3.9 Change the subject of the following formula to W:

$$Q = \exp\left(\frac{W - W_T}{KT}\right) + 1.$$

3.5 Logarithmic Graphing

Logarithms can be used to test hypotheses or models that suggest an exponential behaviour of some kind. Suppose that we have a set of data points (t_i, Q_i) and seek a formula for a possible function $Q(t)$, where $Q(t_i) \simeq Q_i$. We have chosen t as the independent variable since 'time' is often a factor in exponential models.

If faced with a possible exponential graph, such as that in §3.1, it is unlikely to be immediately obvious that it is exponential rather than polynomial in nature, and estimation of parameters would be difficult. In exponential cases we can convert a graph to a linear one by plotting the **logarithm** of the data. In this **log-linear** or **semi-logarithmic** plot we use data $(t_i, \ln Q_i)$.

There is also a **log-log** plot, using data $(\ln t_i, \ln Q_i)$. The log-linear plot is far more common and that is the one we shall start with. In both cases we require some or all of the data to be positive, else the log does not exist.

Suppose that we have plotted $\ln Q_i$ against t_i and have concluded that the data fits a straight line with gradient m and intercept on the vertical axis c. We postulate a model

$$\ln Q(t) = mt + c.$$

From this we deduce

$$Q(t) - e^{mt+c} = e^{mt}e^c = Q_0 c^{mt}. \tag{3.15}$$

Here we have written e^c as Q_0, since setting $t = 0$ in (3.15) gives $Q(0) = e^0 e^c = e^c$ and so e^c measures the initial value of Q.

Hence we conclude that a straight line log-linear graph indicates exponential growth (if the gradient is positive) or exponential decay (if the gradient is negative). The gradient m is the critical parameter. Indeed, the verification of an exponential model and determination of m is often all that is required. Its absolute value is what we earlier called the **rate constant**.

Although we have used the natural log, any log can be used and the analysis is virtually unchanged. The only fundamental difference is that e will be replaced by a different number, e.g., 10.

Example 3.14 An analysis of radioactive decay. An isotope of iodine is used as a tracer in medical diagnosis. An experiment measuring its rate of disintegration produces the following data. Estimate its half-life.

Time (secs)	0	500	1000	1500	2000
Counts (per sec)	975	775	615	490	390
ln(Counts)	6.882	6.653	6.422	6.194	5.966

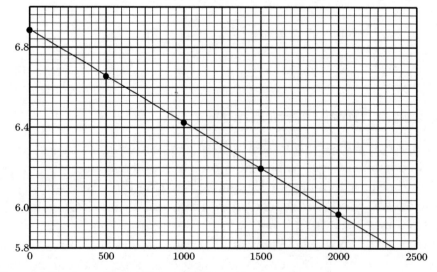

The gradient can be estimated from the graph as

$$m = \frac{5.8 - 6.88}{2350 - 0} = -0.000\,46.$$

Hence

$$R = R_0 e^{-0.000\,46\,t}.$$

In §3.3 we noted the **half-life** for the exponential decay process e^{-kt} is $(\ln 2)/k$. Hence, here it is $(\ln 2)/0.000\,46 \simeq 1507\,\text{s}$, i.e., about 25 min.

Note that the data gives the *rate* of disintegration, not the amount of material. The rate of decay and the amount left share the same half-life, as we shall see in Example 5.16, and the rate R is much easier to measure.

The line drawn above is constructed using a popular method for dealing with data scattered about a straight line: the *best least squares fit* or *regression line*. It can be found using a calculator as:

$$\ln R = 6.8816 - 0.000\,4582\,t,$$

giving a half-life of 25 min, 13 sec. ∎

We now briefly examine **log-log** graphing. Suppose we plot data points $(\ln t_i, \ln Q_i)$ and find a straight line fit: $\ln Q = m \ln t + c$. Then:

$$\ln Q - \ln t^m = c \quad \Rightarrow \quad \ln \frac{Q}{t^m} = c \quad \Rightarrow \quad \frac{Q}{t^m} = e^c.$$

Hence, writing $e^c = A$, we have the final model

$$Q = At^m. \tag{3.16}$$

We cannot write e^c as Q_0, since $t = 0$ may not be allowed, for example if $m < 0$. The simplest interpretation is that A is the value of Q at $t = 1$.

Think about it like this
Note that this formula is *not* an exponential one. That is why the log-linear plot is more common, reflecting the greater importance of the exponential process.

Example 3.15   A quantity Q has values 250, 355 and 430 at times t given by 1, 2 and 3, respectively. Investigate whether Q varies as a power of t.

The log values for t are: 0, 0.693, 1.099; those for Q are: 5.521, 5.872, 6.064.

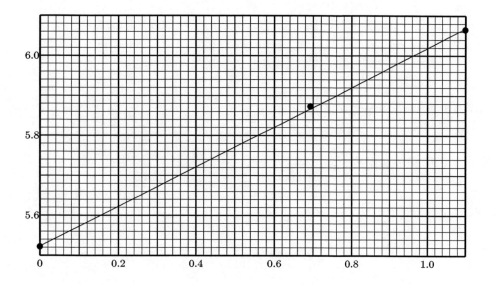

The gradient can be estimated from the graph as

$$m = \frac{6.07 - 5.52}{1.1 - 0} = 0.5.$$

This, and the fact that the points are approximately collinear, suggests a model

$$Q = At^{1/2} = A\sqrt{t}.$$

The line drawn on the graph paper is the *best least squares fit*, calculated as:

$$\ln Q = 5.523\,071 + 0.495\,417 \ln t.$$

Hence $A \simeq e^{5.523\,071} = 250.4$, an approximation to $Q(1)$. Note that the original data gave a measured estimate of 250 for $Q(1)$.   ■

Ex 3.10 For each of the following, express y as a function of x:
(a) $\ln y = -5x + 4$,   (b) $\ln y = -5x + \ln 100$.

Ex 3.11 The following data satisfies approximately the relation: $Q = At^m$.

t	2	4	6	8	10
Q	100	25	11	6	4

(a) Write down an equivalent relation using natural logs.

(b) Graph the data using the natural logs of both quantities.

(c) Hence deduce an appropriate value of m.

3.6 Revision Exercises

Ex 3.12 Use the log rules to simplify each of the following into a single logarithm. Note that the working does not depend on the type of logarithm, which is why 'log' and not 'ln' has been used.

(a) $\log 20 + \log 5$ (b) $\log 20 - \log 5$ (c) $3\log 3 + 2\log 2$
(d) $5\log 2 - 2\log 5$ (e) $\log ab - \log \frac{a}{b}$ (f) $\log ab + \log \frac{a}{b}$
(g) $2\log t^2 - \log t$ (h) $\log xy^2 + \log x^2 y - 3\log xy$

Ex 3.13 Solve, correct to 4 dp:
(a) $x^\pi = 10$,   (b) $\log_5 x = 0.5$,   (c) $2^{x+1} = 3^{x-2}$.

Ex 3.14 Find x, given $y = \ln \dfrac{1}{\sqrt{x}}$.

Ex 3.15 Solve, for x: $\dfrac{e^{-x}}{1 + e^{-x}} = \dfrac{1}{4}$.

Ex 3.16 Find all values of x satisfying $e^{2x} - 6e^x + 8 = 0$.

Ex 3.17 Find the exact value of x for which $\ln x = \frac{1}{2}\ln 16 - 2\ln 5 + 3\ln 2$.

Ex 3.18

(a) Simplify $\exp(2\ln x - 1)$.

(b) Find the base a of the logarithm $\log_a$ if it is known that

$$\log_a 27 - \log_a 3 = 2.$$

Ex 3.19 Solve the equation

$$\ln(x - 2) - 2\ln x = \ln a$$

for x. For which range of values of a is the answer real?

Ex 3.20

(a) A log-linear plot produces the straight line fit $\ln R = 10t + \ln 25$. Find R.

(b) A quantity is defined by the equation

$$\ln Q(t) = 0.5 + 0.25t.$$

Find, to 4 dp, $Q(0)$ and the time T at which $Q(T) = 2Q(0)$.

4 INTRODUCTION TO DIFFERENTIATION

Calculus principally concerns two processes applied to functions: **differentiation** and **integration**. In each case, it provides a method for performing calculations in situations where elementary formulae break down because they require some feature of the problem to be constant. Thus calculus provides a tool for analysing the real 'dynamic' world.

An arithmetic approach to this problem is possible but offers only approximate answers, since exact answers require an infinite number of calculations. Calculus succeeds by using a conceptual leap from approximate (numerical) calculation to precise (symbolic) calculation.

In this chapter we concentrate on **differentiation**, where an **average**, measured over a small interval, is replaced by an **instantaneous** measure.

4.1 Distance and Velocity

We start with a well-known context: velocity v and displacement (or distance) s of a particle from a fixed point. Both the quantities v and s are **functions** of time t and we seek to link them. First, consider the simplest case, that of motion in a straight line with displacement proportional to time, i.e., $s(t) = ut$. This is shown graphically below.

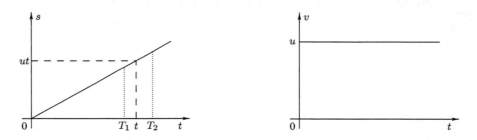

We can work out the average velocity between $t = T_1$ and $t = T_2$ as

$$v_{\mathrm{av}} = \frac{s(T_2) - s(T_1)}{T_2 - T_1} = \frac{uT_2 - uT_1}{T_2 - T_1} = u. \tag{4.1}$$

This value is the same, no matter what time interval we choose. Hence we can safely deduce that the velocity is constant and is given by $v_{\mathrm{av}} = u$. The process of deducing $v = u$ from $s = ut$ is **differentiation** and in this chapter we shall concentrate on extending the idea.

The opposite process, where we deduce $s = ut$ from $v = u$, is the other principal process of calculus: **integration**, considered in Chapter 6.

The familiar 'rules' of motion:

$$\text{velocity} = \frac{\text{distance}}{\text{time}}, \qquad \text{distance} = \text{velocity} \times \text{time}$$

hold only when *the velocity is constant*. They apply more generally if we insert the word 'average' before 'velocity', but that is too imprecise for effective calculations. In general, (4.1) gives a value of v_{av} that depends on T_1 and T_2 and hence cannot give a precise value at any selected time.

Think about it like this

There is a well-known geometrical solution to this problem, namely that:

Velocity is given by the slope or gradient of the graph of $s(t)$.

The difficulty with this is that it 'begs the question': knowing that the gradient is the desired solution helps only if we know how to evaluate that gradient, a problem equivalent to differentiating s to obtain v. Nonetheless, it is a useful rule for some problems, such as those involving piecewise linear functions, whose gradients are easy to calculate.

This problem with simple rules – they apply only when some factor is constant – occurs throughout most disciplines where mathematics is used to provide quantified answers.

Ex 4.1 A car's velocity increases from 0 to $5\,\mathrm{ms}^{-1}$ over $5\,\mathrm{s}$. Following a gear change, this increases to $8\,\mathrm{ms}^{-1}$ over $5\,\mathrm{s}$. Following another gear change, it increases to $10\,\mathrm{ms}^{-1}$ over $5\,\mathrm{s}$. The driver then does an emergency stop, coming to rest in $2.5\,\mathrm{s}$. Compute the average acceleration in each time period.

Now, assume that the velocities increased or decreased at a uniform rate in each time period. Draw graphs of velocity and acceleration against time, explaining where you have relied on this assumption.

4.2 The Approach to Differentiation

Suppose we seek information about the velocity at some chosen time, given the displacement function $s(t)$. The only realistic starting point is to examine the average velocity over the interval $[T_1, T_2]$. For this, we use (4.1), reproduced below:

$$v_{\mathrm{av}} = \frac{s(T_2) - s(T_1)}{T_2 - T_1}. \tag{4.2}$$

This measure will depend on the interval used, but the smaller its width $T_2 - T_1$ is, the less scope there is for s to vary inside it and hence the closer the result is likely to be to what may be regarded as the **instantaneous** velocity at a specific time between T_1 and T_2.

Hence, we wish to move T_1 and T_2 ever closer while trying to **extrapolate** or 'guess', from the trend of the values computed from (4.2), a possible 'instantaneous' velocity at the common value to which T_1 and T_2 approach. This value of the velocity is called the **limit**. (In practice, we usually make one of T_1 or T_2 fixed and move the other towards it, the limit being the velocity at the fixed point.)

Example 4.1 A particle is at position $\sqrt{t}$ at time t. Estimate its velocity at time $t = 1$.

We examine the average velocity between times 1 and $1 + h$:

$$v_{\mathrm{av}} = \frac{\sqrt{1+h} - \sqrt{1}}{h}.$$

h	0.1	0.01	0.001	0.0001	−0.001
v_{av}	0.488 088	0.498 756	0.499 875	0.499 988	0.500 125

It is tempting to guess from these values that $v(t) = 0.5$ at $t = 1$.   ■

Notation

The concept of a limit underpins all of calculus and there are several important notations used. We make a temporary change of independent variable to x, since that is the case for most of our later work.

Suppose we are interested in the limit of the values of $f(x)$ as x approaches a. This approach of x to a is written $x \to a$, in words: 'x tends to a'. If the corresponding limit of $f(x)$ is L, we write '$f(x) \to L$ as $x \to a$' or

$$\lim_{x \to a} f(x) = L.$$

We could apply this limiting idea to (4.2) assuming, as noted earlier, that T_1 remains fixed and $T_2 \to T_1$. But it is neater to replace T_1 by T and T_2 by $T + \Delta t$.

Notation

Here, Δt is regarded as a **change** made in the value of T, a particular value of the variable t. This is a standard notation and applies to any variable. Thus, Δx stands for a **change** – up (positive) or down (negative) – in the current value of the variable x. Δ is the capital version of δ [*delta*].

The form Δx is a 'composite' symbol standing for a single quantity and **not** for the product of Δ and x. Although these changes can be of any size, the notation is only of practical use when the changes are small.

Now, letting T_2 approach T_1 is equivalent to shrinking the interval, i.e., letting its width Δt approach 0. We then use a 'limit' version of (4.2):

$$v(T) = \lim_{\Delta t \to 0} \frac{s(T + \Delta t) - s(T)}{\Delta t}, \qquad (4.3)$$

as our measure of the **instantaneous** velocity at $t = T$. This is the type of limit that is used in **differentiation**. We defer for the moment the question of how to evaluate that limit.

Think about it like this

Note that the fraction in (4.3) is equivalent to that in (4.2),

$$\frac{s(T_2) - s(T_1)}{T_2 - T_1} = \frac{s(T + \Delta t) - s(T)}{\Delta t},$$

where $T_1 = T$ and $T_2 = T + \Delta t$, i.e., $T_1 = T$ is the 'start' time and T_2 follows a (short) time Δt later, or earlier if $\Delta t < 0$. $T_2 - T_1 = \Delta t$.

Ex 4.2 Consider the function $f(x) = \dfrac{1}{x+1}$.

(a) Calculate $f(4)$ and $f(4 + 0.1)$.

(b) Hence calculate $R = \dfrac{f(4 + h) - f(4)}{h}$, where $h = 0.1$, to 6 dp.

(c) Repeat (b), using $h = 0.01$.

(d) Conjecture from (b) and (c) a value for the limit of R as h tends to zero, a value that will be written as $f'(4)$ in the next section.

4.3   The Definition of Differentiation

We now extract from the above the key content, free from the context used. There is a function involved and we use the name f, rather than s. We change the independent variable from t to the more usual x.

Converting (4.3), we define the **derivative** of f at the (fixed) point a by

$$f'(a) = \lim_{\Delta x \to 0} \frac{f(a + \Delta x) - f(a)}{\Delta x}. \tag{4.4}$$

In (4.4) we regard a as a **constant**. It could equally well be regarded as a **variable** if we undertake to ensure it remains constant in value during the time we calculate the limit, when only Δx is allowed to vary. The result of the calculation is $f'(x)$, which can be thought of as a value of a function f' for an input x.

This new function is properly called the **derived function**, but **derivative** is more commonly used. Its definition

$$f'(x) = \lim_{\Delta x \to 0} \frac{f(x + \Delta x) - f(x)}{\Delta x} \tag{4.5}$$

is similar to (4.4) and will be repeated shortly, in a somewhat neater form.

Notation

The derivative for the function defined by $y = f(x)$ is denoted in many ways, e.g.,

$$y', \qquad \frac{dy}{dx}, \qquad \frac{d}{dx}[f(x)], \qquad f'(x), \qquad \frac{df}{dx}.$$

(The symbol f' is read as 'f-dashed' or 'f-prime'.)

If we wish to find the derivative of f at a particular constant value a, say, then the x in $f'(x)$ can be replaced by a, and we write $f'(a)$. Alternatively, we may use the notation

$$\left. \frac{dy}{dx} \right|_{a} \quad \text{or} \quad \left. \frac{dy}{dx} \right|_{x=a},$$

where the vertical bar indicates that the variable is to be replaced by a particular constant value; this is a generally used device.

The process of finding the derivative at a, or the derived function f', is called **differentiation**. We talk of differentiation '**with respect to** x' (or t or u, etc.) when we require to make it clear what is the independent variable. This is often abbreviated to '**w.r.t.** x'.

Think about it like this

At this stage, the notation $\frac{dy}{dx}$ should be thought of as a single composite symbol for the derivative. The items dy and dx, known as *differentials*, can be given an independent existence. We shall occasionally allow ourselves to use dx as a sort of 'limit' of Δx, but only as an *aide-mémoire*.

The link between 'd' and 'Δ' is, however, a useful one to bear in mind: this notation for the derivative is clearly similar to $\frac{\Delta y}{\Delta x}$. In that ratio, Δy represents the change in y caused by the change Δx in x, i.e., it is $f(x + \Delta x) - f(x)$, which is the numerator of the ratio in (4.5). It also appears in the numerator in (4.4), with x given the value a.

The use of Δx can be clumsy in algebraic work, so the definition of the derivative is often rewritten using a single symbol, often h, in its place.

Frame 4.1   Definition of the derivative

$$f'(x) = \lim_{h \to 0} \frac{f(x+h) - f(x)}{h} \qquad (4.6)$$

Think about it like this

This definition is fundamental to the building and analysis of mathematical models, but it is of little help unless the limit can actually be evaluated. It is tempting to set the interval width to zero in (4.6): $h = 0$. This is doomed to failure since it invariably gives the meaningless expression $0/0$.

Algebraic manipulation can often achieve cancellation of the Δx or h before the limiting procedure is set in motion, producing a new version where the limit is easily evaluated. The following examples illustrate this.

Example 4.2   Use the definition in (4.5) to find the derivative of a constant valued function, $f(x) = K$.

We have

$$\frac{f(x + \Delta x) - f(x)}{\Delta x} = \frac{K - K}{\Delta x} = 0 \to 0,$$

as $\Delta x \to 0$. **All constants have derivative 0.**   ∎

Example 4.3   Use the definition in (4.6) to find the derivatives of:

$$\text{(a) } f(x) = x^2, \qquad \text{(b) } f(x) = \sqrt{x}, \qquad \text{(c) } f(x) = \frac{1}{x}.$$

(a) We have

$$\frac{f(x+h) - f(x)}{h} = \frac{(x+h)^2 - x^2}{h} = \frac{x^2 + 2xh + h^2 - x^2}{h}$$

$$= \frac{2xh + h^2}{h} = 2x + h$$

$$\to 2x, \quad \text{as } h \to 0.$$

Hence $f'(x) = 2x$.

(b) This time we use a rather unusual device, the reverse of "rationalising the denominator":

$$\frac{f(x+h) - f(x)}{h} = \frac{\sqrt{x+h} - \sqrt{x}}{h} \times \frac{\sqrt{x+h} + \sqrt{x}}{\sqrt{x+h} + \sqrt{x}}$$

$$= \frac{(x+h) - x}{h\left(\sqrt{x+h} + \sqrt{x}\right)} = \frac{1}{\sqrt{x+h} + \sqrt{x}}$$

$$\to \frac{1}{\sqrt{x} + \sqrt{x}} = \frac{1}{2\sqrt{x}}, \quad \text{as } h \to 0.$$

Hence $f'(x) = \dfrac{1}{2\sqrt{x}}$.

(c) This time we must combine the terms using the algebra of fractions:

$$\frac{f(x+h)-f(x)}{h} = \frac{1}{h}\left[\frac{1}{x+h}-\frac{1}{x}\right]$$

$$= \frac{1}{h}\left[\frac{x-(x+h)}{(x+h)x}\right] = \frac{-1}{(x+h)x}$$

$$\rightarrow \frac{-1}{x\cdot x} = -\frac{1}{x^2}, \quad \text{as } h\rightarrow 0.$$

Hence $f'(x) = -\dfrac{1}{x^2}$.

■

Note that

$$\sqrt{x} = x^{1/2}, \qquad \frac{1}{2\sqrt{x}} = \frac{1}{2}x^{-1/2},$$

and

$$\frac{1}{x} = x^{-1}, \qquad -\frac{1}{x^2} = (-1)\times x^{-2}.$$

Thus, all the results here, as well as others found similarly, fit the template:

$$\frac{d}{dx}[x^n] = nx^{n-1}.$$

This is the first standard result in differentiation and will enable us to perform many practical differentiations. It is well worth memorising. Indeed, for reasons connected with future work, a useful approach is to think of it as a sequence of operations:

multiply by the index (n), subtract one from the index $(n \rightarrow n-1)$.

The examples we have worked through all involve x as the independent variable. We shall soon see other symbols being used and it is important to identify and to indicate what the independent variable is, i.e., what we are differentiating 'w.r.t.'. This is one of the advantages of the $\frac{d}{dx}$ notation: the x in the bottom line tells us the variable that is driving the calculation.

Ex 4.3 Use the definition of a derivative given by

$$f'(x) = \lim_{h\rightarrow 0}\frac{f(x+h)-f(x)}{h}$$

to find $f'(x)$ when $f(x) = x^3$, and when $f(x) = \dfrac{1}{1-x}$.

4.4   The Interpretation of Differentiation

This process was introduced in an attempt to measure instantaneous velocities from a displacement function $s(t)$. There is nothing special about s, and
we can use the same concept to find the **instantaneous rate of change**
for any measured quantity $f(t)$. Indeed, the rate need not be measured with
respect to changes in time: $f'(x)$ measures the rate at which the output of
the function f changes in response to changes in the input, no matter what
x measures. We shall return to this later.

There is also a **geometrical** or **graphical** interpretation, shown below.
A sequence of lines (*chords*) joining

$$\big(x, f(x)\big) \quad \text{to} \quad \big(x + \Delta x, f(x + \Delta x)\big)$$

appear to approach nearer and nearer to the **tangent** to the graph of $f(x)$
at the point x, as $\Delta x \to 0$.

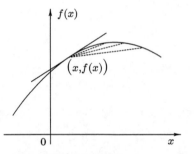

Let Δf stand for the change in the value of $f(x)$ due to the change Δx
in the value of x, i.e., $\Delta f = f(x + \Delta x) - f(x)$. These chords have gradient

$$\frac{f(x + \Delta x) - f(x)}{(x + \Delta x) - x} = \frac{\Delta f}{\Delta x},$$

which tends to $\frac{df}{dx}$. The derivative must therefore measure the gradient of
the **tangent**. That gradient is often referred to as the gradient of the **curve**
itself at that point. Knowing the gradient of the tangent allows us to find the
equation of the tangent, using Frame 1.1. This observation is the origin of
the gradient-velocity link mentioned in §4.1. (The Δf notation ties in rather
nicely with the notation $\frac{df}{dx}$: in the **limit**, Δ becomes d.)

Example 4.4   Find the equation of the tangent to $y = x^2$ at the point
$(3, 9)$.

First of all, note that at $x = 3$, $y = 3^2 = 9$, so the point is on the graph.

From Example 4.3(a), if $f(x) = x^2$, $f'(x) = 2x$, so $f'(3) = 6$. This is the
gradient of the tangent, so its equation is

$$y - 9 = 6(x - 3) \quad \Rightarrow \quad y = 6x - 9.$$

Note that it is essential to substitute $x = 3$ in the derivative, since we require
the gradient at that **fixed** point.   ∎

Example 4.5　Find the equation of the tangent to $y = \sqrt{x}$ at the point $(4, 2)$.

Also, find the equation of the tangent to $y = \sqrt{x}$ at the point $(0, 0)$.

From Example 4.3(b), $\frac{dy}{dx} = \frac{1}{2\sqrt{x}}$, which has value $\frac{1}{4}$ at $x = 4$.

Hence the tangent is $y - 2 = \frac{1}{4}(x - 4)$, i.e., $y = \frac{1}{4}x + 1$.

At $x = 0$, $\frac{dy}{dx}$ is not defined. Also, the function exists only on one side of the point. The best we can say is that the tangent, which is vertical, is the y-axis, with equation $x = 0$. The gradient is 'infinite'.

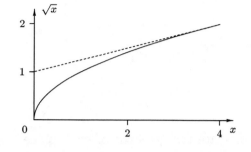

Think about it like this

A good understanding of differentiation requires a secure grasp of the structure and meaning of the ratio in (4.6):

$$\frac{f(x+h) - f(x)}{(x+h) - x} = \frac{f(x+h) - f(x)}{h}. \qquad (4.7)$$

To help achieve this, consider this key quantity algebraically, geometrically and physically. (Note: h is commonly used in this way and it is unfortunate that it is also often used for 'height'.)

Algebraically: Suppose we are given a formula for $f(x)$, a specific value for x and one for h. Then it is straightforward to use (4.7): just find values for the numbers $x+h$ and x, substitute them into the formula and calculate. If, however, we are given only the formula, with x and h to remain as symbols, write down the formula as given, $f(x)$, and then again with every x replaced by $(x + h)$, using brackets for safety. Subtract the two (second minus first), unpick the brackets, tidy up and see if you can divide by h.

Geometrically: Think about what happens on a graph. $f(x)$ is the height at position x, while $f(x + h)$ is the height at position $x + h$, presumed to be a little further on. Hence the top line of the fraction is the increase in height as we move from x to $x+h$. The bottom is the increase in x itself, so overall the fraction is the *gradient* of the line connecting $(x, f(x))$ to $(x + h, f(x + h))$.

Physically: We have already seen an interpretation: (4.1). This is the average velocity over a time period of size h, starting at time x, where $f(x)$ measures the distance travelled. There is another (spatial) interpretation, related to the geometric one. Suppose you are climbing a hill with height at distance x given by $f(x)$ and that at distance X from the start the gradient is 0.1. This means that if you travel a further 100 metres measured horizontally so that $h = 100$, you will climb $0.1 \times 100 = 10$ metres, i.e., $f(X + 100) - f(X) = 10$, ensuring the ratio in (4.7) is $\frac{10}{100} = 0.1$, with $x = X$ and $h = 100$.

In all of these cases, there is the irksome fact that the answer depends on h. If we measure rates of change, gradients, average velocities, etc., in such a way, we do not get a single well-defined value. Can we find a suitable value everyone will agree on? The only possibility is that which is most 'accurate' at x itself: the *instantaneous* rate, gradient, velocity. This is found by letting h shrink and extrapolating the trend of the values of (4.7), i.e., by taking the *limit* as $h \to 0$.

Example 4.6   Use of the gradient to find the derivative. Differentiate $f(x)$, defined in the graph to the left below, and sketch a graph of $f'(x)$.

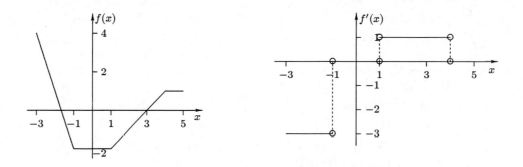

Calculate the gradient of each piece of the function. This gradient is the corresponding derivative value.

x	$-3 < x < -1$	$-1 < x < 1$	$1 < x < 4$	$4 < x < 5$
m	$\frac{-2-4}{-1-(-3)}$	0	$\frac{1-(-2)}{4-1}$	0
$f'(x)$	-3	0	1	0

These derivative values are plotted in the right-hand graph above. There is no derivative at the **knots** at $x = -1$, 1 and 4, since there is no tangent at those points. Hence they are marked with ∘.

■

Ex 4.4 Find the equation of the tangent to the curve $y = \dfrac{1}{x}$ at the point where $x = \frac{1}{2}$.

Ex 4.5 A function $f(x)$ is shown in the graph below. By calculating gradients, draw the graph of $f'(x)$.

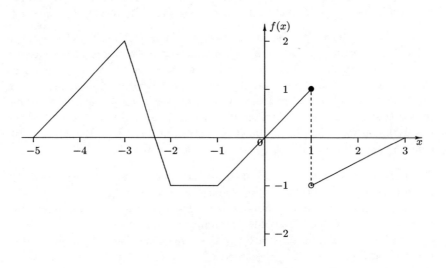

4.5 Further Differentiation

We noted in the previous section that the various derivatives we had found all fitted the following template.

Frame 4.2   *Differentiation of a power function*

$$\frac{d}{dx}[x^n] = nx^{n-1} \qquad\qquad (4.8)$$

Here, n may be a whole number or a rational number, positive or negative.

Example 4.7   Differentiate $f(x) = \dfrac{1}{\sqrt{x}}$.

Rewrite this as $f(x) = x^{-1/2}$ and use Frame 4.2:

$$\frac{d}{dx}\left[x^{-1/2}\right] = \left(-\frac{1}{2}\right)x^{-1/2-1} = -\frac{1}{2}x^{-3/2}.$$

∎

We now extend this to 'compound' functions using the first of the **Rules of Differentiation**. These are easy to prove, but the details are technical and the results are fairly obvious on geometrical grounds.

Frame 4.3   *Sum rule*

$$\frac{d}{dx}[u+v] = \frac{du}{dx} + \frac{dv}{dx} = f'(x) + g'(x) \qquad [u = f(x),\ v = g(x)]$$

Frame 4.4   *Constant multiplication rule*

$$\frac{d}{dx}[ky] = k\frac{dy}{dx} = kf'(x) \qquad [y = f(x),\ k \text{ constant}]$$

These rules allow us to differentiate functions built up by adding together functions we have already treated, such as those of the form x^n, as well as constant multiples of these. In particular, they enable us to differentiate **polynomials**, which are sums of powers of x, multiplied by constants:

$$p(x) = a + bx + cx^2 + dx^3 + \cdots,$$

where a, b, etc. are **constants**.

Example 4.8   Use the two rules to differentiate $\frac{1}{2}x^2 - 7x + 8$.

$$\frac{d}{dx}\left[\frac{1}{2}x^2 - 7x + 8\right] = \frac{1}{2}\frac{d}{dx}\left[x^2\right] - 7\frac{d}{dx}\left[x\right] + \frac{d}{dx}\left[8\right]$$

$$= \frac{1}{2} \times 2x - 7 \times 1 + 0$$

$$= x - 7.$$

■

These rules, however, apply to all functions, not just polynomials.

Example 4.9   The following involves two functions treated earlier:

$$\frac{d}{dx}\left[4\sqrt{x} - \frac{3}{x}\right] = 4\frac{d}{dx}\left[\sqrt{x}\right] - 3\frac{d}{dx}\left[\frac{1}{x}\right]$$

$$= 4 \times \frac{1}{2\sqrt{x}} - 3 \times \left(-\frac{1}{x^2}\right)$$

$$= \frac{2}{\sqrt{x}} + \frac{3}{x^2}.$$

■

Example 4.10   The following differentiation uses two new functions, each covered by the template in Frame 4.2:

$$\frac{d}{dx}\left[6x^{4/3} + \frac{1}{3x^3}\right] = 6\frac{d}{dx}\left[x^{4/3}\right] + \frac{1}{3}\frac{d}{dx}\left[x^{-3}\right]$$

$$= 6 \times \frac{4}{3}x^{1/3} + \frac{1}{3} \times (-3)x^{-4}$$

$$= 8\sqrt[3]{x} - \frac{1}{x^4}.$$

■

Ex 4.6   Differentiate the following:

(a) $-3x^4$ (b) $2x^{11}$ (c) $x^4 + 4x^3 + 6x^2 + 4x + 1$
(d) $Ax^{10} + Bx + C$ (A, B and C are constants)

Ex 4.7

(a) Differentiate $t^5 + 3t^4 - 2t$ with respect to t.

(b) Differentiate $4\left(x^3 - \frac{3x^2}{8} + \frac{1}{x}\right)$ with respect to x.

(c) Find $\frac{dP}{dx}$ when $P = \frac{P_0}{x} - \frac{1}{P_0 x^2}$, with P_0 a constant.

4.6 Applications of Differentiation

The derivative measures 'rate of change', by which we mean the extent to which a change in the value of one quantity – measured by the **independent** variable – affects the value of another – measured by the **dependent** variable. For example, we used **velocity** v as the **rate of change of displacement** s. Similarly, we can regard **acceleration** as the **rate of change of velocity**, i.e., $\frac{dv}{dt}$. Both these rates are 'with respect to time' as independent variable; that is a very common situation but by no means the only one.

Example 4.11   The following derivatives represent rates of change:

(a) Rate of **increase** in quantity Q of a chemical or an isotope w.r.t. time t is $\dfrac{dQ}{dt}$.

(b) Rate of **decrease** in quantity Q of a chemical or an isotope w.r.t. time t is $-\dfrac{dQ}{dt}$, since decrease is opposite to increase.

An alternative way to see this is to assume we start with amount Z. Then $Z - Q$ measures the amount **lost**. Hence the rate of decrease, which is the same as the rate of increase in the amount lost, is $\frac{d}{dt}[Z - Q] = \frac{dZ}{dt} - \frac{dQ}{dt} = 0 - \frac{dQ}{dt}$, since Z is constant.

∎

Example 4.12   Oil leaks from a vessel, forming a slick of area A (varying in time) and thickness δ (constant). What is the rate of leakage?

The volume of the slick is $V = A\delta$. The rate of leakage is the rate of increase in the slick volume. This is

$$\frac{dV}{dt} = \frac{d}{dt}[A\delta] = \delta\frac{dA}{dt},$$

since δ is constant. ∎

Example 4.13   A particle moving in the positive x-direction experiences a frictional force F, proportional to its velocity.

The velocity is $\dfrac{dx}{dt}$ and the force opposes it, so

$$F = -k\frac{dx}{dt} \qquad (k \text{ constant}).$$

∎

If we have a formula for any of these quantities, expressed in terms of the 'w.r.t.' variable, then our differentiation rules and formulae help us calculate these rates of change explicitly.

Example 4.14   Justify the guess made in Example 4.1: the velocity at $t = 1$ for displacement $s = \sqrt{t}$.

We know that $v = \frac{ds}{dt} = \frac{1}{2\sqrt{t}}$, which gives us a formula for $v(t)$, seen to be **non-constant**. At the instant $t = 1$, we have $v(1) = \frac{1}{2}$, as we conjectured arithmetically.

It is important to note that this **exact** value could not be found using the simple formulae for motion: the more general calculus approach was essential. (Even the arithmetical approach cannot guarantee to deliver the answer. We guessed it correctly only because it was a round number.) ■

The link between $\frac{\Delta f}{\Delta x}$ and $f'(x)$ shows that $f(x)$ **increases** as x increases when $f'(x) > 0$, since both Δf and Δx must be positive. Similarly, $f(x)$ **decreases** as x increases, when $f'(x) < 0$. These results are confirmed by recalling the link with the gradient of the tangent from §4.4.

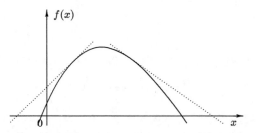

This raises the question of what happens if $f'(a) = 0$ at some point a. The tangent must be horizontal and the function is neither increasing nor decreasing at a, which is called a **stationary point**. Often, this means that the function has been increasing and is about to decrease – a **maximum** value – or has been decreasing and is about to increase – a **minimum** value.

This observation provides a tool for solving many **optimisation** problems. We establish a function f that describes some quantity we wish to optimise, then solve $f'(x) = 0$ to find the stationary points. We can discriminate between them by evaluating $f'(x)$ at $a \pm \epsilon$ for a small ϵ [*epsilon*]. (This letter is often used to represent a very small quantity.) Consider the sign of $f'(x)$ as we pass from $a - \epsilon$ to $a + \epsilon$:

$$+ \quad \rightarrow \quad 0 \quad \rightarrow \quad - \quad \text{means we have a } \textbf{maximum.}$$
$$- \quad \rightarrow \quad 0 \quad \rightarrow \quad + \quad \text{means we have a } \textbf{minimum.}$$

This is illustrated by the first two graphs below, where A is a maximum and B a minimum; the third graph is discussed later.

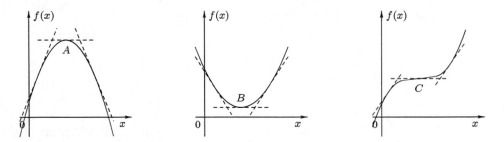

Example 4.15 Use of derivatives in curve-sketching. Investigate the graphical behaviour of the cubic

$$y = x^3 - 3x - 2.$$

First seek information about gradients and stationary points:

$$\frac{dy}{dx} = 3x^2 - 3 = 3(x-1)(x+1)$$
$$= 0 \quad \text{if } x = -1 \text{ or } +1.$$

For other values of x we have:

$$x < -1, \qquad \frac{dy}{dx} > 0, \qquad y \text{ increases,}$$

$$-1 < x < 1, \qquad \frac{dy}{dx} < 0, \qquad y \text{ decreases,}$$

$$1 < x, \qquad \frac{dy}{dx} > 0, \qquad y \text{ increases.}$$

At $x = \pm 1$, y is stationary. The gradients indicate:

$$x = -1: \quad \nearrow \! \rightarrow \! \searrow \quad \text{maximum,}$$
$$x = +1: \quad \searrow \! \rightarrow \! \nearrow \quad \text{minimum.}$$

To help draw the graph, note that $y = 0$ at $x = -1$, 2. The points $(0, -2)$ and $(1, -4)$ also lie on the graph, which is shown below.

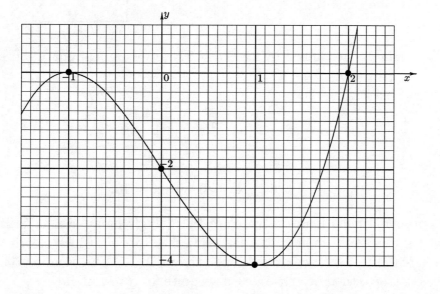

We shall return to this topic later, but there are three points to note at present.

- A stationary point that is a maximum or minimum is a **turning point**. But, not all stationary points are maxima and minima; we can also have a **point of inflection**, such as C in the third graph above, where the derivative does not change sign. An example is $y = x^3$, whose graph is shown in Example 1.11.

- Not all maxima and minima are stationary points; the function $|x|$ has a minimum value of 0 at $x = 0$ (it is positive everywhere else). There is no tangent at that point and hence no derivative. Its graph is shown in §1.4.

- Strictly speaking, we should refer to A and B as **local** maxima and minima since they do not necessarily give the largest and smallest values throughout the entire range of the function; determination of **global** maxima and minima is much harder. They do not necessarily occur at turning points; they may lie at one or other of the ends of the domain. For example, $y = x^2$, $(x$ in $[0, 1])$ has a maximum value at $x = 1$, where the derivative is not zero. The local versions, however, are often useful starting points in the search for the global ones.

Example 4.16   Find the field of maximum area enclosed by 64 metres of fence.

This can be solved using the method below, but in this case the answer is 'obvious'. We should use a square field: $16 \times 16 = 256\,\mathrm{m}^2$.

Now suppose there is a wall available to form one side.

Let the dimensions be x and y, as in the diagram. These are linked, so there is only *one* "degree of freedom". We cannot make both x and y bigger at the same time.

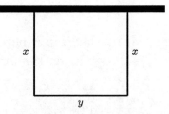

The variables are linked by $2x + y = 64$, so we can eliminate y from the problem by using $y = 64 - 2x$.

If the area is A, we have

$$A = xy = x(64 - 2x) = 64x - 2x^2,$$

and hence

$$\frac{dA}{dx} = 64 - 4x = 0 \quad \text{if} \quad x = 16.$$

The optimum dimensions are therefore 16×32, giving an area of $512\,\mathrm{m}^2$.

But is this a maximum? The derivative is $4(16 - x)$, which clearly moves from $+$ to 0 to $-$ as x increases through the value 16. The function therefore increases, stops, then decreases, as we require for a maximum. ■

Think about it like this

> This example is typical of optimisation problems; we shall see further examples later. The quantity to be optimised depends on two quantities that both should be increased to improve the solution, but they compete for 'resources', in this case the quantity of fencing materials. The mathematical analysis finds the optimum trade-off between them.

Ex 4.8 If $A = 2\pi r^2 + 20\pi r$ find the rate of change of A with respect to r.

Ex 4.9 The quantity **specific energy** is used in the analysis of flow in a water channel with cross-sectional area A and depth y. It is defined by $E = y + \dfrac{Q^2}{2gA^2}$, where Q is the rate of flow in the channel.

For a rectangular channel, width B, $A = By$. Express E in terms of y and hence find a formula for the **critical depth of flow**, where $\dfrac{dE}{dy} = 0$.

Ex 4.10 The velocity of a particle moving in a straight line is $v = \dfrac{ds}{dt}$ where s is displacement (m) and t is time (s). If $s = 3t - t^3$, find the velocity when $t = 1.5$. At what (positive) time is the velocity zero? What happens at this time? What is the formula for the acceleration and what does this tell us?

Ex 4.11 The isothermal compressibility of a gas is defined as $k_T = -\dfrac{1}{v}\dfrac{dv}{dp}$, where v is the volume and p is the pressure of the gas. Note the minus sign: v decreases as p increases.

Suppose that the gas satisfies the **ideal gas law**, $pv = RT$, where R is a constant and T is the temperature, constant in this **isothermal** case. Rearrange the gas law to find a formula for v in terms of p (and RT) and hence find a formula for k_T in terms of p.

Ex 4.12

(a) Verify that $x = 3$ is a turning point for the curve $y = x^3 - 3x^2 - 9x + 10$.

(b) Is it a maximum or a minimum?

(c) Find the second turning point and its nature.

Ex 4.13 Find the value or values of x at which $Q = x^2 + xy$ (where $x^2 y = 4$) has a maximum or minimum value. For each such solution, determine which type of value (maximum or minimum) it is.

4.7 Revision Exercises

Ex 4.14 Consider the function $f(x) = x^2 - 3x + 3$.

(a) Find $f'(x)$ from first principles.

(b) Find the rate of change of $f(x)$ at $x = 2$.

(c) Verify that $P : (2, 1)$ and $Q : (m + 1, m^2 - m + 1)$ lie on the graph of f.

(d) Show that the line PQ has gradient m, and determine the value of m such that the two points P and Q are coincident. What has now happened to the line PQ and why does this value of m agree with $f'(2)$?

(e) Find the equation of the tangent to the graph of f at $(2, 1)$.

(f) Sketch the graph of f over $[0, 3]$ and relate your answers to it.

Ex 4.15 Find the equations of the tangents to the graph of $y = x^2 - x$ at the point with $x = 2$ and at the point with $x = \frac{1}{2}$.

Ex 4.16 Consider the graph of $y = x^{1/3}$.

(a) Find the gradient of the straight line joining the points of this graph with $x = 0$ and $x = 8$.

(b) Find the value a such that the tangent to y at $x = a$ is parallel to the straight line in (a).

Ex 4.17 Consider the function $f(x) = \dfrac{2}{x^2}$.
Find the equation of the **normal** to its graph at $x = 2$.

Ex 4.18 Find the stationary points of $f(x) = 2x^3 - 9x^2 + 12x + 2004$ and determine their nature.

Ex 4.19 A cylindrical tin, like that used to contain baked beans, with height h and base radius r has volume V and surface area S given by

$$V = \pi r^2 h, \qquad S = 2\pi r^2 + 2\pi r h.$$

It is planned to make a tin of fixed capacity $V = 54\pi\,\mathrm{cm}^3$ out of a minimum amount of metal. Find an expression for h in terms of r and hence show that S is minimised when $h = 2r$, i.e., the height equals the base diameter.

Note that this conclusion is true whatever fixed capacity is set. A specific value was given above to reduce the number of symbols in the problem.

5 FURTHER DIFFERENTIATION

It is not sensible to pursue applications further until we have extended the list of functions we can differentiate. We do this in two ways. We find derivatives for basic functions, such as $\sin x$ and e^x; these are called **standard forms**. We also find ways of dealing with more complicated functions generated by combining these standard forms; these are called **rules of calculus**. We shall identify some of these rules and then look for standard forms.

But first, we revisit the one standard form we already know, that in Frame 4.2 :

$$\frac{d}{dx}[x^n] = nx^{n-1}. \tag{5.1}$$

We accept this as a reasonable conjecture based on the special cases we have examined.

The previous chapter also introduced the first two 'rules'. The following example illustrates how to use the standard form and rules together.

Example 5.1   Differentiate $y = 1 + x + \frac{1}{2}x^2 + \frac{1}{6}x^3 + \frac{1}{24}x^4 + \frac{1}{120}x^5$.

Use (5.1) and the rules in Frames 4.3 and 4.4:

$$y' = 0 + 1 + \frac{1}{2}(2x) + \frac{1}{6}(3x^2) + \frac{1}{24}(4x^3) + \frac{1}{120}(5x^4)$$
$$= 1 + x + \frac{1}{2}x^2 + \frac{1}{6}x^3 + \frac{1}{24}x^4.$$

This is the same as y, except for the last term, which has disappeared.

This striking property occurs because y consists of a series of terms of the form $\frac{1}{n!}x^n$ and

$$\frac{d}{dx}\left[\frac{1}{n!}x^n\right] = \frac{1}{n!}nx^{n-1} = \frac{1}{(n-1)!}x^{n-1},$$

the previous term in the series.   ∎

Now polynomials do not always appear in the form in Example 5.1. We could encounter ones such as

$$f(x) = (3x-1)^9, \qquad g(x) = (3x^2-2)(x^3-5x), \qquad h(x) = (x^2+x+1)^3.$$

In such cases we can, in theory, expand by removing the brackets and proceed to differentiate as above. This would clearly be unattractive in the case of $f(x)$. In fact, all three of these can be differentiated in their original form using rules we are about to meet.

5.1 The Product Rule

For the case of the function $g(x) = (3x^2-2)(x^3-5x)$ above, we have a **product** or multiplication of (the output of) the functions $3x^2-2$ and x^3-5x, each of which is easily differentiated. What we would like is a rule that allows us to differentiate this product using these two simpler derivatives. This can be done using the following whose justification can be found, as a technical calculation, in textbooks.

Frame 5.1   *The Product Rule*

$$\frac{d}{dx}[uv] = u\frac{dv}{dx} + v\frac{du}{dx} = f(x)g'(x) + g(x)f'(x) \qquad (5.2)$$

$$[u = f(x), \ v = g(x)]$$

Think about it like this

You may think it unfortunate that there is no simpler rule for this task, but we could not expect anything simpler, if we think about dimensions or units. A derivative is a rate, e.g., a 'per sec' measure. An expression such as $u'(x)v'(x)$ – often wrongly used for the derivative of $u(x)v(x)$ – makes no sense since its dimensions would relate to 'per sec^2'. Hence any term in the correct rule can involve only one derivative. Each term must also contain a product of two functions, to preserve other units in use. Add to this the requirement to be symmetric in u and v and the formula in Frame 5.1 is the simplest possible.

Example 5.2   Differentiate (a) $(3x^2 - 2)(x^3 - 5x)$,   (b) $x^{3/2}$

(a) (This is the function $g(x)$ at the start of the chapter.) Let

$$u = 3x^2 - 2, \qquad v = x^3 - 5x,$$

$$\frac{du}{dx} = 6x, \qquad \frac{dv}{dx} = 3x^2 - 5.$$

Hence $y' = (3x^2 - 2)(3x^2 - 5) + 6x(x^3 - 5x)$.

(b) Although this is not really a product, we can write $x^{3/2} = x^{1/2} \times x$, both of which we can differentiate:

$$u = x^{1/2}, \qquad v = x,$$

$$\frac{du}{dx} = \tfrac{1}{2}x^{-1/2}, \qquad \frac{dv}{dx} = 1.$$

Hence

$$y' = x^{1/2} \cdot 1 + \tfrac{1}{2}x^{-1/2} \cdot x$$
$$= x^{1/2} + \tfrac{1}{2}x^{1/2} = \tfrac{3}{2}x^{1/2}.$$

This also fits the general 'nx^{n-1}' result in (5.1), with $n = 3/2$.

■

The formula in Frame 5.1 applies to any function whose output can be written as a product of two quantities. More complicated products can be broken up into steps: differentiate uvw by doing vw first, then write $uvw = u(vw)$, i.e., as the product of u and vw.

Ex 5.1 Differentiate the following functions of x:

(a) $(2x-1)(2x+1)$,　(b) $(x^2+1)(x^4-7x^3+5)$,　(c) $\left(3x^2 + \dfrac{4}{x^2} + 2\right)\left(x^3 - \dfrac{1}{x}\right)$.

5.2　The Quotient Rule

It is a short step from the product of two functions to the **quotient** or division of the output of two functions.

Frame 5.2　　*The Quotient Rule*

$$\frac{d}{dx}\left[\frac{u}{v}\right] = \frac{v\,{}^{du}/_{dx} - u\,{}^{dv}/_{dx}}{v^2} = \frac{g(x)f'(x) - f(x)g'(x)}{[g(x)]^2} \qquad (5.3)$$

$$[u = f(x), \; v = g(x)]$$

Think about it like this

Note that, unlike the Product Rule, this is *not* symmetric in u and v. This lack of symmetry is not surprising: although $u \times v = v \times u$, we have $\frac{u}{v} \neq \frac{v}{u}$, so $\frac{u}{v}$ is not symmetric. Particular care is needed with the position of the minus sign. One can ensure this is placed correctly by remembering that both the top and bottom lines start with v.

Before using this rule, note the following special case, where $u = f(x) = 1$.

$$\frac{d}{dx}\left[\frac{1}{v}\right] = -\frac{{}^{dv}/_{dx}}{v^2} = -\frac{f'(x)}{[f(x)]^2} \qquad [v = f(x)]. \qquad (5.4)$$

Think about it like this

Some people prefer to differentiate quotients by treating them as products. Thus, they treat the quotient $\frac{u}{v}$ as $u \cdot \frac{1}{v}$, differentiating $\frac{1}{v}$ using (5.4). This method is, of course, perfectly acceptable. The crafty differentiator will always use whichever method is easiest for a given problem.

Example 5.3　Differentiate　(a) $\dfrac{x-1}{x+1}$,　(b) $\dfrac{2x-3}{x^2-4x+5}$.

(a) Let

$$u = x - 1, \qquad v = x + 1,$$
$$u' = 1, \qquad\quad v' = 1.$$

Then, using the Quotient Rule,

$$\frac{dy}{dx} = \frac{(x+1)\cdot 1 - (x-1)\cdot 1}{(x+1)^2} = \frac{2}{(x+1)^2}.$$

(b) Let

$$u = 2x - 3, \qquad v = x^2 - 4x + 5,$$
$$u' = 2, \qquad v' = 2x - 4.$$

Then, using the Quotient Rule,

$$\frac{dy}{dx} = \frac{(x^2 - 4x + 5)2 - (2x - 3)(2x - 4)}{(x^2 - 4x + 5)^2} = \frac{-2x^2 + 6x - 2}{(x^2 - 4x + 5)^2},$$

on tidying up the top line.

∎

The quotient rule is not restricted to ratios of polynomials; it can be applied to ratios involving other types of functions.

Example 5.4 Differentiate $x^{-1/2}$.

We have $x^{-1/2} = \dfrac{1}{x^{1/2}}$, so use the special formula (5.4) (or the full Quotient Rule, if preferred):

$$v = x^{1/2}, \qquad v' = \tfrac{1}{2}x^{-1/2} \quad \text{(from Chapter 4)}.$$

Then,

$$\frac{dy}{dx} = -\frac{\tfrac{1}{2}x^{-1/2}}{\left(x^{1/2}\right)^2} = -\tfrac{1}{2}x^{-1/2}x^{-1} = -\tfrac{1}{2}x^{-3/2}.$$

This result fits the 'nx^{n-1}' rule in (5.1), with $n = -1/2$. ∎

Ex 5.2 Differentiate the following functions of x:

(a) $\dfrac{1}{x^2 - 4x + 1}$,   (b) $\dfrac{x^2}{x - 2}$,   (c) $\dfrac{x^3 - 4x}{x + 1}$.

5.3 Function Composition

Suppose we have two functions f and g, and use the output of g as the input of f (assuming this is valid). This is shown in the diagram below.

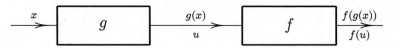

We note that the final output can be described in the single expression $f\big(g(x)\big)$. There is a special notation for this process, which is known as the **composition of f and g**.

Frame 5.3   *Composition of functions*

$$z = f \circ g(x) \quad \text{if} \quad u = g(x), \; z = f(u) \qquad [\text{or} \quad z = f\big(g(x)\big)]$$

Think about it like this

Note that $g \circ f$, which involves $g(f(x))$, is likely to be different from $f \circ g$. One way to remember this is that, in the expression $f \circ g(x)$, g being nearest to x gets 'first go' at x, then $g(x)$ is the argument for f.

We have assumed, above, that the output of the first function is a valid input to the second. Strictly speaking, x is only in the domain of $f \circ g$ if x is in the domain of g **and** $g(x)$ is in the domain of f.

Example 5.5 Find both possible compositions of $f(x) = \ln x$ and $g(x) = x^2 + 1$.

From Frame 5.3,

$$f \circ g(x) = f\left(x^2 + 1\right) = \ln\left(x^2 + 1\right),$$
$$g \circ f(x) = g\left(\ln x\right) = \left(\ln x\right)^2 + 1.$$

These are not the same function. In fact, they have different domains:

$f \circ g(x)$ is defined for all x, since $x^2 + 1 > 0$;

$g \circ f(x)$ requires $x > 0$, for $\ln x$ to be defined. ■

For our purposes, it is the opposite process that is required, which we shall call **decomposition**. We seek to take a complicated function, $y = F(x)$ say, and write it in the form $y = f(u)$, $u = g(x)$.

Think about it like this

There is a guide to help identify f, u, etc., whether we use the boxes set out in the diagram above or any of the notations in Frame 5.3. Start where x appears. The simplest function that uses it is $u = g(x)$. Then work away from this expression. Suppose we have a composition of three functions. Then we identify $u = h(x)$, $v = g(u)$ and finally f. This reflects the order in which h, g and f appear in $f \circ g \circ h(x)$, as we move away from x.

Example 5.6 'Decompose' the functions   (a) $(x^2 + x + 1)^3$,   (b) $\sin x^2$.

(a) Identifying the function that first operates on x, we define $u = x^2 + x + 1$, then $y = u^3$.

(b) Identifying the function that first operates on x, we define $u = x^2$, then $y = \sin u$.

Note that this result is different from $u = \sin x$, $y = u^2$, which defines the function $y = \sin^2 x$.

■

Decomposing functions does not produce a unique answer:

$$y = 4\sin^2 x \quad \Rightarrow \quad y = 4u^2,\ u = \sin x \quad \textit{or} \quad y = u^2,\ u = 2\sin x.$$

This is of no consequence, as far as differentiation is concerned.

Ex 5.3 Suppose $f(x)$ has formula $f(x) = \dfrac{x-1}{x+1}$.

Write down, and 'tidy up', the expressions $f\left(x^2 + 1\right)$, $f\left(\frac{1}{x}\right)$, i.e., the compositions $f \circ g(x)$ and $f \circ h(x)$, where $g(x) = x^2 + 1$ and $h(x) = \frac{1}{x}$.

Ex 5.4

(a) Find the formula for $f \circ g(x)$, where $f(x) = \sqrt{1-x}$ and $g(x) = \dfrac{x}{x+1}$.

For which values of x is $f \circ g(x)$ defined?

(b) Find functions f and g such that $f \circ g(x) = 1/(x^2 + x + 1)^2$.

Ex 5.5 The function $\ln \sin x$ can be viewed as the composition $f \circ u(x)$ or $f(u(x))$, where $f(x) = \ln x$, $u(x) = \sin x$. Express each of the following as such a composition:

$$\sqrt{x^3 + 1}, \qquad \tan \frac{1}{x}.$$

5.4   The Chain Rule

Now suppose we have a function y of x and that we have identified it to be a **composition** of functions f and g. We have the situation in the diagram below, which is based on that in the previous section.

Our aim is to find $\frac{dy}{dx}$ for this composite function. Hence, make a small change Δx in x. We find corresponding changes Δu in u and Δy in y. Considering the two 'boxes' in the diagram separately,

$$\frac{\Delta u}{\Delta x} \to g'(x) = \frac{du}{dx}, \qquad \frac{\Delta y}{\Delta u} \to f'(u) = \frac{dy}{du},$$

as $\Delta x \to 0$. Using the obvious relationship $\frac{\Delta y}{\Delta u} = \frac{\Delta y}{\Delta u} \cdot \frac{\Delta u}{\Delta x}$ and taking limits, we obtain a rule for differentiating y.

Frame 5.4   *The composite-function or Chain Rule*

$$\frac{dy}{dx} = \frac{dy}{du}\frac{du}{dx} = f'(u)g'(x) \qquad [y = f(u), \ u = g(x)] \qquad (5.5)$$

This is called the **Chain Rule**, because of the way the functions 'chain' together as in the diagram. Longer chains are possible if we find more than two functions are composed; the extension of the rule is straightforward.

Think about it like this

A sketch 'proof' has been given here, since it reflects the natural properties of such input-output linked systems. One interpretation of the derivative is that it 'scales' the size of a small change in the input. If we track the effect of this small change as it passes through a chain of processes, it will be scaled by each in turn, i.e., its final scaling will be the *product* of the individual scale factors. That is how the proof works and the product is seen in the format of the Chain Rule.

Some comment is called for concerning the temptation to 'cancel' du in $\frac{dy}{du} \cdot \frac{du}{dx}$, which would make the result in Frame 5.4 an obvious one. We have yet to give any convincing meaning for the differentials dx, etc. as isolated quantities, but it is permissible to rely on ideas such as the 'cancellation' just referred to as a memory aid and as a means of grasping the symbolic structure.

Example 5.7 Differentiate (a) $(x^2 + x + 1)^3$, (b) $\sqrt{1 - x^2}$.

(a) (This is the function $h(x)$ at the start of the chapter.) The first step is to 'decompose' the function, which was done in the Example 5.6(a): $u = x^2 + x + 1$ and $y = f(u) = u^3$.

Now complete the differentiation using the Chain Rule:

$$u = x^2 + x + 1, \qquad y = u^3,$$
$$\frac{du}{dx} = 2x + 1, \qquad \frac{dy}{du} = 3u^2.$$

Then

$$\frac{dy}{dx} = 3u^2(2x + 1) = 3(2x + 1)(x^2 + x + 1)^2.$$

(b) Decompose using $u = 1 - x^2$. Then use $y = f(u) = \sqrt{u}$.

Now complete the differentiation using the Chain Rule:

$$u = 1 - x^2, \qquad y = \sqrt{u},$$
$$\frac{du}{dx} = -2x, \qquad \frac{dy}{du} = \frac{1}{2\sqrt{u}}.$$

Then

$$\frac{dy}{dx} = -2x \frac{1}{2\sqrt{u}} = -\frac{x}{\sqrt{1 - x^2}}.$$

Differentiation of functions of this form is a common task: they tend to be generated by application of Pythagoras' Theorem.

∎

Ex 5.6 Differentiate the following functions of x:
   (a) $f(x) = \sqrt{1 - x^3}$, (b) $\sqrt[3]{5x^2 + 1}$.

5.5 Linear Arguments

We now examine a special case that occurs much more frequently than the general one. This is where the function $g(x)$ is a **linear** one: $g(x) = ax + b$, so that $u = ax + b$ and $y = f(ax + b)$. Using the terminology from §1.5, the function f has a **linear argument**. The reason for its frequency is that such an argument is equivalent to changing the origin and/or the scale for the x-axis, as we saw there.

Example 5.8   The following functions have **linear arguments**.

$$
\begin{aligned}
(3x-1)^9 &\quad:\quad u^9, &\quad u = 3x-1; \\
\sqrt[3]{1-2x} &\quad:\quad \sqrt[3]{u}, &\quad u = -2x+1; \\
\ln(1+x) &\quad:\quad \ln u, &\quad u = x+1; \\
\sin(\omega x + \phi) &\quad:\quad \sin u, &\quad u = \omega x + \phi; \\
\cos 5x &\quad:\quad \cos u, &\quad u = 5x + 0; \\
e^{1-x} &\quad:\quad e^u, &\quad u = -x + 1.
\end{aligned}
$$

∎

Now, in this case we have $\frac{du}{dx} = a$, so that the rule simplifies.

Frame 5.5   *Linear composite rule for differentiation*

$$
\frac{dy}{dx} = af'(ax+b) \qquad [y = f(ax+b),\ a,\ b\ \text{constants}] \qquad (5.6)
$$

Think about it like this

Graphically, $f(ax+b)$ looks like $f(x)$, except that

- it is moved left or right;
- it is *shrunk* by a factor a.

The first of these does not affect the gradients, but the second *expands* them by a factor of a. This explains why the factor a appears as a multiplier in (5.6).

Example 5.9   Differentiate:

$$
\text{(a) } (3x-1)^9, \quad \text{(b) } (1-x)^2, \quad \text{(c) } \sqrt{1-2x}, \quad \text{(d) } \frac{1}{(2x-1)^3}.
$$

(a) (This is the function $f(x)$ at the start of the chapter.) As given in Example 5.8(a), $u = 3x - 1 \equiv ax + b$ with $a = 3$ and $y = u^9$.

   The derivative of u^9 is $9u^8$, so the derivative of the original function is

$$
9(3x-1)^8 \times 3 = 27(3x-1)^8.
$$

(b) $u = 1 - x \equiv ax + b$ with $a = -1$ and $y = u^2$.

   Derivative: $2(1-x) \times (-1) = -2(1-x)$ (via $2u$).

(c) $u = -2x + 1 \equiv ax + b$ with $a = -2$ and $y = \sqrt{u}$.

   Derivative: $\dfrac{1}{2\sqrt{1-2x}} \times (-2) = -\dfrac{1}{\sqrt{1-2x}}.$

(d) $u = 2x + 1 \equiv ax + b$ with $a = 2$ and $y = u^{-3}$.

Derivative: $-3(2x + 1)^{-4} \times 2 = -\dfrac{6}{(2x + 1)^4}$.

■

Think about it like this

It is important to realise that $f'(ax + b)$ is not the same as $\frac{d}{dx}[f(ax + b)]$. Here, f' is the **derived function** for f and its formula must be found **before** introducing the argument $ax + b$. Thus, for $f(x) = x^2$, we find $f'(x) = 2x$ and **only then** deduce that $f'(ax + b) = 2(ax + b)$, using the new argument in f'. Multiplying this by a completes the task of differentiating $(ax + b)^2$.

Ex 5.7 Differentiate the following functions of x:

(a) $(2x + 6)^2$,   (b) $(2x + 6)^{100}$,   (c) $(5x + 1)^2(2x - 1)^3$,   (d) $\dfrac{(x - 1)^2}{(x + 3)^3}$.

Ex 5.8 An open water conduit is to be cut with a cross-section in the shape of a trapezium. It is then to be lined with material available in a standard width of 1 m, as shown in the figure below.

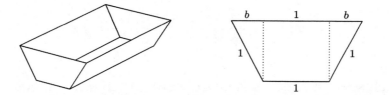

To achieve maximum potential capacity, the designer must maximise the area of the cross-section, which depends on the length b. Show that this area is

$$A(b) = \left[(1 + b)^3(1 - b)\right]^{1/2}.$$

Now, we wish to maximise $A(b)$, which would appear to involve the differentiation of a function with a nasty square root. Explain why this problem is the same as the problem of maximising $[A(b)]^2$.

This new problem involves only a polynomial. Show that the maximum occurs when $b = 0.5$ m. [The product rule is recommended for the differentiation, since it retains some useful structure.]

5.6   Circular Functions

We now commence extending the list of **standard forms**, i.e., the derivatives of basic functions that cannot be built up using x^n, our only standard form to date. The first type we examine are the circular or trigonometric functions. A natural starting point is $\sin x$ or $\cos x$. It is possible to show, using 'differentiation from first principles' that

$$\frac{d}{dx}[\sin x] = \cos x.$$

The details can be found in many textbooks, relying on a special limit we have not yet encountered. At present you should take this result on trust.

We can now differentiate $\cos x$ by using complementary angles, together with the **linear composite rule**, $u = \frac{\pi}{2} - x$ and $a = -1$:

$$\frac{d}{dx}[\cos x] = \frac{d}{dx}\left[\sin\left(\frac{\pi}{2} - x\right)\right] = -\cos\left(\frac{\pi}{2} - x\right) = -\sin x.$$

The other functions require the Quotient Rule. We shall work through one of these soon, but there is a very important matter to note first.

These results are true only if x is measured in radians. It is possible to differentiate circular functions with their arguments in degrees – see later – but the formulae are untidy. From now on we shall avoid reference to degrees and work entirely with radians.

Example 5.10   Differentiate $\tan x$.

Let $u = \sin x$ and $v = \cos x$, so $u' = \cos x$ and $v' = -\sin x$. Then

$$\frac{d}{dx}[\tan x] = \frac{d}{dx}\left[\frac{\sin x}{\cos x}\right]$$

$$= \frac{\cos x \times \cos x - \sin x \times (-\sin x)}{\cos^2 x}$$

$$= \frac{\cos^2 x + \sin^2 x}{\cos^2 x} = \frac{1}{\cos^2 x} = \sec^2 x.$$

∎

The full set of derivatives is given below. Alternative versions are given for $\tan x$ and $\cot x$, using identities from Frame 2.7.

Frame 5.6   Derivatives for trigonometric functions

$$\frac{d}{dx}[\sin x] = \cos x \tag{5.7}$$

$$\frac{d}{dx}[\cos x] = -\sin x \tag{5.8}$$

$$\frac{d}{dx}[\tan x] = \sec^2 x = 1 + \tan^2 x \tag{5.9}$$

$$\frac{d}{dx}[\sec x] = \sec x \tan x \tag{5.10}$$

$$\frac{d}{dx}[\operatorname{cosec} x] = -\operatorname{cosec} x \cot x \tag{5.11}$$

$$\frac{d}{dx}[\cot x] = -\operatorname{cosec}^2 x = -(1 + \cot^2 x) \tag{5.12}$$

Example 5.11   Differentiate:

(a) $\cos \dfrac{x}{2}$,   (b) $x^2 \cos x$,   (c) $\dfrac{\tan 2x}{x}$,   (d) $\sin(\pi t - \alpha)$,   (e) $\sin x \sin 2x$.

(a) This has a **linear argument** $\frac{1}{2}x + 0$. Derivative is:

$$\left(-\sin\frac{x}{2}\right) \times \frac{1}{2} = -\frac{1}{2}\sin\frac{x}{2}.$$

(b) This is a **product**, with $u = x^2$, $v = \cos x$. Derivative is:

$$x^2(-\sin x) + (\cos x)2x = -x^2\sin x + 2x\cos x.$$

(c) This is a **quotient**, with $u = \tan 2x$, $v = x$ and there is a **linear argument** involved in $\tan 2x$. Derivative is:

$$\frac{x \cdot 2\sec^2 2x - (\tan 2x) \cdot 1}{x^2} = \frac{2x\sec^2 2x - \tan 2x}{x^2},$$

where there is no simplification possible.

(d) Note that this appears to be a function of t, so we shall use differentiation w.r.t. t. It is again a **linear argument** example, with $a = \pi$. The derivative is $\pi\cos(\pi t - \alpha)$.

(e) This is a **product**, with $u = \sin x$, $v = \sin 2x$, and there is a **linear argument** in v. Derivative is:

$$(\sin x)(2\cos 2x) + (\cos x)(\sin 2x) = 2\sin x \cos 2x + \cos x \sin 2x.$$

■

Example 5.12   Differentiate $\sin x^2$ and $\sin^2 x$.

First, recall from Example 5.6(b) that these are different functions: the first is the sin of the angle x^2 (input squared) and the second the square of $\sin x$ (output squared). Both require the **Chain Rule**. The decompositions were found in that previous example.

$y = \sin x^2$ can be decomposed using $u = x^2$, $y = \sin u$. Then $\frac{dy}{du} = \cos u$ and $\frac{du}{dx} = 2x$, giving

$$\frac{dy}{dx} = (\cos u)2x = 2x\cos x^2.$$

We have reversed the order in the answer, to avoid the clumsy form $\cos x^2 2x$.

$y = \sin^2 x$ can be decomposed using $u = \sin x$, $y = u^2$. Then $\frac{dy}{du} = 2u$ and $\frac{du}{dx} = \cos x$, giving

$$\frac{dy}{dx} = (2u)\cos x = 2\sin x \cos x,$$

which can also be written as $\sin 2x$, using (2.17). ■

Finally, recall the earlier statement that it is ill-advised to use degree measure in calculus. If this is unavoidable and you really must work with $\sin x°$, say, the following example shows what you will have to deal with.

Example 5.13   Differentiate $\sin x°$.

   We proceed as follows: change to radians and use Frame 5.5 with $a = \frac{\pi}{180}$. We have

$$\frac{d}{dx}[\sin x°] = \frac{d}{dx}\left[\sin\left(\tfrac{\pi}{180}x\right)\right] = \tfrac{\pi}{180}\cos\left(\tfrac{\pi}{180}x\right) = \tfrac{\pi}{180}\cos x°.$$

■

Ex 5.9   Differentiate the function f where:
   (a) $f(t) = \sin\left(\omega t - \frac{\pi}{4}\right)$,   (b) $f(x) = \tan^2 x$.

Ex 5.10   Differentiate each of the following functions with respect to the variable in the formula:

   (a) $\cos(3x)$ (b) $\sin x \cos x$ (c) $\dfrac{1}{\cos x}$

   (d) $\sin^2(5t + 8)$ (e) $\sin(\omega t + \phi)$

Ex 5.11   Prove the identity $\cos^2 x + \sin^2 x = 1$ by following these steps:

   (a)   Consider the function $f(x) = \cos^2 x + \sin^2 x$. Differentiate to show $f'(x) = 0$.

   (b)   Conclude that f is constant.

   (c)   Find the constant value of f by evaluating it at a convenient x.

5.7   Logarithms and Exponentials

As in the case of the circular functions, these functions cannot easily be built up using x^n and hence need a different approach 'from first principles'. This is a difficult task and we shall again take the results on trust. The outcome is a remarkably simple standard form.

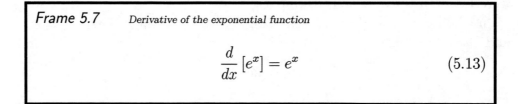

Frame 5.7   *Derivative of the exponential function*

$$\frac{d}{dx}[e^x] = e^x \qquad\qquad (5.13)$$

Think about it like this

   Pay particular attention to the form of e^x. It is precisely opposite to x^n. The positions of the variable and the constant are reversed and there is therefore no connection whatever between their standard forms.

Example 5.14   Differentiate   (a) e^{2x+3},   (b) $e^{-x}\sin x$.

   (a)   Use the linear composite rule with $ax + b \equiv 2x + 3$. Derivative is:

$$e^{2x+3} \times 2 = 2e^{2x+3}.$$

(b) This is a **product**, with $u = e^{-x}$, $v = \sin x$, so $u' = -e^{-x}$, $v' = \cos x$. Derivative is:

$$e^{-x} \cos x - e^{-x} \sin x = e^{-x}(\cos x - \sin x).$$

This function models damped harmonic motion, like that exhibited by a 'real' spring; the amplitude is e^{-x}, which dies away as x increases. The result of Example 2.13 could now be used to rewrite the result as $\sqrt{2}e^{-x} \sin\left(x + \frac{3\pi}{4}\right)$, which more clearly shows the way the amplitude and phase are connected with those for the original function.

∎

The **linear composite** rule gives the following very useful results, which are used frequently, especially in time-related problems. That is why we switch notation from x to t :

$$\frac{d}{dt}\left[e^{kt}\right] = ke^{kt}, \qquad \frac{d}{dt}\left[e^{-kt}\right] = -ke^{-kt}. \qquad (5.14)$$

Think about it like this

It is important to avoid misunderstandings about the application of (5.14).

- It applies only to cases where the exponent kt is a constant k times the variable t. It cannot be applied to e^{-t^2}, for example, as we see in the following example.

- It is the *constant* k that multiplies e^{kt} in the result.

Example 5.15   Differentiate $\exp\left(-\frac{1}{2}x^2\right)$.

This is a composition and hence requires the Chain Rule. Let

$$y = e^u, \qquad u = -\tfrac{1}{2}x^2,$$
$$\frac{dy}{du} = e^u, \qquad \frac{du}{dx} = -x.$$

Then we have

$$\frac{dy}{dx} = -xe^u = -x \exp\left(-\tfrac{1}{2}x^2\right).$$

∎

Example 5.16   A quantity decays exponentially according to the formula $Q = Q_0 e^{-kt}$. Verify that its rate of decay $R = -\frac{dQ}{dt}$ also decays exponentially, with the same half-life.

Use the linear composite rule, $at + b \equiv -kt + 0$, to obtain

$$R = -\frac{dQ}{dt} = -\left[-kQ_0 e^{-kt}\right] = kQ_0 e^{-kt}.$$

Hence R also decays exponentially with the same rate constant k and hence the same half-life, shown to be $(\ln 2)/k$ in §3.3.

This is important since R is much easier to measure than Q and so is used in determining half-lifes, as in Example 3.14. ∎

We now turn attention to the derivative of $\ln x$. This is most easily done using the final differentiation rule, **the inverse-function rule**. Unlike the other rules, this is not used in regular calculations, but remains on the side lines to be brought into play on a very few occasions, to deal with a 'new' function. In *Mathematical Methods 1* it is required just once, to differentiate $\ln x$.

Assume, as usual, that a small change Δx in x corresponds to a small change Δy in y. Now

$$\frac{\Delta x}{\Delta y} = 1 \bigg/ \frac{\Delta y}{\Delta x},$$

so the limit as $\Delta x \to 0$ gives the following.

Frame 5.8   *The inverse-function rule*

$$\frac{dy}{dx} = \frac{1}{dx/dy} = \frac{1}{f'(y)} \qquad [y = f^{-1}(x),\ x = f(y)] \qquad (5.15)$$

Now use the fact that the natural logarithmic function is the inverse of the exponential function.

Let $y = \ln x$. Then $x = e^y$ and $\frac{dx}{dy} = e^y$, on differentiating w.r.t. y. Using (5.15):

$$\frac{dy}{dx} = \frac{1}{dx/dy} = \frac{1}{e^y} = \frac{1}{x},$$

since $e^y = x$. The key result now follows.

Frame 5.9   *Differentiation of the logarithmic function*

$$\frac{d}{dx}[\ln x] = \frac{1}{x} \qquad\qquad (5.16)$$

This can be extended to more complicated cases using the differentiation rules.

Example 5.17   Differentiate   (a) $x \ln x$,   (b) $\ln(1-x)$,   (c) $\ln(x^2+1)$.

(a) Use the Product Rule, with $u = x$ and $v = \ln x$. We have

$$\frac{d}{dx}[x \ln x] = x \cdot \frac{1}{x} + 1 \cdot \ln x = 1 + \ln x.$$

(b) This has a **linear argument** $(-1)x + 1$. Derivative is:

$$\frac{1}{1-x} \times (-1) = \frac{1}{x-1}.$$

(c) This requires the **Chain Rule** with $y = \ln u$, $u = x^2 + 1$. Hence $\frac{dy}{du} = \frac{1}{u}$, $\frac{du}{dx} = 2x$. Derivative is:

$$\frac{1}{u} \times (2x) = \frac{2x}{x^2 + 1}.$$

∎

This last example is a special case of a result that will prove immensely useful in integration. Suppose $y = \ln(f(x))$, which we decompose using $y = \ln u$, $u = f(x)$. Hence

$$\frac{dy}{dx} = \frac{1}{u} \times f'(x) = \frac{f'(x)}{f(x)}. \tag{5.17}$$

Example 5.18 Differentiate $\ln(\cos x)$.
As above, $y = \ln u$, $u = \cos x$. Then

$$\frac{dy}{dx} = \frac{1}{u} \cdot (-\sin x) = -\frac{\sin x}{\cos x} = -\tan x.$$

∎

Finally, having noted that it is foolish to use degree measurement for calculus, it is also inadvisable to use logarithms to a base other than e or an exponential function with a base other than e. There are formulae for any base – see below – but they are not pleasant.

Recall, from Chapter 3, that any logarithmic value can be calculated using the natural log. This is the method by which we differentiate general log functions. Thus, using Frame 3.8,

$$\frac{d}{dx}[\log_a x] = \frac{d}{dx}\left[\frac{\ln x}{\ln a}\right] = \frac{1}{x}\frac{1}{\ln a}. \tag{5.18}$$

Also, we can write any exponential function in terms of **the** exponential function, using Frame 3.7:

$$\frac{d}{dx}[a^x] = \frac{d}{dx}\left[e^{x \ln a}\right] = (\ln a)e^{x \ln a} = (\ln a)a^x. \tag{5.19}$$

Think about it like this

Note that setting $a = e$, so that $\ln a = \ln e = 1$, in both (5.18) and (5.19) gives us back the simpler (base e) results in (5.16) and (5.13). This shows why the **natural** log and **the** exponential function are almost universally those used in calculus.

Example 5.19 Differentiate (a) $\log_{10} x$, (b) 10^x.

(a) As in (5.18),

$$y = \log_{10} x = \frac{\ln x}{\ln 10} \quad \Rightarrow \quad \frac{dy}{dx} = \frac{1}{\ln 10}\frac{1}{x}.$$

(b) As in (5.19),

$$10^x = e^{x \ln 10} \quad \Rightarrow \quad \frac{dy}{dx} = (\ln 10)e^{x \ln 10} = (\ln 10)\, 10^x.$$

∎

Ex 5.12 Differentiate the following functions, w.r.t. x:

$$e^{-2x}, \qquad \ln(1-2x), \qquad x\ln(x) - x, \qquad \frac{\ln x}{x^2}, \qquad e^{2x}\cos x, \qquad e^{x^2/2}.$$

Ex 5.13

(a) The displacement of an object undergoing damped harmonic motion can be modelled by $x(t) = Ae^{-kt}\sin(\omega t + \phi)$, where A, k, ω and ϕ are constants. Find a formula for $\frac{dx}{dt}$.

(b) 'Logistic' population growth modifies the exponential model to include restricted food etc., using expressions like $P(t) = \dfrac{10}{1 + 9e^{-2t}}$.

Show that $\frac{dP}{dt} = 2P\left(1 - \frac{P}{10}\right)$.

5.8   Second and Higher Derivatives

Differentiation is an 'operation' that takes one function as its input and produces another as its output. There is no reason, in principle, why we should not apply that operation to the output, in other words, differentiate the derived function. In effect, we would differentiate the function a second time. The result is called the **second derivative** of the function or a derivative of **order** 2.

This has various notations that are extensions of those used for 'first' derivatives. If $y = f(x)$ we may write the second derivative as, e.g.,

$$y'', \qquad \frac{d^2y}{dx^2}, \qquad \frac{d^2}{dx^2}[f(x)], \qquad f''(x), \qquad \frac{d^2f}{dx^2}.$$

Notation

The superscripts '2' may seem oddly placed. The explanation follows from

$$\frac{d^2y}{dx^2} = \frac{d}{dx}\left[\frac{dy}{dx}\right] = \frac{d}{dx}\left[\frac{d}{dx}[y]\right].$$

This can be thought of as the operation '$\frac{d}{dx}$' applied twice to y, becoming $\frac{d^2}{(dx)^2}$. The brackets on the bottom may then be omitted since dx is regarded as a single entity, not $d \times x$.

This idea can clearly be extended to **third (order) derivatives**, and so on. One type of notation adapts in an obvious manner: $\frac{d^3y}{dx^3}$, etc. The f'' type becomes cumbersome after the third derivative and there are two common devices used, typified by $f^{iv}(x)$ and $f^{(4)}(x)$. In the latter case, brackets are needed to distinguish from the use of superscripts for powers.

Example 5.20 Differentiate $y = x^4$ repeatedly.

$$y' = 4x^3, \quad y'' = 12x^2, \quad y''' = 24x, \quad y^{iv} = 24, \quad y^v = 0.$$

∎

More generally, for the function $y = x^n$ we have

$$\frac{d^2y}{dx^2} = \frac{d}{dx}\left[nx^{n-1}\right] = n(n-1)x^{n-2},$$

$$\frac{d^3y}{dx^3} = \frac{d}{dx}\left[n(n-1)x^{n-2}\right] = n(n-1)(n-2)x^{n-3},$$

and so on. Since we lose one degree each time we differentiate, we must eventually reach a constant:

$$\frac{d^n}{dx^n}\left[x^n\right] = n(n-1)(n-2)\cdots 3 \cdot 2 \cdot 1 = n!, \tag{5.20}$$

and all subsequent derivatives are zero.

Since all polynomials can be built up using terms involving x^n, we can deduce that the mth derivative of any polynomial of degree less than m is zero. In particular, the second derivative of a linear function is zero.

Think about it like this

These higher derivatives may have direct interpretations, e.g., in kinematics we have the following relationships between acceleration a, velocity v and displacement s:

$$v = \frac{ds}{dt}, \quad a = \frac{dv}{dt} \quad \Rightarrow \quad a = \frac{d^2s}{dt^2}.$$

There are also applications to graph-drawing, as we see later.

Example 5.21 Differentiate $\sin \omega t$ twice, w.r.t. t, and interpret the result. Use the **linear composite rule**, $at + b \equiv \omega t + 0$:

$$\frac{d}{dt}\left[\sin \omega t\right] = \omega \cos \omega t,$$

$$\frac{d^2}{dt^2}\left[\sin \omega t\right] = \omega \frac{d}{dt}\left[\cos \omega t\right] = -\omega^2 \sin \omega t.$$

This shows that $y = \sin \omega t$ describes a motion with acceleration proportional to the displacement y and acting opposite to it. This is typical of a 'spring' system. $y = \cos \omega t$ has the same property, as do simple combinations of the two. ∎

The first derivative measures the rate at which a function increases: its **gradient**. Hence the second derivative measures the rate at which the gradient is increasing. This interpretation provides much useful information about graphs.

We observed in §4.6 that a positive derivative means an increasing function. This implies that a **positive second** derivative means an **increasing derivative**, in other words, an increasing gradient. Examine the graphs in

§4.6. In the middle graph, the gradient of the tangent goes from −ve to 0 to +ve, i.e., it is increasing. This gives us a useful method for finding the nature of such a stationary point. We have a **minimum** at $x = a$ if $f'(a) = 0$ and $f''(a) > 0$.

Similarly, consideration of the left-hand graph shows that the gradient is decreasing and so we have a **maximum** at $x = a$ if $f'(a) = 0$ and $f''(a) < 0$.

Think about it like this

Note that the rules here are rather counter-intuitive: a maximum (big!) corresponds to $f''(a) < 0$ (small!) and a minimum (small!) corresponds to $f''(a) > 0$ (big!).

Although these tests are rightly popular, there are occasions when calculation of the second derivative is likely to involve considerably more work than using the test already described in §4.6. Functions requiring the Quotient Rule for their differentiation are prime examples. That original method may also be required in certain other situations, as we see later.

Example 5.22   Check the nature of the stationary points $x = -1$ and $x = 1$ for the function $f(x) = x^3 - 3x - 2$, analysed in Example 4.15.

$f'(x) = 3x^2 - 3$ and $f''(x) = 6x$.

$x = -1$: $f''(-1) = -6 < 0$, hence this gives a **maximum**.

$x = +1$: $f''(+1) = +6 > 0$, hence this gives a **minimum**.

This agrees with the results found before.   ■

Example 5.23   The stiffness of a rectangular beam varies directly as the cube of its height h and directly with its breadth b. Find the best way to cut a beam from a circular log, diameter 1 unit.

From the diagram, $h^2 + b^2 = 1$. We are told that the stiffness (S) satisfies

$$S \propto h^3, \quad S \propto b.$$

Hence

$S = kh^3 b$ (for some constant k)

$\quad = k\left[h^6 b^2\right]^{1/2}$

$\quad = k\left[h^6(1 - h^2)\right]^{1/2}.$

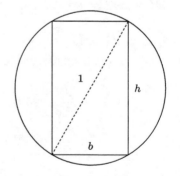

Now computing $\frac{dS}{dh}$ would necessitate the Chain Rule and would produce a complicated function to analyse, particularly if the second derivative is required.

Instead, note that maximising S is equivalent to maximising S^2 and the latter is very much easier to accomplish, since it contains no square root.

$$\frac{d}{dh}\left[S^2\right] = \frac{d}{dh}\left[k^2 h^6 - k^2 h^8\right] = 6k^2 h^5 - 8k^2 h^7$$
$$= 2k^2 h^5(3 - 4h^2)$$
$$= 0 \quad \text{if } h = 0, \ \pm\tfrac{\sqrt{3}}{2}.$$

The only physically relevant solution is $h = +\frac{\sqrt{3}}{2}$ and hence $b = \frac{1}{2}$.

The second derivative is

$$\frac{d^2}{dh^2}\left[S^2\right] = 30k^2h^4 - 56k^2h^6 = 2k^2h^4(15 - 28h^2).$$

Its sign is determined by the sign of $15 - 28h^2$ at $h^2 = \frac{3}{4}$, which has value

$$15 - 28 \times \tfrac{3}{4} = 15 - 21 = -6.$$

Since this is negative, the solution is a maximum.

For a different unit system, where the diameter is d units, say, we simply scale the above solution to find the optimal dimensions:

$$h = \frac{\sqrt{3}}{2}d, \qquad b = \frac{1}{2}d.$$

$\blacksquare$

In the right-hand graph in §4.6, the gradient decreases to zero then increases again, i.e., it is also at a minimum at $x = a$, so $f''(a) = 0$. This suggests that at a point of inflection we have $f''(a) = 0$.

However, a point for which $f''(a) = 0$ is not necessarily a point of inflection. For example, $f(x) = x^4$ has a minimum at $x = 0$, yet $f'(0) = f''(0) = 0$. The best advice is that cases where $f''(a) = 0$ should be investigated graphically.

The sign of $f''(x)$ gives information about the graph even in the absence of a stationary point. We say that a curve is **concave up** when $f''(x) > 0$, and **concave down** when $f''(x) < 0$. The graphs in §4.6 show the difference in behaviour: the left-hand graph is concave down and the middle one is concave up.

The size of the second derivative gives *some* information about how curved the graph is, but a precise measure of its **curvature**, κ [*kappa*], is more complicated. The formula is given here for reference:

$$\kappa = \frac{f''(x)}{\left[1 + (f'(x))^2\right]^{3/2}}. \tag{5.21}$$

The extra factor (on the denominator) is required to ensure the result does not depend on the orientation of the coordinate axes. The curve is, at the point where κ is being evaluated, behaving like a circle with radius ρ [*rho*]:

$$\rho = \frac{1}{\kappa}. \tag{5.22}$$

This is the **radius of curvature**.

Ex 5.14 Obtain an expression for the nth derivative of $g(x) = (3x + 2)^k$, where $k > n$.

Ex 5.15 Find the third derivative of $e^x \sin x$.

Ex 5.16 The displacement of an object undergoing simple harmonic motion is given by $x(t) = 2\sin\left(\pi t - \frac{\pi}{4}\right)$. Find the velocity and the acceleration. When does the particle pass through $x = 0$? When is it stationary?

Ex 5.17 Consider the problem of pulling a heavy weight of mass M along a horizontal surface against a frictional force with (constant) coefficient of friction μ. Suppose the pulling rope is at an angle θ to the surface, as shown below.

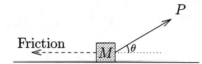

The force required to keep the mass just moving is given by

$$P = \frac{\mu M g}{\mu \sin\theta + \cos\theta}.$$

Find an equation giving the angle θ that minimises this force.

Ex 5.18 Consider the function $f(x) = (x+1)e^{-ax}$. Find its stationary point and discuss its nature for each of $a < 0$ and $a > 0$. What happens when $a = 0$?

5.9   Revision Exercises

Ex 5.19

(a) Use the product rule to differentiate $(x-1)(x^2 + x + 1)$.

    Remove all brackets in the answer and tidy up the terms. The answer should be very simple. Can you explain why?

(b) Differentiate, without any final tidying: $(x^2 + x - 2)(3x^2 - 5x + 1)$.

Ex 5.20 Differentiate $\dfrac{x}{x^3 + x + 6}$.

Ex 5.21 In each of the following cases, find the formulae for $f \circ g(x)$ and $g \circ f(x)$.

    (a) $f(x) = x^2 + 1$, $g(x) = \dfrac{1}{x}$;   (b) $f(x) = \ln x$, $g(x) = \sqrt{x}$.

Ex 5.22 Differentiate $\sqrt{1 + x^2}$ with respect to x.

Ex 5.23 Find the equation of the tangent to the graph of $y = \sqrt{3 + x^4}$ at the point $(1, 2)$.

Ex 5.24 Differentiate the following:
    (a) $(x + 1)^4$,   (b) $(2x - 1)^3$,   (c) $(5x + 3)^9$,   (d) $(2 - 3x)^2$.
    Compare the answer to (a) with that for Exercise 4.6(c).

Ex 5.25 Differentiate the following:
    (a) $(5x + 1)^3(3 - 2x)^4$,   (b) $\dfrac{1}{(3x - 2)^4}$,   (c) $(1 - 2x)^{-3}$.

Ex 5.26 Differentiate the following functions of x:

(a) $\sin 3x$ (b) $\cos \frac{\pi x}{2}$ (c) $\sin(2x+3)$ (d) $\tan 3x$
(e) $\sec 2x$ (f) $x \sin x$ (g) $\sin 2x \cos 3x$ (h) $x^{3/2} \sin x$
(i) $\dfrac{\cos x}{x}$ (j) $\cot x = \dfrac{\cos x}{\sin x}$ (k) $\sin^4 x$ (l) $\ln(\sec x + \tan x)$

Ex 5.27 Differentiate $\dfrac{1 - \cos t}{\sin t}$ with respect to t.

Ex 5.28 Find the equation of the tangent to the graph of $y = \sin(2x)$ at the point with $x = \frac{\pi}{6}$.

Ex 5.29 The following unusual result underlines one of the properties of logarithms. Using the linear composite rule, with $f(x) = \ln x$ and $ax + b \equiv 2x$, gives the following:

$$\frac{d}{dx}[\ln 2x] = \frac{1}{2x} \times 2 = \frac{1}{x}.$$

But this is the result of differentiating $\ln x$. Where has the '2' gone?

Ex 5.30 Differentiate $x^2 \ln\left(x^5\right)$ with respect to x.
 [Hint: simplify the logarithm first.]

Ex 5.31

(a) Differentiate $f(x) = x^3 - 2x^2 + x + 3$ repeatedly until you obtain zero.

(b) Find the first three derivatives for $g(x) = (2x - 1)^5$.

 Extrapolate from these answers to suggest a *general* formula for the mth derivative of $(ax + b)^n$, where $m \leqslant n$.

Ex 5.32 Find the second derivative of $f(x) = \sin x \cos x$.

6   INTRODUCTION TO INTEGRATION

There are two ways in which to approach the other major theme of calculus, **integration**, neither of which is adequate on its own. One method is essential for *expressing* the solution to problems as **integrals**, while the other is the only feasible way of *evaluating* these integrals, assuming a precise value can be found. That the two approaches find the same quantity is guaranteed by the **Fundamental Theorem of Calculus**.

Rather than concentrate on the first approach, which is difficult to manipulate in symbols, or the second, which appears merely mechanical when there is no clear interpretation available, we shall start with an example using both approaches. (This will provide good evidence for the truth of the Fundamental Theorem.) Then we shall concentrate on the more mechanical approach, using a geometrical interpretation as an anchor.

6.1   Introduction

The context for this first example is the same as that used when differentiation was introduced in Chapter 4, namely the velocity $v(t)$ and displacement $s(t)$ of a body moving in a straight line. The simple formula **velocity = distance/time** breaks down when the velocity is not constant. It was to overcome this that we introduced the technique of differentiation. We now examine how to adapt its rearrangement **distance = velocity×time**, which also requires constant velocity.

Example 6.1   Estimate the distance travelled between $t = 0$ and $t = 8$ by a body with velocity profile $v(t) = t(8 - t)$.

First note that v is not constant and neither is the acceleration $\frac{dv}{dt} = 8 - 2t$. Hence none of the simple rules of motion will deliver an exact answer.

Suppose we sample the velocity at times separated by 4 units, i.e., at $t = 4$, $v = 16$; at $t = 8$, $v = 0$. An **estimate** of the distance travelled can be calculated using the simple rule – velocity × time – in each subinterval between the sample times. For simplicity we use, in the formula, the value of the velocity at the right-hand end of each subinterval:

$$D \simeq 16 \times 4 + 0 \times 4 = 64.$$

We would expect a better estimate if we sampled every 2 units of time – see the graph below – with velocities (at $t = 2, 4, 6, 8$) of 12, 16, 12, 0, respectively:

$$D \simeq 12 \times 2 + 16 \times 2 + 12 \times 2 + 0 \times 2 = 80.$$

Reducing to an interval of 1 unit of time gives a value of 84. It seems clear that these estimates are getting progressively better and that the differences between successive estimates is shrinking. This recalls the **limiting** idea we encountered in differentiation. In this context, we hope that shrinking the time interval between observations, Δt say, will reduce the amount by which the range of velocities in each subinterval differs from the one chosen value, and hence the result will be more accurate.

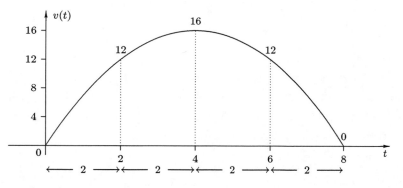

Tentatively, we conjecture that

$$D = \lim_{\Delta t \to 0} \left[v(t_1)\,\Delta t + v(t_2)\,\Delta t + v(t_3)\,\Delta t + \cdots + v(t_{n-1})\,\Delta t + v(t_n)\,\Delta t \right],$$

(6.1)

where $t_k = k\,\Delta t$, $k = 1, 2, \ldots, n$. (There are n steps of Δt between 0 and 8, i.e., $n\Delta t = 8$. We start at $t = 0$ and make the first evaluation at the *right-hand end*, so $t_1 = 0 + 1 \times \Delta t$, etc.)

This equation is the definition of an integral using the first approach. It can be relaxed somewhat, but we defer that – and the matter of notation – until later. The problem at the moment is that we have no obvious method for evaluating this limit and the trend in the values 60, 80, 84 is not clear enough for us to guess the value. Instead, consider an alternative approach.

Suppose we know $s(t)$ and wish to find $v(t)$. We know how to perform that calculation: $v(t) = \frac{ds}{dt}$. This suggests that if we can spot a function $s(t)$ whose derivative is the **given** $v(t)$, it would represent the distance travelled at time t, from which we could easily solve our problem. Here, we can check that

$$\frac{d}{dt}\left[4t^2 - \tfrac{1}{3}t^3 \right] = 8t - t^2 = t(8 - t) = v(t).$$

Hence we propose that $s(t) = 4t^2 - \tfrac{1}{3}t^3$ gives the distance travelled. From that we can solve the original problem by calculating $s(8) - s(0) = 85\tfrac{1}{3}$.

Although this formula for $s(t)$ has been produced without any indication of a method, we shall see that there are indeed simple rules for finding it in many cases. That the two approaches to the problem must give the same answer should be clear from the context and is supported by the numerical evidence. Formal justification requires the Fundamental Theorem of Calculus. ∎

It is now time to introduce notation and some names for the items in this example. First, however, we shall change to standard notation: we use $f(x)$ in place of $v(t)$ and we seek to calculate from $x = a$ to $x = b$. The counterpart to (6.1) is

$$\lim_{\Delta x \to 0} \left[f(x_1)\,\Delta x + f(x_2)\,\Delta x + \cdots + f(x_n)\,\Delta x \right],$$

where $x_k = a + k\Delta x$. (We start at $x = a$ rather than $t = 0$.) Rewrite this, moving to 'sigma' form:

$$\lim_{\Delta x \to 0} [f(x_1)\,\Delta x + f(x_2)\,\Delta x + \cdots + f(x_n)\,\Delta x] = \lim_{\Delta x \to 0} \sum_{k=1}^{n} f(x_k)\,\Delta x. \quad (6.2)$$

We assume there are n steps from a to b so that $n\Delta x = (b - a)$. Again we evaluate $f(x)$ at the right-hand end of each subinterval. This limit is known as the **(definite) integral** of $f(x)$ from a to b. It has a special notation that evolved from the sigma one:

$$\int_a^b f(x)\,dx.$$

In this notation, a and b correspond to the lower and upper limits on the sum (and are known as the **limits** for the integral) while 'dx' replaces Δx in the sum. The function $f(x)$ is the **integrand**.

Notation

The notation of the integral is unusual, but is directly related to the limit itself. The new symbol $\int$ evolved from the original use of S for 'sum'. The Δ has changed into d, exactly as it did in differentiation, after taking the limit. The dx part plays the same critical role here, telling the reader what the independent variable is.

Think about it like this

The analysis we undertook to establish (6.2) offers no mechanism for evaluating the limit. Its purpose is to show an argument used to define many useful concepts, such as area, centre of gravity, moment of inertia, indeed any quantity that can be built up by adding small contributions from a quantity that keeps changing. We shall see in a later chapter how to extract the essence of this construction, without the cumbersome detail. First, we consider how to evaluate the result.

In the second approach, we sought a function $s(t)$ whose derivative was $v(t)$. In this new context we seek a function $F(x)$ whose derivative is $f(x)$, often known as an **anti-derivative** of $f(x)$, since it 'undoes' the differentiation process.

Frame 6.1   *Definition of an anti-derivative $F(x)$ for $f(x)$*

$$\frac{d}{dx}[F(x)] = f(x) \qquad (6.3)$$

To sum up what we have constructed so far: we define a quantity by a definite integral given by the limit of a sum as in (6.2); we calculate it by first finding an anti-derivative as in (6.3), then evaluating as follows.

> **Frame 6.2**   *Use of an anti-derivative to evaluate an integral*
>
> $$\int_a^b f(x)\,dx = \Big[\, F(x) \,\Big]_a^b = F(b) - F(a) \qquad (6.4)$$

The part in the middle of (6.4) is a standard notation used as an intermediate step in the calculation. Its use will be illustrated soon.

It is not a practical long-term solution to write the anti-derivative as $F(x)$, since capital letters are sometimes used for ordinary functions. We require a special notation. Recognising that the Fundamental Theorem of Calculus links $F(x)$ to integration, it is normally written as

$$\int f(x)\,dx, \qquad (6.5)$$

without any limits, and is known as the **indefinite integral**.

Example 6.2   Returning to Example 6.1, we can set out the calculation more formally.

We must evaluate the **definite integral**

$$\int_0^8 t(8 - t)\,dt.$$

This we do by finding the **indefinite integral** (an anti-derivative)

$$\int t(8 - t)\,dt = 4t^2 - \tfrac{1}{3}t^3.$$

We then perform the evaluation

$$\Big[4t^2 - \tfrac{1}{3}t^3\Big]_0^8 = 4 \times 8^2 - \tfrac{1}{3} \times 8^3 - \left(4 \times 0^2 - \tfrac{1}{3} \times 0^3\right) = 85\tfrac{1}{3}.$$

∎

There are two matters we must attend to before putting this technique into practice. One is easily dealt with. It is not always the case that the limit in (6.2) exists, but for the simple functions we are to encounter this will not be an issue. When the limit does exists, we need not be so prescriptive about the size of Δx and the placement of the x_k. We may vary the size of Δx between subintervals provided the size of the largest subinterval tends to zero. Also, we can choose x_k to be **any** point in the appropriate subinterval, not necessarily the right-hand end-point.

The other matter is more serious. The anti-derivative is not uniquely defined. There are an infinite number of possible $F(x)$, although we can show they are identical except for an added constant, the so-called **constant**

of integration or **arbitrary constant**. This constant is usually written as
C. Suppose that $F(x)$ is an anti-derivative of $f(x)$. Then

$$\frac{d}{dx}[F(x)] = f(x), \qquad \frac{d}{dx}[F(x) + C] = f(x) + 0 = f(x),$$

so $F(x) + C$ is also an anti-derivative. For this reason we always include
'$+C$' in the indefinite integral, unless we are proceeding directly to a definite
integral. For example:

$$\int x(8 - x)\,dx = 4x^2 - \tfrac{1}{3}x^3 + C.$$

Think about it like this

Although C appears to be unnecessary for evaluating definite integrals, it is
good practice to include it when writing down indefinite ones. It may appear
to be a nuisance but is often vital.

It is essential for any calculation involving anti-differentiation where a definite
integral is not known to be the ultimate aim. There are applications
where C is essential for matching mathematical models to the starting point
for the processes they model.

That is not the only way in which an arbitrary constant matches physical
experience. It is well-known that potential energy cannot be uniquely defined. We may choose any position we wish as the 'base level'. Calculations
succeed because we require only the *difference* in energy values, so this arbitrariness cancels out. This is reminiscent of the indefinite/definite integral
phenomenon and that is no surprise. Potential energy is properly defined as
an integral: formulae such as $E = mgh$ are values of such an integral where
simplifying assumptions, such as the constancy of g, are made.

Returning to the context of motion, knowing the velocity of a body does not
tell us where it is; it may be anywhere in the universe. Hence we cannot fix
the function $s(t)$ unless we are given one more piece of information, such as
where the action originates. That would allow us to tie down $s(t)$.

We have already stated that we can dispense with C in a definite integral,
because C will cancel when we subtract the values at the limits. This relates
to the fact that the distance travelled is the difference of two s values and
that is independent of where the action is taking place.

Ex 6.1 A car is observed over 1 minute. It travels behind a bus for $10\,\text{s}$ at velocity
$15\,\text{ms}^{-1}$, overtakes to travel at velocity $20\,\text{ms}^{-1}$ for $20\,\text{s}$, is stopped at traffic lights
for $15\,\text{s}$, and then follows a lorry at velocity $10\,\text{ms}^{-1}$. Assuming velocities change
instantaneously, draw a graph of velocity against time.

For a constant velocity u over a time period t, the distance travelled is ut. Use
this to complete the table below, to find the *total* distance travelled from the start
of the 1 minute period.

Time elapsed	0	10	30	45	60
New distance (ut)	0	150			
Total distance	0			550	

Plot this data on a distance-time graph, and hence find the complete graph by
filling in between the isolated points. Explain why it is legitimate to do so using
straight line segments.

6.2 A Standard Form and Two Simple Rules

Our plan is to examine our differentiation results to identify those where the answer $F'(x) = f(x)$ has a particularly useful form. This immediately generates an integration result.

Frame 6.3   *Reversing differentiation results*

$$\frac{d}{dx}[F(x)] = f(x) \quad \Rightarrow \quad F(x) + C = \int f(x)\,dx$$

Think about it like this

This process can be thought of as 'dividing' by $\frac{d}{dx}$ on the left and 'multiplying' by $\int \ldots dx$ on the right. The link can be read in the other direction, using an integration result to give a differentiation one, but this is very rarely used.

The key observation is: **every differentiation result provides an integration one, free of charge.**

To see how this works, consider the first standard form for differentiation that we found:

$$\frac{d}{dx}[x^n] = nx^{n-1}.$$

Reversing this gives

$$\int nx^{n-1}\,dx = x^n + C.$$

This is clumsy in two ways. One is the extra n on the left. It is tempting to divide both sides by it and we shall see soon that this is valid, **but only because n is a constant**:

$$\int x^{n-1}\,dx = \frac{1}{n}x^n + C \qquad (n \neq 0).$$

The case $n = 0$ is excluded since we cannot divide by zero. Now, having $n-1$ on the left is not very neat, but this is easily fixed by replacing **every** n by $n+1$ to obtain our first standard form for integration.

Frame 6.4   *Integrating powers*

$$\int x^n\,dx = \frac{1}{n+1}x^{n+1} + C \qquad (n \neq -1) \tag{6.6}$$

As in the differentiation case, this is best approached as a sequence of operations. First, recall the differentiation ones:

multiply by the index (n), subtract one from the index $(n \to n-1)$.

The integration operations are:

add one to the index $(n \to n+1)$, divide by the new index $(n+1)$.

Think about it like this

> These are the opposite operations to the differentiation ones. That should not be a surprise since integration is the reverse of differentiation. But also, the **order** of the operations reverses. This is no surprise, since undoing operations should be carried out in reverse order. This is generally true, not only in mathematics, but in everyday life: we put on our socks, then our shoes; we take off our shoes, then our socks.

Example 6.3   Integrate: (a) x^7,   (b) $\dfrac{1}{x^5}$,   (c) $\sqrt[3]{x}$,   (d) $\dfrac{1}{\sqrt{x}}$.

(a) $\displaystyle \int x^7\, dx = \frac{x^{7+1}}{7+1} + C = \frac{1}{8}x^8 + C.$

(b) Write this as x^{-5} and then

$$\int x^{-5}\, dx = \frac{x^{-5+1}}{-5+1} + C = -\frac{1}{4}x^{-4} + C = -\frac{1}{4x^4} + C.$$

(c) $\displaystyle \int \sqrt[3]{x}\, dx = \int x^{1/3}\, dx = \frac{x^{1/3+1}}{1/3+1} + C = \frac{3}{4}x^{4/3} + C.$

(d) Write this as $x^{-1/2}$ and then

$$\int x^{-1/2}\, dx = \frac{x^{-1/2+1}}{-1/2+1} + C = 2x^{1/2} + C = 2\sqrt{x} + C.$$

∎

Before searching for more standard forms, it is appropriate to introduce the following two rules, which enable us to deal with slightly more complicated functions. These are easy to prove, but the details are quite technical and the results are fairly obvious from the geometrical interpretation with which we shall end this chapter.

Frame 6.5   *Sum rule*

$$\int [f(x) \pm g(x)]\, dx = \int f(x)\, dx \pm \int g(x)\, dx$$

Frame 6.6   *Constant multiplication rule*

$$\int k f(x)\, dx = k \int f(x)\, dx \qquad\qquad [k \text{ constant}]$$

Think about it like this

One process is simple addition: the integral of the sum of two functions is the sum of their integrals, in abbreviated symbolic form $\int (f+g) = \int f + \int g$. It is the reverse of the differentiation rule in Frame 4.3.

The other is multiplication by a constant: the integral of a scaled function is its integral similarly scaled, $\int kf = k \int f$. Again this relates to a differentiation rule, that in Frame 4.4. Pay particular attention to this one since 'taking a constant outside' an integral or derivative is a very common process; it removes a possible distraction and allows us to concentrate on the core calculation. This refers only to **constants** multiplying a function, which can be treated merely as scale factors and hence do not interact with the limiting processes.

Example 6.4 Integrate: (a) $10x^{99}$, (b) $9x^2 - 2 + \dfrac{3}{x^2}$, (c) $\tfrac{1}{2}x^{-3/4}$.

(a) $\displaystyle \int 10x^{99}\, dx = 10 \int x^{99}\, dx = \frac{10}{100}x^{100} + C = 0.1x^{100} + C.$

(b) $\displaystyle \int \left(9x^2 - 2 + \frac{3}{x^2} \right) dx = 9\int x^2\, dx - 2\int 1\, dx + 3\int x^{-2}\, dx$

$\displaystyle = 9 \cdot \frac{1}{3}x^3 - 2x + 3 \cdot \frac{1}{-1}x^{-1} + C = 3x^3 - 2x - \frac{3}{x} + C.$

(c) $\displaystyle \int \tfrac{1}{2}x^{-3/4}\, dx = \tfrac{1}{2}\frac{x^{1/4}}{1/4} + C = 2x^{1/4} + C.$

■

Think about it like this

Note the following points about the second of these calculations.

1. We require only one arbitrary constant even though each separate integration can generate one. The use of $C_1 + C_2$ cannot generate any value that C cannot take on its own.

2. With practice, one would see that it is quicker to split $9x^2$ as follows: $\int 9x^2\, dx = 3\int 3x^2\, dx = 3x^3 + C$, thereby avoiding intermediate fractions.

3. Most people would write directly $\int 2\, dx = 2x + C$, rather than taking the 2 outside the integration: in general $\int a\, dx = ax + C$.

Example 6.5 Find that value of a for which $\displaystyle \int_1^2 (x^3 - ax)\, dx = 0.$

We call the target integral I, which is a common notational device:

$$I = \left[\tfrac{1}{4}x^4 - \tfrac{1}{2}ax^2 \right]_1^2 = 4 - 2a - \tfrac{1}{4} + \tfrac{1}{2}a = \tfrac{15}{4} - \tfrac{3}{2}a = 0$$

if $a = \tfrac{2}{3} \cdot \tfrac{15}{4} = \tfrac{5}{2}.$ ■

244 Mathematical Methods 1

Ex 6.2 Find the following integrals:

$$\int x^3\,dx, \qquad \int_{-1}^{2}(5x+2)\,dx, \qquad \int 3\sqrt{t}\,dt, \qquad \int_{1}^{2}\frac{1}{z^2}\,dz.$$

Ex 6.3 Evaluate the following:

$$\int_{-1}^{1}x^3\,dx, \qquad \int_{-1}^{1}x^4\,dx, \qquad \int_{0}^{1}\sqrt[3]{x}\,dx, \qquad \int_{1}^{4}\frac{1}{x^{3/2}}\,dx.$$

Ex 6.4 Find the value(s) of a for which $\displaystyle\int_{0}^{a}x(1-x)\,dx = 0.$

6.3 Further Standard Forms

We now embark on a search through Chapter 5 for other useful differentiation results.

The easiest of all to reverse is the differentiation result for the exponential function:

$$\frac{d}{dx}[e^x] = e^x \quad \Rightarrow \quad \int e^x\,dx = e^x + C.$$

Although this is useful, recall that most exponentials contain a **rate constant**. Hence we are more likely to use:

$$\frac{d}{dx}[e^{kx}] = ke^{kx} \quad \Rightarrow \quad \int ke^{kx}\,dx = e^{kx} + C,$$

from which we derive the following standard form.

Frame 6.7   Integrating the exponential function

$$\int e^{kx}\,dx = \frac{1}{k}e^{kx} + C \tag{6.7}$$

Example 6.6   Integrate   (a) $e^{0.025x}$,   (b) e^{-x}.

(a) $\displaystyle\int e^{0.025x}\,dx = \frac{1}{0.025}e^{0.025x} + C = 40e^{0.025x} + C$

(b) $\displaystyle\int e^{-x}\,dx = \frac{1}{-1}e^{-x} + C = -e^{-x} + C$

∎

The next useful standard forms are from trigonometry. We start from

$$\frac{d}{dx}[\sin x] = \cos x \quad \Rightarrow \quad \int \cos x = \sin x + C,$$

$$\frac{d}{dx}[\cos x] = -\sin x \quad \Rightarrow \quad \int -\sin x = \cos x + C,$$

but recognise that we are much more likely to encounter these with a variety of different **angular frequencies**. A similar argument to that used for the exponential function provides standard forms.

Frame 6.8   *Integrating circular functions*

$$\int \sin \omega x\, dx = -\frac{1}{\omega} \cos \omega x + C \qquad (6.8)$$

$$\int \cos \omega x\, dx = \frac{1}{\omega} \sin \omega x + C \qquad (6.9)$$

Example 6.7   Integrate   (a) $\cos 2x$,   (b) $\sin \frac{\pi x}{2}$,   (c) $\cos x°$.

(a) $\omega = 2$, so (6.9) gives the answer $\frac{1}{2}\sin 2x + C$.

(b) $\omega = \frac{\pi}{2}$, so (6.8) gives the answer $-\frac{2}{\pi}\cos \frac{\pi x}{2} + C$.

(c) Convert to radians: $\cos x° = \cos\left(\frac{\pi}{180}x\right)$, giving $\omega = \frac{\pi}{180}$. The integration is completed as

$$\int \cos x°\, dx = \int \cos\left(\tfrac{\pi}{180}x\right)\, dx = \tfrac{180}{\pi}\sin\left(\tfrac{\pi}{180}x\right) + C = \tfrac{180}{\pi}\sin x° + C,$$

again illustrating the need to use radians to obtain a neat answer.

∎

The other differentiation results for trigonometric functions also reverse, but only one is really significant:

$$\frac{d}{dx}[\tan x] = \sec^2 x + C \quad \Rightarrow \quad \int \sec^2 x\, dx = \int \frac{1}{\cos^2 x}\, dx = \tan x + C.$$

The final standard form that we examine here is the one that plugs the hole in the standard form for x^n derived in the previous section. There, we were unable to find a function of the form x^n whose derivative involved x^{-1}. But in Chapter 5 we did find that:

$$\frac{d}{dx}[\ln x] = \frac{1}{x}.$$

We reverse this to find an extremely important integral, and yet another illustration of the key nature of the logarithm:

$$\int \frac{1}{x}\,dx = \ln x + C. \qquad (6.10)$$

Example 6.8   The work done by a gas changing its volume from v_0 to v_1 is

$$W = \int_{v_0}^{v_1} p\,dv.$$

Find an explicit formula for an isothermal change (T remains constant), assuming the gas obeys the ideal gas law, $pv = RT$, where R is a constant.

We have $p = \frac{RT}{v}$ and hence

$$
\begin{aligned}
W &= \int_{v_0}^{v_1} \frac{RT}{v}\,dv \\
&= RT \int_{v_0}^{v_1} \frac{1}{v}\,dv \quad (R,\,T \text{ are constant}) \\
&= RT \Big[\ln v\Big]_{v_0}^{v_1} = RT\,(\ln v_1 - \ln v_0) \\
&= RT \ln \frac{v_1}{v_0}.
\end{aligned}
$$

The assumption that T is constant is critical, else it cannot be taken outside the integral and we would need to know how it relates to v (as a function) in order to proceed further.   ■

Textbooks often contain a slightly different version of the standard form, and this is the one we shall adopt.

Frame 6.9   *Integration of $1/x$*

$$\int \frac{1}{x}\,dx = \ln |x| + C \qquad (6.11)$$

The reason for this is that $\int (1/x)\,dx$ makes sense when $x < 0$, whereas $\ln x$ requires $x > 0$.

Assume $x < 0$; then $\ln |x| = \ln(-x)$ and hence, using Frame 5.5,

$$\frac{d}{dx}\,[\ln(-x)] = \frac{1}{-x} \times (-1) = \frac{1}{x}.$$

The reversed result (6.11) holds for negative, as well as positive, x.

Notation

Note the following special notation. When integrating $\dfrac{1}{f(x)}$, the 1 on the top line is often replaced by dx, to neaten the formula. Thus, assuming $1 \times dx = dx$, we write $\int \dfrac{dx}{f(x)}$.

The use of the standard form in Frame 6.9 requires considerable care, as shown by the following example.

Example 6.9 Evaluate (a) $\int_{-6}^{-3} \frac{dx}{x}$, (b) $\int_{-2}^{4} \frac{dx}{x}$.

(a) This integral can be evaluated using Frame 6.9:

$$\int_{-6}^{-3} \frac{dx}{x} = \left[\ln|x|\right]_{-6}^{-3} = \ln|-3| - \ln|-6| = \ln\frac{3}{6} = \ln\frac{1}{2} = -\ln 2.$$

Alternatively, it can be rewritten as $-\int_{-6}^{-3} \frac{dx}{-x}$, which avoids a negative argument for ln, since $-x$ is positive between the (negative) limits.

(b) Using the same approach as in (a):

$$\int_{-2}^{4} \frac{dx}{x} = \left[\ln|x|\right]_{-2}^{4} = \ln|4| - \ln|-2| = \ln\frac{4}{2} = \ln 2.$$

Unfortunately, this answer is entirely **wrong**. The integrand is infinite at $x = 0$, between the limits, and the integral is not defined.

∎

This demonstrates the danger of using Frame 6.9 without careful inspection of the limits. $\int_{a}^{b} \frac{1}{x}\, dx$ is defined only if a and b have the same sign.

Ex 6.5 Find the following integrals:

$$\int e^{3x}\, dx, \qquad \int_{0}^{\pi/4} \sin 2\theta \, d\theta, \qquad \int_{1}^{2} \left(\frac{1}{x} + \frac{1}{x^3}\right) dx, \qquad \int 2\cos\frac{t}{2}\, dt.$$

Ex 6.6

(a) An electric current is defined as the rate of flow of electric charge, so that $i = \frac{dq}{dt}$, where q measures charge. The unit of charge is the *coulomb* defined as the charge that flows in 1s for a current of 1 *ampere* (A). For a varying current, the charge flowing between times t_1 and t_2 is $Q = \int_{t_1}^{t_2} i(t)\, dt$. Suppose a current from the AC mains has a maximum size 5A. Then we have $i(t) = 5\sin 100\pi t$, since the frequency of mains current is 50Hz. Compute the charge that flows between $t = 0$ and $t = 0.01$s. Also show that the charge flowing over a period of 0.02s is zero. Why is this the case?

(b) In a chemical process, the *standard heat of reaction* Δh is often assumed to depend linearly on $T : \Delta h(T) = a + bT$, with known values for a and b.

Derive a formula for the *standard free energy change of reaction* Δg, given that $\frac{\Delta g}{T} = A + \int_{T_0}^{T} -\frac{\Delta h}{T^2}\, dT$, where A is a known constant.

Ex 6.7 Evaluate:

(a) $\int_{1}^{2} \left(\frac{2}{t} - \frac{t^2}{3}\right) dt$, (b) $\int_{1}^{4} (x^2 - 2x + 1)\, dx$, (c) $\int_{1}^{2} \frac{du}{4u^2}$, (d) $\int_{0}^{\frac{\pi}{2}} \sin\frac{x}{2}\, dx$.

6.4   A Geometrical Interpretation

We return to the calculation of distance using a large number of samples of velocity, taken during short time intervals. For the function $f(x)$, this calculation involves breaking the interval $[\,a,b\,]$ into n subintervals. We assume – although it is not essential to do so – that each has the same width Δx. Then $n\Delta x = b - a$. Also, we 'sample' $f(x)$ in each subinterval by choosing the right-hand end in each: $x_k = a + k\Delta x$ for $k = 1, 2, \ldots, n$. This structure is shown in the diagrams below, with the kth subinterval enlarged, but telescoped vertically, in the diagram on the right.

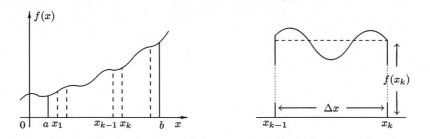

The 'summation' definition of the integral, used in the velocity-distance model in §6.1, is

$$\int_a^b f(x)\,dx = \lim_{\Delta x \to 0}\left[f(x_1)\,\Delta x + f(x_2)\,\Delta x + \cdots + f(x_n)\,\Delta x\right]$$

$$= \lim_{\Delta x \to 0} \sum_{k=1}^{n} f(x_k)\,\Delta x. \qquad (6.12)$$

Now the kth term in this expression is the area of the rectangle with the dashed line at the top, and hence **approximately** the area under the curve itself. Adding these up gives an approximation to the total area under the curve (between a and b). Our contention is that, on taking the limit, **the integral in (6.12) measures the exact area.**

Think about it like this

> The behaviour of this limit is less clear than the limit for differentiation, since there is an error in **every** subinterval and, as we shrink Δx, we have more and more subintervals and so more and more errors. But we can show that these errors shrink faster than the size of the rectangles themselves and the conjecture is justified.

Area is sometimes claimed to be a 'definition' of an integral and used to solve integration problems, such as the calculation of the work done by a force or the impulse generated by it, without formal calculus. But it must be borne in mind that justification of this link requires calculus techniques and area evaluation, in all but the simplest cases, requires calculus.

Interpretation of the integral as area leads immediately to useful rules, such as

$$\int_a^b f(x)\,dx + \int_b^c f(x)\,dx = \int_a^c f(x)\,dx. \qquad (6.13)$$

This merely states that the area from a to b plus that from b to c is the same as that from a to c, an obvious fact.

This raises the question of what happens if b is not between a and c. This in turn raises the question of how we interpret an integral with limits in the 'wrong' order, i.e., where we encounter $\int_a^b$ with $a > b$.

Suppose we swap the limits a and b in (6.4). Noting that $F(b) - F(a) = -\big(F(a) - F(b)\big)$, we find the following result, which is often used to force limits to adopt the natural order.

Frame 6.10   *Reversing the limits in an integral*

$$\int_a^b f(x)\, dx = -\int_b^a f(x)\, dx \qquad\qquad (6.14)$$

This result ensures that there are no restrictions needed for the limits in (6.13) and other such formulae.

Before exploiting the link with area further, there is a problem we must address: **area has no sign**. It is always regarded as positive. Integrals, on the other hand, can be negative since they add up values of a function, which can be negative. This is similar to the way 'speed' involves no direction, while 'velocity' does.

We implicitly assumed above that $f(x) \geqslant 0$ for all x in $[\,a, b\,]$, so this part of its graph lies on or above the x-axis. We now remove that restriction. The diagrams below show what can happen.

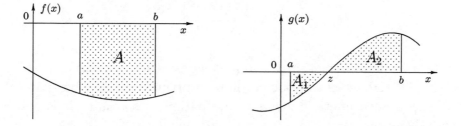

To use an area measure to evaluate an integral, we must attach a minus sign to any part of that area that lies below the x-axis. For the situations in the figures above,

$$\int_a^b f(x)\, dx = -A, \qquad \int_a^b g(x)\, dx = A_2 - A_1.$$

To use an integral to measure an area, we must evaluate the integral separately for negative and positive parts of the function, then add the results using the absolute value for each part. For the situations in the figures above, this gives

$$A = -\int_a^b f(x)\, dx, \qquad A_1 + A_2 = -\int_a^z g(x)\, dx + \int_z^b g(x)\, dx.$$

Now examine the graphs below, which establish two very useful results; these can simplify or even avoid the calculation of the value of an integral, when the limits span a **symmetric** interval, i.e., $[-a, a]$ for some $a > 0$.

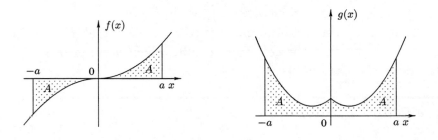

The integral of an **odd** function over a symmetric interval is simple:

$$\int_{-a}^{a} f(x)\, dx = A - A = 0, \tag{6.15}$$

and for an **even** function:

$$\int_{-a}^{a} g(x)\, dx = A + A = 2A = 2\int_{0}^{a} g(x)\, dx. \tag{6.16}$$

Example 6.10   Evaluate   (a) $\displaystyle\int_{-2}^{2} \left(x^2 - x^4\right) dx$,   (b) $\displaystyle\int_{-\pi}^{\pi} \sin 3x\, dx$.

(a) A direct calculation gives

$$I = \left[\frac{x^3}{3} - \frac{x^5}{5}\right]_{-2}^{2},$$

which leads to a plethora of minus signs: they appear in $(-2)^3$ and $-(-2)^5$, and the entire bottom limit contribution must be subtracted. There are arithmetic dangers in evaluation as a result. It is easier to use the evenness of the integrand and calculate

$$I = 2\int_{0}^{2} \left(x^2 - x^4\right) dx = 2\left[\frac{x^3}{3} - \frac{x^5}{5}\right]_{0}^{2} = 2\left(\frac{8}{3} - \frac{32}{5}\right) = -\frac{112}{15}.$$

(b) A direct calculation gives

$$I = \left[-\frac{1}{3}\cos 3x\right]_{-\pi}^{\pi} = -\frac{1}{3}[\cos 3\pi - \cos(-3\pi)] = -\frac{1}{3}[-1 - (-1)] = 0,$$

a result that could have been written down without calculation, using the oddness of the sin function.

∎

We have yet to investigate the connection between an **anti-derivative** and a **definite integral** for a general function. The following discussion, which is included for background reading, covers the key points. Briefly, we will provide an alternative definition of the indefinite integral, $F(x)$ say, using the idea of a definite integral. What the **Fundamental Theorem of Calculus** does is to show that $F'(x) = f(x)$, so that this alternative definition is an anti-derivative. That ties together the two approaches to integration: construction and evaluation.

There is a notational point to consider first. The quantity $\int_a^b f(x)\,dx$ is a **number**, containing no 'x' in its value. Hence we would obtain the same number with any symbol in place of x:

$$\int_a^b f(t)\,dt = \int_a^b f(r)\,dr = \int_a^b f(\theta)\,d\theta, \text{ etc.}$$

The value depends only on f, a and b. The variables x, t, r and θ, as used here, are called **dummy variables**. Their function is to help write the formula for f and to indicate which symbol is driving the integration process.

Notation

This is not the first time you should have encountered the idea of a dummy variable. It is also used in our summation notation: in $\sum_{k=1}^n a_k$, the symbol k is a dummy index and both instances of it could be replaced by i or j or r, etc., without changing the value of the sum.

The indefinite integral can be defined as follows.

Frame 6.11   *Alternative definition of an indefinite integral*

$$F(x) = \int_c^x f(t)\,dt \qquad\qquad (6.17)$$

The value of c can be **any** constant, which is the reason for the use of 'indefinite'; it is related to the $+C$ encountered before, although they are quite different values. Also, it is possible to use x both as a dummy variable inside the integral and as a limit, although it is often sensible to avoid confusion by using a different dummy variable, as here.

The function $F(x)$ measures the area under the curve, from c to x, shaded in the diagram below. Here x denotes the upper limit and t labels the axis. (The label on the horizontal axis is not important since it is a dummy variable.) This diagram has $f(t) \geqslant 0$ throughout, but this is not a necessary restriction, provided we add minus signs to areas below the x-axis, as we see in the next example.

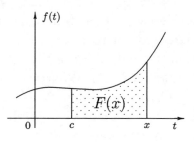

Example 6.11   Evaluate $F(x) = \displaystyle\int_{-3}^{x} f(t)\,dt$, for f given by the graph below (on the left), and sketch a graph of the result.

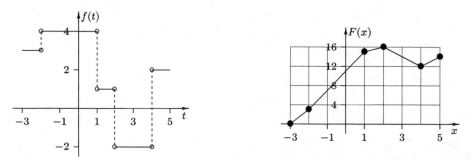

We need to measure the area from -3 to each x value. We do so by calculating the area of each rectangle bounded by the graph, the dashed lines and the x-axis. This gives the extra integral value that has accumulated after the last 'jump' point. It must be added to the integral value to date – except for the rectangle between 2 and 4, which must be **subtracted**, since it lies below the axis. (This is emboldened in the table.)

x	-3	-2	1	2	4	5
Area	0	3×1	4×3	1×1	$\mathbf{2 \times 2}$	2×1
$F(x)$	0	3	15	16	**12**	14

Now plot these values on the graph above (on the right). They may be safely joined by straight line segments: since $f(t)$ is piecewise constant we accumulate area at a constant rate as we move across each rectangle.   ■

We can use the indefinite integral to find definite integrals just as before:

$$\int_{a}^{b} f(x)\,dx = \int_{c}^{b} f(x)\,dx - \int_{c}^{a} f(x)\,dx = F(b) - F(a), \qquad (6.18)$$

since the area from a to b is the difference of the areas from c to b and c to a, no matter what value c has. The diagram below illustrates this in the case where c lies to the left of both a and b, although (6.14) ensures this is not a real restriction.

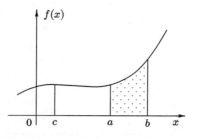

Example 6.12 For the function in Example 6.11, evaluate $\int_0^4 f(t)\,dt$.

From the graph of F, we can read off $F(0) = 11$, $F(4) = 12$.

Hence $\int_0^4 f(t)\,dt = F(4) - F(0) = 12 - 11 = 1$.

This can be verified directly by area-counting in the original graph. ∎

Ex 6.8 In each of the following cases find the area between the graphs of the function f and the x-axis over the given interval.

(a) $f(x) = x^2$, $0 \leqslant x \leqslant 3$;

(b) $f(x) = x^2$, $-2 \leqslant x \leqslant 2$;

(c) $f(x) = \sin x$, $0 \leqslant x \leqslant 2\pi$.

Ex 6.9 Verify that the curve with equation $y = x^3 + x^2 - 2x$ cuts the x-axis at the points $(0,0)$, $(1,0)$ and $(-2,0)$. Calculate $\int_{-2}^{0}(x^3 + x^2 - 2x)\,dx$ and $\int_0^1 (x^3 + x^2 - 2x)\,dx$. Hence write down the total area enclosed between the curve and the x-axis.

Ex 6.10 Find the following integrals:

$$\int_{-5}^{5} x^{101}\,dx, \qquad \int_{-1}^{1} x^8 \sin x\,dx, \qquad \int_{-1}^{2} x^7\,dx.$$

Ex 6.11 Find $\int_{-2}^{4} (x^2 - x)\,dx$ and interpret your result in terms of areas.

Ex 6.12 The graph below is that for the velocity of a particle, increasing uniformly to a value 20 over 5 time units.

Assume that the distance travelled from time $t = 0$ until time $t = T$ is given by the area under the graph between these two values. Construct a table of distance s against time for $T = 0, 1, 2, 3, 4, 5$. Verify that the values satisfy $s = 2t^2$ for the given t values, and sketch the graph of s.

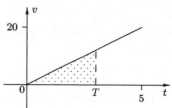

Can you justify the formula for s, using the assumption about area?

Ex 6.13 A function $f(x)$ has graph shown below, for $0 \leqslant x \leqslant 6$. The objective is to sketch a graph of $\int_0^x f(t)\,dt$ over the same interval.

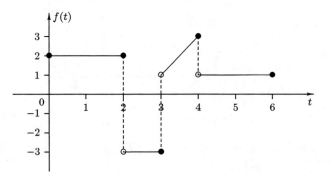

Recall that this integral is the area 'under' the graph from 0 to x, taking appropriate account of any negative areas. Hence construct a table of values of the integral, for $x = 0, 1, 2, 3, 4, 5, 6$.

Finally, plot the tabulated data and fill in the gaps between.

6.5   Revision Exercises

Ex 6.14 Integrate the following:

    (a) $7x^6$ (b) $-18x^5$ (c) $x^3 + 3x^2 + 3x + 1$
    (d) $Ax^{10} + Bx + C$ (A, B and C are constants)

Ex 6.15 Boyle's Law ($pv = $ const.) does not apply, even as an approximation, for so-called *adiabatic* processes, where heat energy is conserved but temperature is allowed to vary. The correct law is

$$pv^\gamma = \text{const.},$$

where γ is related to the specific heats of the gas, and a value in the region of 1.4 is typical for diatomic gases (and hence air).

When a gas expands from volume v_0 to volume v_1, it does work

$$W = \int_{v_0}^{v_1} p\,dv.$$

Suppose that air in a cylinder has pressure p (in $\mathrm{N\,m^{-2}}$) and volume v (in $\mathrm{m^3}$) related by

$$pv^{1.4} = 5000.$$

The gas expands from 0.2 to $0.3\,\mathrm{m^3}$ and drives a piston. Calculate the work done.

Ex 6.16 Draw the graph of $\sin(2x)$ for $0 \leqslant x \leqslant \frac{3\pi}{4}$. Find the area of the region between this graph and the x−axis for $0 \leqslant x \leqslant \frac{3\pi}{4}$.

Ex 6.17

(a) Draw the graph of the function $f(x) = x(1-x)$ for $0 \leqslant x \leqslant 2$.

(b) Find the area of the region enclosed between the x-axis and the graph of f for $0 \leqslant x \leqslant 2$.

Ex 6.18 Evaluate $\displaystyle\int_{-\pi}^{\pi} \left(x^3 \cos x + x^2\right) \, dx$.

Ex 6.19 Evaluate $\displaystyle\int_{-1}^{1} \left(x^7 \cos x + x^2\right) \, dx$.

7   FURTHER INTEGRATION

Integration is at least as important a process as differentiation for practical applications, but it is harder to perform the calculations. They are mostly carried out by reversing differentiation and operating **in reverse** is usually harder than in a forward sense. This emerges in three principal ways:

1. There are simple functions for which there is no **anti-derivative** in terms of similarly simple functions. Some of these are very important. The best known is e^{-x^2}, whose integral underpins a large part of statistical calculation, not to mention diffusion problems such as heat flow. There is no function with a simple formula $F(x)$, where $F'(x) = e^{-x^2}$. Hence evaluation of, say

$$\int_a^b e^{-x^2}\, dx$$

is impossible using an indefinite integral. The only solution is to use an approximation method.

2. There are far fewer **rules of integration**. Attempts to reverse some of the differentiation rules do not deliver useful results. Thus, there are no general rules for integrating products and quotients. This means that on occasion we have no alternative but to perform long technical calculations. The following (real-life) example illustrates this.

   Example 7.1   In viscous fluid flow parallel to a flat plate, a quantity known as the *momentum thickness* is defined by

   $$\theta = \Delta \int_0^1 \frac{u}{u_0}\left(1 - \frac{u}{u_0}\right) dz,$$

   where u is the velocity (a function of z) and u_0 is the undisturbed velocity far from the plate. Find θ, given that $\frac{u}{u_0} = 2z - 2z^3 + z^4$. Although the integral

   $$I = \int_0^1 (2z - 2z^3 + z^4)(1 - 2z + 2z^3 - z^4)\, dz,$$

   contains a product, the only reasonable approach is to expand:

   $$I = \int_0^1 \left[(2z - 4z^2 + 4z^4 - 2z^5) + (-2z^3 + 4z^4 - 4z^6 + 2z^7)\right.$$
   $$\left. + (z^4 - 2z^5 + 2z^7 - z^8)\right] dz$$
   $$= \int_0^1 (2z - 4z^2 - 2z^3 + 9z^4 - 4z^5 - 4z^6 + 4z^7 - z^8)\, dz$$
   $$= \left[z^2 - \tfrac{4}{3}z^3 - \tfrac{1}{2}z^4 + \tfrac{9}{5}z^5 - \tfrac{2}{3}z^6 - \tfrac{4}{7}z^7 + \tfrac{1}{2}z^8 - \tfrac{1}{9}z^9\right]_0^1$$
   $$= 1 - \tfrac{4}{3} - \tfrac{1}{2} + \tfrac{9}{5} - \tfrac{2}{3} - \tfrac{4}{7} + \tfrac{1}{2} - \tfrac{1}{9} = \tfrac{37}{315}.$$

   Hence $\theta = \frac{37}{315}\Delta$. ∎

3. Consider the following differentiation, using the Product Rule:

$$\frac{d}{dx}\left[(x+1)^4(x+2)^5\right] = (x+1)^4\,5(x+2)^4 + 4(x+1)^3\,(x+2)^5 \quad (7.1)$$

$$= (x+1)^3(x+2)^4\left[5(x+1)+4(x+2)\right]$$

$$= (9x+13)(x+1)^3(x+2)^4. \quad (7.2)$$

The form (7.1) could be recognised as the result of applying the Product Rule, while the tidied up version (7.2) is unrecognisable as such.

If asked to integrate (7.1), we could do so in one step, simply reversing the Product Rule. If asked to integrate (7.2), we would probably end up resorting to the kind of calculation in Example 7.1. The moral here is that integration sometimes forces us to 'untidy' functions in order to proceed. The technical name for such a step is **rearrangement**. There are two important cases where it is frequently used, which we shall examine in §7.2. (It is also required – usually in a simple way – in §7.3.)

7.1 Linear Arguments

There is one integration rule that is particularly heavily used. Indeed, we anticipated it with some of the standard forms in §6.3.

This rule is the counterpart of the special form of the **Chain Rule** for a **linear argument**. It has the form:

Frame 7.1   *Linear composite rule*

$$\int f(ax+b)\,dx = \frac{1}{a}F(ax+b) + \text{constant}$$

$$[a,b \text{ constants}, a\neq 0, F'(x)=f(x)]$$

This appears more complicated than the differentiation version, but that is only because the notation is less neat. The mechanics are virtually identical. If the function can be written in terms of a linear function u, as in $(2x+1)^7 = u^7$ with $u = 2x+1$, we integrate w.r.t. u, then adjust for 'a' although this time **dividing** by a. (Integration always does the opposite of differentiation.)

Notation

As for differentiation, the calculus must be done before the argument is used. What this means is that we integrate f to find the indefinite integral $F(x)$, then use the argument $ax+b$. For $f(x)=x$, we have $F(x)=\frac{1}{2}x^2$ and then $F(ax+b)=\frac{1}{2}(ax+b)^2$. The calculation is completed by dividing by a.

Think about it like this

This rule can be used **directly** to verify the integrations of e^{kx}, $\sin \omega x$ and $\cos \omega x$ that we carried out in the previous chapter by reversing differentiations. There we **divided** by k and ω.

Example 7.2   Integrate: (a) $(3x - 1)^9$,   (b) $(1 - x)^2$.

(a) Let $u = 3x - 1 \equiv ax + b$ with $a = 3$.

The integral of u^9 is $\frac{1}{10}u^{10}$, so the integral of the original function is

$$\frac{1}{10}(3x - 1)^{10} \div 3 + C = \frac{1}{30}(3x - 1)^{10} + C.$$

(b) Let $u = 1 - x \equiv ax + b$ with $a = -1$.

Integral: $\frac{1}{3}(1 - x)^3 \div (-1) + C = -\frac{1}{3}(1 - x)^3 + C$ (via $\frac{1}{3}u^3$).

∎

Example 7.3   Integrate   (a) $\dfrac{1}{(1 - 3x)^2}$,   (b) $\sqrt[3]{1 - 2x}$.

(a) Let $u = ax + b \equiv -3x + 1$, writing the integrand as $(1 - 3x)^{-2}$.

Integral: $\dfrac{1}{-2+1}(1 - 3x)^{-2+1} \div (-3) + C = \dfrac{1}{3(1 - 3x)} + C.$

(b) Let $u = ax + b \equiv -2x + 1$, writing the integrand as $(1 - 2x)^{1/3}$.

Integral: $\dfrac{3}{4}(1 - 2x)^{4/3} \div (-2) + C = -\dfrac{3}{8}(1 - 2x)^{4/3} + C.$

∎

Example 7.4   Integrate $\cos(100\pi t - \alpha)$, which is the oscillatory factor in AC voltage.

Use Frame 7.1 with $at + b \equiv 100\pi t - \alpha$:

$$I = \frac{1}{100\pi} \sin(100\pi t - \alpha) + C.$$

∎

Example 7.5   Integrate e^{5-2x}.

Use Frame 7.1, with $ax + b \equiv -2x + 5$.

$$I = e^{5-2x} \div (-2) + C = -\frac{1}{2}e^{5-2x} + C.$$

∎

The following more general result follows directly from applying the linear composite rule to $1/x$. It underpins part of the next section.

Frame 7.2   *Integration of the reciprocal of a linear function*

$$\int \frac{1}{ax+b}\, dx = \frac{1}{a}\ln|ax+b| + C$$

Think about it like this

The result in this Frame is particularly worthy of note. It tends to catch people out. Firstly, it is not immediately clear that there is such a simple answer, since $1/(ax+b)$ looks quite different from $1/x$. Then, once that has been accepted, it is all too tempting to assume that any function of the form $1/f(x)$ has a simple log as its integral. **Only functions that are a reciprocal of a linear function $ax+b$ have this property.**

Example 7.6   Integrate $\dfrac{1}{2x+3}$ and evaluate $\displaystyle\int_{-4}^{-2} \frac{dx}{2x+3}$.

Use Frame 7.1 to obtain the indefinite integral: $\dfrac{1}{2}\ln|2x+3| + C$.

An attempt to evaluate this at the limits fails unless the absolute value is used. Without it we would find $\ln\left[2\times(-2)+3\right] = \ln(-1)$, which is undefined.

It is safe to use the full version, because the limits do not enclose the problematic value $x = -3/2$, where the bottom line is zero. We obtain:

$$\left[\tfrac{1}{2}\ln|2x+3|\right]_{-4}^{-2} = \tfrac{1}{2}\ln 1 - \tfrac{1}{2}\ln 5 = -\tfrac{1}{2}\ln 5 \simeq -0.8047.$$

■

Think about it like this

Although you should aim to use these linear composite rules – for differentiation as well as integration – without the need for intermediate working, it may be safer at the start to set out more steps. There are various ways of setting out the calculations, some of which now follow. No matter which you prefer, the underlying steps are effectively the same, as is the final answer.

A very safe method is to set $u = ax+b$ and work with $f(u)$. Compute $\frac{df}{du}$ or $\int f(u)\,du$, convert u back to $ax+b$ and adjust by the factor a (differentiation) or $\frac{1}{a}$ (integration). The u versions of the calculations are both 'w.r.t. u' and the adjustments are necessary to convert the answers to 'w.r.t. x'.

An equivalent but quicker method is to avoid introducing and then removing u, instead treating $ax+b$ as a 'composite' symbol with, for the moment, no separate existence for a, x or b. The calculation is carried out 'w.r.t. $(ax+b)$' as the variable and then the adjustment by a or $\frac{1}{a}$ is made.

There is a third variation, used by some people, particularly for integration. This relies on the notion of *differentials dx, du*, not considered here.

Finally, in the differentiation case we noted that the rule was a special case of the Chain Rule. **In integration there is no straightforward rule for which this is a special case, so it is wrong to try to extend the linear composite rule to non-linear arguments.** We return to this in §7.3.

Ex 7.1 Evaluate the following integrals:

$$\int \left[7\cos(2x+1) - 3\sin(5x)\right] dx, \quad \int \frac{1}{6x-2}\, dx, \quad \int (x+1)^2\, dx.$$

Ex 7.2 Evaluate the following integrals:

$$\int e^{3x+2}\, dx, \quad \int \frac{1}{2x+4}\, dx, \quad \int \sqrt{9-u}\, du, \quad \int (3t-4)^5\, dt \quad \int \cos\left(10t - \frac{\pi}{4}\right) dt.$$

7.2   Integration by Rearrangement

There are two cases where **rearrangement** is regularly used in a systematic way. We start with a case that underpins the important topic of *Fourier Series*: integration of the product of two sin and/or cos terms.

Recall that we have no counterpart of the **Product Rule** for differentiation, guaranteed to integrate all products. Hence products of functions tend to be difficult to integrate. In the trigonometric case, the identities in Frame 2.10, reproduced below, enable us to convert any of these products into a sum or difference, for which the rules of integration, including the linear composite rule, can be used.

We switch from x, y to A, B, to avoid a clash with the x used as default variable in integration.

Frame 7.3   *Products of circular functions*

$$2\sin A\cos B = \sin(A+B) + \sin(A-B) \qquad (7.3)$$
$$2\cos A\sin B = \sin(A+B) - \sin(A-B) \qquad (7.4)$$
$$2\cos A\cos B = \cos(A+B) + \cos(A-B) \qquad (7.5)$$
$$2\sin A\sin B = \cos(A-B) - \cos(A+B) \qquad (7.6)$$

This procedure is best illustrated by examples.

Example 7.7   Integrate $\sin 3x\cos 2x$ and evaluate $\displaystyle\int_0^{2\pi} \sin 2x\cos 3x\, dx.$

Use (7.3), $A = 3x$, $B = 2x$.

$$I = \tfrac{1}{2}\int 2\cos 3x\sin 2x\, dx = \tfrac{1}{2}\int (\sin 5x - \sin x)\, dx$$
$$= \tfrac{1}{2}\left[-\tfrac{1}{5}\cos 5x + \cos x\right] + C = -\tfrac{1}{10}\cos 5x + \tfrac{1}{2}\cos x + C.$$

Note the use of Frame 7.1 – as anticipated in Frame 6.8 – to integrate $\cos 5x$.

Using the given limits produces an answer of zero. Although the various cos values, such as $\cos 2\pi$ and $\cos 0$, are non-zero, they cancel due to the periodicity of cos. ∎

The result found above is typical for integrations of products of $\sin mx$, and $\cos nx$ over an interval of width 2π.

Think about it like this

> (7.3) and (7.4) appear to deal with the same matter: a product of sin and cos. Even though the answers seem different, this is illusory since there are various subtractions that cancel out. The best advice is to use (7.3) if the sin angle is larger than the cos one, and (7.4) otherwise; this avoids negative angles.

Example 7.8 Integrate $\sin(3x+1)\sin(x-2)$.
Use (7.6), $A = 3x+1$, $B = x-2$:

$$I = \tfrac{1}{2}\int 2\sin(3x+1)\sin(x-2)\,dx$$
$$= \tfrac{1}{2}\int [\cos(2x+3) - \cos(4x-1)]\,dx$$
$$= \tfrac{1}{2}\left[\tfrac{1}{2}\sin(2x+3) - \tfrac{1}{4}\sin(4x-1)\right] + C$$
$$= \tfrac{1}{4}\sin(2x+3) - \tfrac{1}{8}\sin(4x-1) + C.$$

∎

There are two related integrations that are even more important. They can be deduced from the above identities but are more naturally done using the **double-angle formulae** (2.18). In general:

$$\int \sin^2 x\,dx = \int \frac{1}{2}(1-\cos 2x)\,dx = \frac{1}{2}x - \frac{1}{4}\sin 2x + C, \qquad (7.7)$$
$$\int \cos^2 x\,dx = \int \frac{1}{2}(1+\cos 2x)\,dx = \frac{1}{2}x + \frac{1}{4}\sin 2x + C. \qquad (7.8)$$

Example 7.9 Integrate $\cos^2\frac{x}{2}$.
Using a **half-angle formula**, $\cos x = 2\cos^2\frac{x}{2} - 1$. Solve for the integrand and complete the straightforward integration:

$$I = \int \frac{1}{2}(1+\cos x)\,dx = \frac{1}{2}x + \frac{1}{2}\sin x + C.$$

∎

Example 7.10 Evaluate $\displaystyle\int_0^{\pi/2} \sin^2 2x\,dx$.
Start with $\cos 4x = 1 - 2\sin^2 2x$, rearranging to find $\sin^2 2x = \tfrac{1}{2} - \tfrac{1}{2}\cos 4x$:

$$I = \int_0^{\pi/2} \sin^2 2x\,dx = \int_0^{\pi/2}\left(\frac{1}{2} - \frac{1}{2}\cos 4x\right)dx$$
$$= \left[\frac{1}{2}x - \frac{1}{8}\sin 4x\right]_0^{\pi/2} = \frac{1}{2}\frac{\pi}{2} = \frac{\pi}{4},$$

using Frame 7.1 and noting that $\sin m\pi = 0$ for all integers m. ∎

Think about it like this

> These 'square' integrals for sin and cos arise in many applications, including computing the power in an electrical circuit, normalising wave functions in quantum mechanics, frequency analysis for vibrations, buckling of shell structures and certain 'root mean square' calculations (see Chapter 8). *There is no sensible alternative, so the method set out above must be thoroughly mastered.* This should be approached by learning the method, rather than memorising the formulae (7.7) and (7.8).

The second use of rearrangement is required to integrate rational functions. A **rational function** is a quotient of two polynomials:

$$f(x) = \frac{a_n x^n + a_{n-1} x^{n-1} + \cdots + a_0}{b_m x^m + b_{m-1} x^{m-1} + \cdots + b_0} = \frac{p(x)}{q(x)}. \tag{7.9}$$

The key to integrating these is to use **partial fractions**. This is covered in detail in *Applicable Mathematics 1*, §4.11. A brief summary of one approach is given here.

We may need an extra initial step: unless the degree of the numerator $p(x)$ is less than that of the denominator $q(x)$ in (7.9), perform a division

$$\frac{p(x)}{q(x)} = s(x) + \frac{r(x)}{q(x)}, \tag{7.10}$$

where $s(x)$ is a polynomial and the degree of $r(x)$ is less than the degree of $q(x)$.

Integration of $s(x)$ is straightforward. To integrate $r(x)/q(x)$, we resolve it into **partial fractions**. The first step is to factorise the denominator $q(x)$. **We assume that this can be done, producing a set of *linear* factors only.** (The case of quadratic factors that cannot be further factorised requires integration tools not yet within our grasp.)

In this situation, $r(x)/q(x)$ can be written as a sum of terms of the form $\frac{A}{ax+b}$ or, in some rare cases when $q(x)$ has 'repeated' linear factors, $\frac{A}{(ax+b)^n}$, with $n > 1$. These can be integrated using **the linear composite rule**:

$$\int \frac{A}{ax+b}\, dx = \frac{A}{a} \ln|ax+b| + C,$$

$$\int \frac{A}{(ax+b)^n}\, dx = -\frac{1}{a}\frac{1}{(n-1)}\frac{A}{(ax+b)^{n-1}} + C \quad (n \neq 1).$$

Think about it like this

> It is possible to work entirely with $a = 1$, dealing with terms such as $\frac{A}{x+b}$, but the more general form is useful, since an expression such as $\frac{1}{x+\frac{1}{2}}$ is more neatly written in the form $\frac{2}{2x+1}$.

Example 7.11   Integrate   (a) $\dfrac{3x-5}{(2x-1)(x+3)}$,   (b) $\dfrac{3x+1}{x(x+1)^2}$.

(a) Let

$$\frac{3x-5}{(2x-1)(x+3)} = \frac{A}{2x-1} + \frac{B}{x+3} = \frac{A(x+3) + B(2x-1)}{(2x-1)(x+3)}.$$

Then, matching the numerators forces

$$3x - 5 \equiv A(x+3) + B(2x-1).$$

Let $x = \frac{1}{2}$: $\frac{3}{2} - 5 = \frac{7}{2}A$ $\Rightarrow$ $A = -1$.

Let $x = -3$: $-9 - 5 = -7B$ $\Rightarrow$ $B = 2$.

$$I = \int \left[\frac{-1}{2x-1} + \frac{2}{x+3} \right] dx = -\tfrac{1}{2}\ln|2x-1| + 2\ln|x+3| + C.$$

(b) Let

$$\frac{3x+1}{x(x+1)^2} = \frac{A}{x} + \frac{B}{x+1} + \frac{C}{(x+1)^2} = \frac{A(x+1)^2 + Bx(x+1) + Cx}{x(x+1)^2}.$$

Then, matching the numerators forces

$$3x + 1 \equiv A(x+1)^2 + Bx(x+1) + Cx.$$

Let $x = 0$: $1 = A$ $\Rightarrow$ $A = 1$.

Let $x = -1$: $-2 = -C$ $\Rightarrow$ $C = 2$.

The coefficients of x^2 on each side must be the same, so $0 = A + B$ and $B = -1$. The integration is

$$\int \left[\frac{1}{x} - \frac{1}{x+1} + \frac{2}{(x+1)^2} \right] dx = \ln|x| - \ln|x+1| - \frac{2}{(x+1)} + C.$$

∎

Finally, there are other rearrangements that are either 'one-offs' or cannot be readily categorised. We shall look at three of these.

Example 7.12   Integrate $\tan^2 x$.

Use the identity included in (5.9) prior to reversing the derivative of $\tan x$:

$$\int \tan^2 x \, dx = \int (\sec^2 x - 1) \, dx = \tan x - x + C.$$

∎

Example 7.13   Integrate $\dfrac{1}{\sqrt{x} + \sqrt{x-1}}$.

First of all, we *rationalise the denominator*:

$$\frac{1}{\sqrt{x} + \sqrt{x-1}} \times \frac{\sqrt{x} - \sqrt{x-1}}{\sqrt{x} - \sqrt{x-1}} = \frac{\sqrt{x} - \sqrt{x-1}}{x - (x-1)},$$

leading to

$$I = \int \left(\sqrt{x} - \sqrt{x-1} \right) dx = \frac{2}{3}x^{3/2} - \frac{2}{3}(x-1)^{3/2} + C.$$

∎

Example 7.14   Integrate $x(x+1)^9$.

Expansion using the binomial theorem is the worst of several possible methods. The easiest conceptually is the rearrangement:

$$x(x+1)^9 \equiv [(x+1)-1](x+1)^9 = (x+1)^{10} - (x+1)^9,$$

leading to the simple integration

$$I = \int \left[(x+1)^{10} - (x+1)^9\right] dx = \frac{1}{11}(x+1)^{11} - \frac{1}{10}(x+1)^{10} + C$$

$$= \frac{1}{110}(10x-1)(x+1)^{10} + C,$$

on taking out a common factor of $(x+1)^{10}$.   ∎

Ex 7.3 Integrate the following:

   (a) $\sin^2(3x)$ (b) $\sin x \cos x$ (c) $\sin(2x)\cos(3x)$
   (d) $\cos x \cos(5x)$ (e) $\sin(3x)\sin(4x)$ (f) $\cos^2\left(\frac{\pi x}{2}\right)$

Ex 7.4 Integrate the following:

  (a) $\dfrac{1}{x(x+2)}$,   (b) $\dfrac{x+1}{(x+5)(x+3)}$,   (c) $\dfrac{4x^2-9x+11}{(x-3)(x-1)(x+2)}$.

Ex 7.5 Integrate $\dfrac{2x^3+17x^2+39x+16}{(x+5)(x+3)}$.

7.3   Introduction to Substitution

The next integration method we examine is **substitution**, which may be thought of as a way of **changing the variable**. There are many integrals for which there is no obvious standard form or integration rule to use, but which can be converted to an easier problem if the variable is changed. In some cases this is an indication that the originator of the problem made a poor choice of variable from the outset.

Suppose, then, that we wish to evaluate $\int f(x)\,dx$. There are two approaches.

(a) We try to change to a new variable u, where $u = g(x)$ for some function g. It is not always possible to construct a new integral free of x, so the attempt may fail.

(b) We change to a new variable v where $x = h(v)$ for some function h. This is always possible to implement but may lead to an even more intractable integral.

In this chapter we shall concentrate on the first approach. Most of the examples are integrands that could have arisen as the result of a differentiation using the **Chain Rule**. The method is often called the **function**

of a function rule (because of the link with function composition) or the **Reverse Chain Rule**. Applying the Fundamental Theorem of Calculus to the **Chain Rule**, removing the $\frac{d}{dx}$ and inserting $\int$ on the other side, gives the method.

Frame 7.4   *Substitution (Reverse Chain Rule)*

$$\int f\big(u(x)\big)\frac{du}{dx}\,dx = F(u) + C, \quad \text{where} \quad F'(x) = f(x) \qquad (7.11)$$

Think about it like this

It is not particularly easy to express this method in symbols. The way to read it is as follows. If the integrand fits the template on the left, then we must find an anti-derivative (or indefinite integral) $F(x)$ for $f(x)$ and use it, replacing x by $u(x)$. A close study of the solutions to Chain Rule problems can help develop a feel for this integration method: reversing the result of any calculation using the Chain Rule will produce an example.

Example 7.15   Integrate the following:

$$\text{(a)} \ f(x) = 3(2x+1)(x^2+x+1)^2, \qquad \text{(b)} \ g(x) = 2x\cos x^2.$$

Each of these is precisely the result of a differentiation in Chapter 5. Hence their integrals should be the functions tackled there.

(a) Example 5.6(a): let $u = x^2 + x + 1$, $\frac{du}{dx} = 2x + 1$. Then

$$I = \int 3u^2 \frac{du}{dx}\,dx = \int 3u^2\,du$$
$$= u^3 + C = (x^2+x+1)^3 + C.$$

(b) Example 5.12: let $u = x^2$, $\frac{du}{dx} = 2x$. Then

$$I = \int \cos u\,\frac{du}{dx}\,dx = \int \cos u\,du$$
$$= \sin u + C = \sin x^2 + C.$$

■

There are two problems associated with this new method: identifying when to use it, and implementing it. We start with the second of these since studying examples helps understand when it can succeed. A recommended procedure – assuming it is valid to use the method – is as follows.

Suppose the integrand is a product of the form $f(x)g(x)$.

Identify which of these is the derivative of a fairly simple function u of x; suppose $g(x) = \frac{du}{dx}$.

Replace $g(x)\,dx$ by $\frac{du}{dx}\,dx = du$ (noting the 'cancellation' of dx).

Then decompose $f(x)$ so that it can be written in terms of u **only**; if you cannot get rid of some x it may be that the integral cannot be done in this way or you have chosen an inappropriate u.

Having done this, you should now have an integral involving u only, which may be easier than the one you started with. Evaluate it.

Now replace all occurrences of u by its expression in x.

This last step assumes we wish an indefinite integral as the answer. There is, in fact, a useful shortcut available for definite integrals, which we shall defer until later.

There are many cases where this rule can be applied even when the integrand does not immediately fit the template in (7.11). A simple rearrangement may immediately reproduce this template. For example, we may adjust a constant, writing x as $\frac{1}{2}(2x) = \frac{1}{2}\frac{du}{dx}$, where $u = x^2$.

Example 7.16   Integrate: $h(x) = x(x^2 + 1)^4$

Note that $x = \frac{1}{2}(2x) = \frac{1}{2}\frac{d}{dx}\left[x^2\right]$. Hence $u = x^2$ looks promising. This will succeed, although using $u = x^2 + 1$, also with $\frac{du}{dx} = 2x$, is a little easier.

$$I = \tfrac{1}{2}\int 2x(x^2 + 1)^4\,dx = \tfrac{1}{2}\int u^4 \frac{du}{dx}\,dx$$

$$= \tfrac{1}{2}\int u^4\,du = \tfrac{1}{10}u^5 + C = \tfrac{1}{10}(x^2 + 1)^5 + C.$$

∎

Example 7.17   The following two problems relate to forces on a cylinder in uniform fluid flow. Evaluate the following integrals:

$$\text{(a)}\ \int \sin^2\theta \cos\theta\,d\theta, \qquad \text{(b)}\ \int \sin^3\theta\,d\theta.$$

(a) We note that if $u = \sin\theta$ then $\frac{du}{d\theta} = \cos\theta$.

$$I = \int u^2 \frac{du}{d\theta}\,d\theta = \int u^2\,du$$

$$= \tfrac{1}{3}u^3 + C = \tfrac{1}{3}\sin^3\theta + C.$$

(b) There is no obvious u, $\frac{du}{d\theta}$ pair, but we can write

$$\sin^3\theta = \sin^2\theta \cdot \sin\theta = (1 - \cos^2\theta)\sin\theta,$$

which suggests using $u = \cos\theta$ and $\frac{du}{d\theta} = -\sin\theta$. Then

$$I = \int (1 - u^2)\left(-\frac{du}{d\theta}\right)d\theta = -\int (1 - u^2)\,du$$

$$= -\left[u - \tfrac{1}{3}u^3\right] + C = \tfrac{1}{3}\cos^3\theta - \cos\theta + C.$$

∎

Think about it like this

This method is a powerful one, but there is one significant pitfall to avoid, as warned at the end of §7.1. We may regard the Chain Rule as an extension of the linear composite rule, **but there is no similar extension of Frame 7.1.** Consider the following:

$$y = e^{2x}, \quad \int y\, dx = \frac{1}{2}e^{2x}, \qquad y = e^{x^2}, \quad \int y\, dx = \frac{1}{2x}e^{x^2}.$$

The first is **correct**; the second is **wrong**. The point here is that the division (by the derivative of 'u') must be done **before integrating**. In the first case the order does not matter since the divisor 2 ($= \frac{d}{dx}[2x]$) is a constant; in the second case it does: $2x = \frac{d}{dx}[x^2]$ is not constant. In fact there is no indefinite integral for e^{x^2}, just as we pointed out at the start of the chapter, for e^{-x^2}.

The following, however, is valid:

$$\int 2xe^{x^2}\, dx = \int e^u\, du = e^u = e^{x^2}, \qquad (u = x^2),$$

since the $2x$ is divided (and cancelled) **before** integrating.

There is a special case of this method that is of common occurrence. This is when the integrand has the form of a fraction with the numerator (top line) being the derivative of the denominator (bottom line). Apply (7.11) with $u = f(x)$ to obtain

$$\int \frac{1}{u}\frac{du}{dx}\, dx = \int \frac{1}{u}\, du = \ln|u| + C.$$

This gives the following rule, which can be applied without any intermediate working:

Frame 7.5   *Special substitution rule*

$$\int \frac{f'(x)}{f(x)}\, dx = \ln|f(x)| + C \qquad\qquad (7.12)$$

The $f'(x)$ part is essential here and care must be taken to avoid the following careless error:

NOT TRUE: $\displaystyle\int \frac{1}{f(x)}\, dx = \ln|f(x)| + C.$

Our first application of (7.12) is to integrate an important trigonometric function:

$$\int \tan x\, dx = -\int \frac{-\sin x}{\cos x}\, dx = -\ln|\cos x| + C.$$

This is sometimes written as $\ln|\sec x| + C$, by using $\ln\frac{1}{z} = -\ln z$.

Example 7.18   Evaluate $\displaystyle\int_1^3 \frac{x}{x^2+1}\,dx.$

Write $x = \frac{1}{2}(2x)$ to achieve the f/f' form. Then:

$$I = \frac{1}{2}\int_1^3 \frac{2x}{x^2+1}\,dx = \frac{1}{2}\Big[\ln(x^2+1)\Big]_1^3$$
$$= \tfrac{1}{2}\left[\ln 10 - \ln 2\right] = \tfrac{1}{2}\ln\tfrac{10}{2} = \tfrac{1}{2}\ln 5.$$

■

There is a useful shortcut available for a **definite integral**. The way (7.11) has been written suggests that the result is ultimately to be converted back from u to x. For a definite integral, however, we may leave it in terms of u, *provided we also change the limits*, to become values of u corresponding to those of x:

$$\int_a^b f\big(u(x)\big)\frac{du}{dx}\,dx = \int_{u(a)}^{u(b)} f(u)\,du. \tag{7.13}$$

Think about it like this

> The right-hand side is an integral in terms of u, which produces a numerical answer without any need to return to x. When we change from dx to du, the limits must change from x values to the corresponding u values. The limits are values of whatever variable follows 'd' on the right of the integral. For example, in the original integral the lower limit a is the starting point for x. When we change variable from x to u, the new integral starts at the corresponding value of u. Hence, the lower limit is deduced from: $x = a \Rightarrow u = u(a)$.

Example 7.19   Evaluate $\displaystyle\int_1^4 \frac{1}{\sqrt{x}(\sqrt{x}+1)}\,dx.$

The problem here is $\sqrt{x}$. This has derivative $\frac{1}{2\sqrt{x}}$, most of which is already present. Hence try

$$u = \sqrt{x}, \qquad \frac{du}{dx} = \frac{1}{2\sqrt{x}}.$$

Change the limits to correspond: $x = 4 \Rightarrow u = 2, \quad x = 1 \Rightarrow u = 1.$
Then

$$I = 2\int_1^4 \frac{1}{2\sqrt{x}}\frac{1}{\sqrt{x}+1}\,dx = 2\int_1^4 \frac{1}{\sqrt{x}+1}\frac{du}{dx}\,dx$$
$$= 2\int_1^2 \frac{1}{u+1}\,du = 2\Big[\ln|u+1|\Big]_1^2$$
$$= 2(\ln 3 - \ln 2) = 2\ln{}^3\!/_2.$$

■

Example 7.20   The following integral arises in finding the electric potential for a charged disc. Evaluate $\displaystyle\int_0^R \frac{r}{(r^2+z^2)^{1/2}}\,dr.$

Note the presence of $r = \frac{1}{2}\frac{d}{dr}[r^2]$. This suggests the use of (7.11) with either $u = r^2 + z^2$ or $u = r^2$. Choose the latter:

$$r = 0 \quad \Rightarrow \quad u = 0, \qquad r = R \quad \Rightarrow \quad u = R^2.$$

Then

$$I = \frac{1}{2}\int_{r=0}^{r=R} \frac{1}{(u+z^2)^{1/2}} \frac{du}{dr}\, dr = \frac{1}{2}\int_{u=0}^{u=R^2} (u+z^2)^{-1/2}\, du$$
$$= \frac{1}{2}\cdot 2\left[(u+z^2)^{1/2}\right]_0^{R^2} = \left(R^2 + z^2\right)^{1/2} - \left(z^2\right)^{1/2}$$
$$= \sqrt{R^2 + z^2} - |z|.$$

∎

A final example illustrates a common occurrence: the new limits are in reverse order and can be swapped using (6.14), so the sign also reverses.

Example 7.21 Evaluate $\displaystyle\int_0^{\pi/3} \frac{\sin\theta}{\cos^2\theta}\, d\theta$.

The substitution required is $u = \cos\theta$, for which $\frac{du}{d\theta} = -\sin\theta$. Also,

$$\theta = 0 \quad \Rightarrow \quad u = \cos 0 = 1, \qquad \theta = \frac{\pi}{3} \quad \Rightarrow \quad u = \cos\frac{\pi}{3} = \frac{1}{2},$$

so the integral becomes

$$\int_0^{\pi/3} \frac{1}{u^2}\left(-\frac{du}{d\theta}\right)d\theta = -\int_1^{1/2} \frac{du}{u^2} = \int_{1/2}^1 \frac{du}{u^2},$$

on using (6.14).

This integral is now easily evaluated:

$$I = \left[-\frac{1}{u}\right]_{1/2}^1 = -1 + \frac{1}{1/2} = -1 + 2 = 1.$$

∎

Think about it like this

It is no accident that a convenient minus sign also appeared. The limits get the wrong way round because the u function is **decreasing**. Such functions have a negative derivative, so we expect an explicit minus sign to appear, allowing a swap of the limits to the more normal order.

Ex 7.6 Use the substitution $u = 4 + x^3$ to evaluate $\displaystyle\int_0^2 \frac{x^2}{4+x^3}\, dx$.

Ex 7.7 Use the given substitutions to evaluate the following

$$\text{(a)} \quad \int x(x^2+1)^{10}\,dx \qquad [u=x^2+1];$$

$$\text{(b)} \quad \int xe^{-x^2}\,dx \qquad [u=-x^2];$$

$$\text{(c)} \quad \int \frac{\cos x}{\sqrt{\sin x}}\,dx \qquad [u=\sin x];$$

$$\text{(d)} \quad \int \frac{1}{\sqrt{x}}\left(\sqrt{x}+1\right)^3 dx \qquad [u=\sqrt{x}].$$

Ex 7.8 Find $\displaystyle\int \frac{x^2}{x^3+1}\,dx$ and $\displaystyle\int \cot x\,dx$.

Ex 7.9 Find $\displaystyle\int v\sqrt{1-v^2}\,dv$ using an appropriate substitution.

7.4 Piecewise Functions

In this final section, we consider the situation where the function has several formulae, i.e., it is a **piecewise** function. Clearly we will not get a single formula for an indefinite integral, so we shall not pursue that approach here.

Definite integrals are straightforward: we break the problem up at the *knots*, into separate definite integrals for each piece within the limits. Then we add the answers.

Example 7.22 Evaluate $\displaystyle\int_0^3 f(x)\,dx$, where

$$f(x) = \begin{cases} x, & \text{if } 0 \leqslant x < 1; \\ 1, & \text{if } 1 \leqslant x < 2; \\ 3-x, & \text{if } 2 \leqslant x \leqslant 3. \end{cases}$$

The graph is shown on the right. The integral can be calculated geometrically, as the area below the graph, between 0 and 3. The sum of the three sub-areas is $1/2 + 1 + 1/2 = 2$.

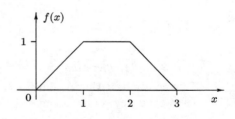

The calculus method is:

$$\int_0^3 f(x)\,dx = \int_0^1 f(x)\,dx + \int_1^2 f(x)\,dx + \int_2^3 f(x)\,dx$$

$$= \int_0^1 x\,dx + \int_1^2 1\,dx + \int_2^3 (3-x)\,dx$$

$$= \left[\tfrac{1}{2}x^2\right]_0^1 + \left[x\right]_1^2 + \left[3x - \tfrac{1}{2}x^2\right]_2^3$$

$$= (1/2 - 0) + (2 - 1) + (9 - 9/2 - 6 + 2) = 2.$$

Note how the three bracketed quantities here agree with the three sub-areas.

If the limits are not 0 and 3, then care is needed in selecting the pieces. Thus

$$\int_0^{3/2} f(x)\, dx = \int_0^1 x\, dx + \int_1^{3/2} 1\, dx.$$

■

The final example is a reminder that a function may be piecewise and have what appears to be a single formula. The biggest danger here is the *absolute value* function, which has no simple indefinite integral. There is no shortcut: the function should be converted into the pieces it represents and integrated as above.

Example 7.23   Evaluate $\displaystyle\int_0^5 |x-3|\, dx.$

The graph is shown on the right; it is the graph of the absolute value function, but shifted to the right by 3. This integral can also be calculated geometrically, as the area below the graph, between 0 and 5, which is $6\tfrac{1}{2}$.

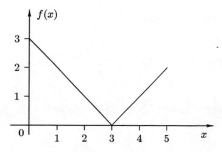

A calculus method needs to consider $[0,3]$ and $[3,5]$ separately. In the first the function is $3 - x$; in the second it is $x - 3$. The details are:

$$\int_0^5 f(x)\, dx = \int_0^3 (3-x)\, dx + \int_3^5 (x-3)\, dx$$

$$= \left[3x - \tfrac{1}{2}x^2\right]_0^3 + \left[\tfrac{1}{2}x^2 - 3x\right]_3^5$$

$$= 4\tfrac{1}{2} + 2 = 6\tfrac{1}{2}.$$

Note that both integrals are positive. A negative quantity would indicate an error since this function is never negative.

■

Ex 7.10 Evaluate $\displaystyle\int_0^4 f(x)\, dx$, where $f(x) = \begin{cases} 4x, & \text{if } 0 \leqslant x \leqslant 2; \\ (4-x)^3, & \text{if } 2 < x \leqslant 4. \end{cases}$

Ex 7.11 Draw a graph of the function defined by $f(x) = \begin{cases} \sqrt{x}, & \text{if } 0 \leqslant x \leqslant 4; \\ 6-x, & \text{if } 4 < x \leqslant 6. \end{cases}$

Evaluate $\displaystyle\int_0^6 f(x)\, dx.$

7.5   Revision Exercises

Ex 7.12 Integrate the following:
(a) $(x+1)^3$,   (b) $(2x-1)^3$,   (c) $(5x+3)^9$,   (d) $(2-3x)^2$.
Compare the answer to (a) with that for Exercise 6.14(c).

Ex 7.13 Evaluate

$$\int_0^\alpha (W - eEx)^{1/2}\, dx,$$

where $\alpha = W/eE$. (W, e and E are all constants.)

Ex 7.14 Evaluate $\displaystyle\int_0^\pi \sin(3x)\, \sin x\, dx$.

Ex 7.15 Find $\displaystyle\int \cos(5x)\sin(2x)\, dx$.

Ex 7.16 Find $\displaystyle\int \frac{5x-6}{x(x-2)}\, dx$.

Ex 7.17 Find $\displaystyle\int \frac{3x+1}{(x+3)(x+4)}\, dx$.

Ex 7.18 Use an appropriate substitution to find $\displaystyle\int \frac{\cos x}{\sqrt{2+\sin x}}\, dx$.

Ex 7.19 Evaluate $\displaystyle\int_1^3 \frac{\ln x}{x}\, dx$.

Ex 7.20 Use an appropriate substitution to find $\displaystyle\int \frac{\sin x}{(1+\cos x)^2}\, dx$.

Ex 7.21 Find the area between the graph of the function f and the x-axis over the interval $[-1,1]$, where:

$$f(x) = \begin{cases} 1+x, & \text{if } -1 \leqslant x < 0, \\ 1-x, & \text{if } 0 < x \leqslant 1. \end{cases}$$

Ex 7.22

(a) Draw the graph of the function

$$f(x) = \begin{cases} x^2, & 0 \leqslant x < 1; \\ 2-x, & 1 \leqslant x \leqslant 2. \end{cases}$$

(b) Find the area of the region between the x-axis and the graph of f.

8   APPLICATIONS OF INTEGRATION

We have seen two approaches to integration: a **summation** one and an **anti-differentiation** one. Applications that revolve round the latter are often modelled as *differential equations*, a major topic in its own right, which will not be pursued here. We concentrate on the former.

8.1   The Basic Procedure

First, we repeat the definition of an integral as the limit of a sum. In this case it is best to use the $\sum$ notation and to use the more general version, which allows different subinterval lengths and the choice of *any* point in each subinterval:

$$\int_a^b f(x)\, dx = \lim_{\substack{n\to\infty \\ \max \Delta x_k \to 0}} \sum_{k=1}^n f(x_k)\Delta x_k. \tag{8.1}$$

The interpretation of the various items in this formula are given within the following procedure for using it.

1. Divide whatever is being considered into a number of small **elements**. Each should have some associated size, typically described as Δx_k (for a spatial problem) or Δt_k (for a temporal problem).

2. Concentrate on a representative element, somewhere in the middle of the set. Suppose it is the kth one and is positioned around the value x_k or t_k. Write down its contribution to the answer; this is likely to involve x_k or t_k.

3. Add up these contributions simply by placing a summation sign in front; there is usually no need to be concerned about limits for the summation. You should obtain a quantity in a form such as $\sum f(x_k)\,\Delta x_k$ (or a similar one using t).

4. Take the limit as all $\Delta x_k \to 0$. This requires no calculation; it is carried out merely by a *transcription* to a new integral form:

$$\sum f(x_k)\,\Delta x_k \to \int_a^b f(x)\, dx. \tag{8.2}$$

The only extra feature is the need to insert limits; these are just the range of values of x (or t) being summed over. (Strictly speaking, they are related to the limits on the summation.)

Before studying various real applications of this method, note that the subdivision of the problem may be into any appropriate small pieces. They need not necessarily be space intervals. We can use time intervals or patches of area or slices of volume, etc. The important point is that each subdivision must be small enough that the quantity we 'add up' *can be treated as if constant throughout it.*

8.2   Geometrical Applications

8.2.1   Area between Curves

The link between area and integral was explored in Chapter 6. There, we noted the need to be cautious because area is always positive, although integrals may be positive or negative. The examples related to the area **under a curve**, by which we mean the area between the curve and the x-axis, which may actually lie **above** the curve in some cases.

The situation for the area between two curves is similar and can be investigated by subtracting the areas measured as before. But it is instructive to start afresh, using the 'element' analysis set out above.

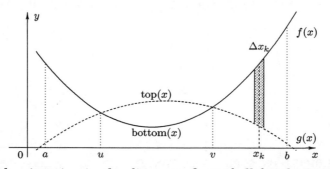

Consider the situation in the diagram, first of all for the interval between v and b. We imagine this interval to have been broken up into small pieces and select just one (representative) piece: that in which a (representative) point x_k is located and which has width Δx_k. This is shaded in the diagram. It is approximately a rectangle – the more so as it shrinks – whose area is its width times its approximate height: $\Delta x_k\big(f(x_k) - g(x_k)\big)$.

Add up the contributions of all these elements to find an approximation to the total area:

$$A \simeq \sum \big(f(x_k) - g(x_k)\big)\,\Delta x_k,$$

where the limits have been omitted from the summation. Finally, take the limit as $\Delta x_k \to 0$, changing $\sum$ to $\int$, Δ to d, dropping the subscripts k and inserting the end-points of the x-interval as limits in the integral:

$$A = \int_v^b [f(x) - g(x)]\,dx.$$

Now consider the full problem of finding the area between the curves from a to b. The same argument holds, with new limits on the integral, but this time it becomes clear that it is not necessarily $f(x_k) - g(x_k)$ that gives the height of the approximate rectangle, but $\mathrm{top}(x_k) - \mathrm{bottom}(x_k)$. This leads to the formula

$$A = \int_a^b [\mathrm{top}(x) - \mathrm{bottom}(x)]\,dx$$

$$= \int_a^u [f(x) - g(x)]\,dx + \int_u^v [g(x) - f(x)]\,dx + \int_v^b [f(x) - g(x)]\,dx.$$

Example 8.1 Find the area enclosed between the graphs of

$$y = 5 - 10x + 7x^2 - x^3 \quad \text{and} \quad y = 4x - 3.$$

The graphs are shown below, with the desired area shaded.

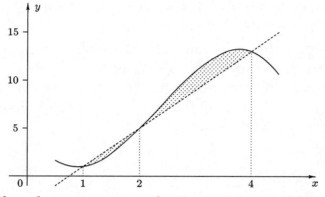

We note that the curves cross when $x = 1, 2, 4$ and hence the area is given by

$$A = \int_1^2 \left[(4x - 3) - (5 - 10x + 7x^2 - x^3) \right] dx$$

$$+ \int_2^4 \left[(5 - 10x + 7x^2 - x^3) - (4x - 3) \right] dx$$

$$= \int_1^2 \left[x^3 - 7x^2 + 14x - 8 \right] dx + \int_2^4 \left[8 - 14x + 7x^2 - x^3 \right] dx.$$

$$= \left[\frac{x^4}{4} - \frac{7x^3}{3} + 7x^2 - 8x \right]_1^2 + \left[8x - 7x^2 + \frac{7x^3}{3} - \frac{x^4}{4} \right]_2^4$$

$$= [4 - {}^{56}\!/_3 + 28 - 16 - {}^1\!/_4 + {}^7\!/_3 - 7 + 8]$$

$$+ [32 - 112 + {}^{448}\!/_3 - 64 - 16 + 28 - {}^{56}\!/_3 + 4]$$

$$= {}^5\!/_{12} + {}^8\!/_3 = {}^{37}\!/_{12}.$$

Note that each of the final two numbers is positive, suggesting that we had carried out the top − bottom subtractions in the correct order. ∎

Ex 8.1 Find the area between the graphs of the functions $f(x) = 8 - 2x^2$ and $g(x) = 4 - x^2$ over the interval $[-2, 2]$.

Ex 8.2 Repeat the previous question, but this time using the interval $[-4, 4]$.

8.2.2 Volume of a Solid of Revolution

We consider the so-called **solid of revolution**, which is a body in 3-D space whose surface is generated by revolving a curve $y = f(x)$, defined in the xy-plane, through 360° about the x-axis.

Think about it like this

A good example of this is a flat-packed Xmas decoration. This can be opened by rotating one cover through 360° to reveal a bell or globe, etc. Every cross-section of this body, perpendicular to the hinge (x-axis), will be a circle.

Another way to think of the final solid is as a pile of coins of different diameters and negligible thickness, piled on top of each other and viewed along the line joining their centres. The way we proceed to find the volume is to divide the solid into such a pile.

Our objective is to find a formula for the volume of the body, given the equation of the generating shape. Following the scheme in §8.1, slice the solid into thin discs by cuts perpendicular to the x-axis, with the kth disc having width Δx_k. The radii of the faces of the disc are approximately y_k, where $y_k = f(x_k)$ for some x_k in the kth interval.

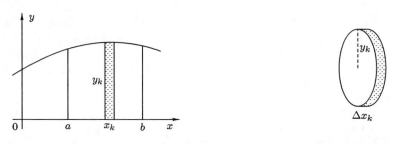

Hence the volume of the disc is approximately $\pi y_k^2 \, \Delta x_k$ (area of faces times thickness) and so the volume of the body is approximately

$$\sum_k \pi y_k^2 \, \Delta x_k.$$

Take the limit as $\Delta x_k \to 0$ to find an expression for the volume.

Frame 8.1   *Volume of a solid of revolution*

$$V = \int_a^b \pi y^2 \, dx = \pi \int_a^b [f(x)]^2 \, dx \qquad (8.3)$$

Example 8.2   A sphere of radius a is generated by rotating the curve $y = +\sqrt{a^2 - x^2}$ about the x-axis. Find the volume of the 'cap' from $x = \alpha$ to $x = a$.

The volume is given by

$$V = \pi \int_\alpha^a \left(\sqrt{a^2 - x^2}\right)^2 dx$$

$$= \pi \int_\alpha^a \left(a^2 - x^2\right) dx$$

$$= \pi \left[a^2 x - \tfrac{1}{3}x^3\right]_\alpha^a$$

$$= \pi \left[a^3 - \tfrac{1}{3}a^3 - a^2\alpha + \tfrac{1}{3}\alpha^3\right]$$

$$= \tfrac{1}{3}\pi \left[2a^3 - 3a^2\alpha + \alpha^3\right].$$

This quantity is used in a model of 'porosity' of materials. In that context it is required in terms of the angle θ: see diagram. Since $\alpha = a\cos\theta$, we have

$$V = \tfrac{1}{3}\pi a^3 \left[2 - 3\cos\theta + \cos^3\theta\right].$$

This clearly shows the 'units' to be length^3, since the cosine terms are pure numbers. ∎

Example 8.3 A beer barrel with maximum width 1 unit and height 2 units has its curved sides described as follows. Any end-to-end cross-section through its centre has the shape of the ellipse

$$\frac{x^2}{4} + \frac{y^2}{0.25} = 1,$$

with the portions for $|x| > 1$ removed. (The 'width' is along the y-axis and the 'height' along the x-axis.) Find its volume.

The barrel is generated by rotating the solid portion of the ellipse, lying above the x-axis, about that axis.

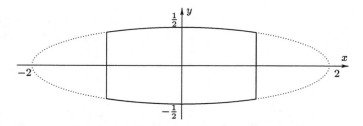

The formula requires y^2, which can be extracted from the equation of the ellipse as $y^2 = \tfrac{1}{4}\left(1 - \tfrac{1}{4}x^2\right)$. Also, note that we can take advantage of evenness to 'double-up' to obtain an integral with rather easier limits. The volume is:

$$V = \pi \int_{-1}^{1} y^2 \, dx = \pi \int_{-1}^{1} \tfrac{1}{4}\left(1 - \tfrac{1}{4}x^2\right) \, dx$$

$$= 2 \times \pi \times \frac{1}{4} \int_{0}^{1} \left(1 - \frac{1}{4}x^2\right) \, dx = \frac{\pi}{2}\left[x - \frac{1}{12}x^3\right]_{0}^{1}$$

$$= \frac{\pi}{2}\left(1 - \frac{1}{12}\right) = \frac{11\pi}{24} \simeq 1.44 \, \text{cu. units.}$$

Note the useful check: this volume is near that of the containing cylinder, which is $\pi \times \left(\tfrac{1}{2}\right)^2 \times 2 = \tfrac{\pi}{2} \simeq 1.57 \, \text{cu. units.}$ ∎

Ex 8.3 Find the volume of the solid of revolution obtained by rotating the curve $y = \sin(3x)$, $0 \leqslant x \leqslant \pi$ through 360° about the x-axis.

Ex 8.4 Find the volume of the solid of revolution obtained by rotating the curve $y = \dfrac{1}{\cos x}$, $0 \leqslant x \leqslant \tfrac{\pi}{4}$ through 360° about the x-axis.

8.2.3   Arc-length

Consider a curve defined by $y = f(x)$. Suppose we require its length between $x = a$ and $x = b$: this would be the length of a piece of thread constrained to follow the curve, then pulled into a straight line and measured. This is known as the length of the **arc of the curve** or **arc-length**.

This problem can be solved using integration, by summing the lengths of many small 'arclets'. With this in mind, we break the interval $[\,a, b\,]$ into small pieces of width Δx_k and, in each piece, we approximate the curve by a small straight line segment. The length of a straight line is well-defined and this is treated as the length of the arclet: in the limit, as we shrink the intervals, this becomes more and more accurate.

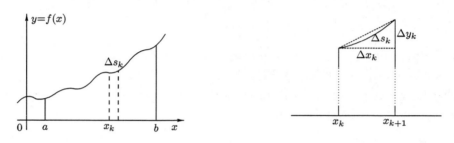

We see from the diagram that the kth arclet's length is approximately given by

$$(\Delta s_k)^2 \simeq (\Delta x_k)^2 + (\Delta y_k)^2$$

from which we deduce

$$(\Delta s_k)^2 \simeq \left\{ 1 + \left(\frac{\Delta y_k}{\Delta x_k} \right)^2 \right\} (\Delta x_k)^2$$

and hence

$$\Delta s_k \simeq \left\{ 1 + \left(\frac{\Delta y_k}{\Delta x_k} \right)^2 \right\}^{1/2} \Delta x_k.$$

Now the arc-length from $x = a$ to $x = b$ is approximately the sum of the Δs_k from each subinterval. In the limit this sum becomes an integral, following the usual adjustments.

Frame 8.2   Length of an arc

$$s = \int_a^b \left\{ 1 + \left(\frac{dy}{dx} \right)^2 \right\}^{1/2} dx = \int_a^b \sqrt{1 + (f'(x))^2} \, dx \qquad (8.4)$$

Example 8.4 Find the length of an 'arch' of a sine curve.
We have

$$y = \sin x \quad \Rightarrow \quad \frac{dy}{dx} = \cos x.$$

This gives the length as

$$s = \int_0^\pi \sqrt{1 + \cos^2 x}\, dx.$$

There is no anti-derivative available to complete the calculation. Instead we must turn to approximation methods – not covered here – one of which gives $s \simeq 3.8202$, correct to 4 dp. ∎

Example 8.5 Find the length of that part of the **semi-cubical parabola** $y = x^{3/2}$ from $x = 0$ to 1.

We have $\dfrac{dy}{dx} = \dfrac{3}{2}x^{1/2} \quad \Rightarrow \quad \left(\dfrac{dy}{dx}\right)^2 = \dfrac{9}{4}x,$ which leads to the length:

$$s = \int_0^1 \sqrt{1 + \tfrac{9}{4}x}\, dx = \int_0^1 \left(1 + \tfrac{9}{4}x\right)^{1/2} dx$$

$$= \left[\tfrac{2}{3}\left(1 + \tfrac{9}{4}x\right)^{3/2} \cdot \tfrac{4}{9}\right]_0^1$$

$$= \tfrac{8}{27}\left[\left(\tfrac{13}{4}\right)^{3/2} - 1\right] \simeq 1.44.$$

This integration uses the **linear composite rule** with $ax + b \equiv \frac{9}{4}x + 1$.

Note that the length of the straight line joining $(0,0)$ to $(1,1)$ is $\sqrt{2} \simeq 1.41$.

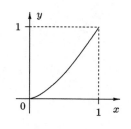

∎

Think about it like this

Note the difference between this problem and that of finding the area under the curve. In the case of the area we were able to ignore the fluctuation of the function over the small subinterval, since this was negligible compared with the area of the column on which it stood. **But this is not the case with the arc-length.** If it were, we would be able to write $\Delta s_k \simeq \Delta x_k$, and $s = \lim \sum \Delta x_k$. But that sum is equal to the length of the interval $b - a$, no matter what the curve actually is. Such a result is impossible; e.g., we know that the length of the arc of a unit circle, centred at the origin, from $x = 0$ to $x = 1$, is $\frac{\pi}{2}$, not 1.

The point is that the length of the arclet depends on its slope. The earlier graph shows the steeper the slope of the hypotenuse, the larger is Δs, assuming Δx is fixed. That is why the derivative – the gradient – gets sucked into the formula.

This difference is not peculiar to this context. It is effectively a dimensional issue: we can use quite rudimentary approximations to small quantities if they have a lower dimension than the target quantity – as in a one-dimensional Δx compared with a two-dimensional area – but not when the two dimensions are the same, as in Δx and Δs.

Ex 8.5 Find an integral giving the arc-length of the curve $y = e^{-x}$ for $0 \leqslant x \leqslant 2$. _Do not attempt to evaluate this integral._

Ex 8.6 Find the arc-length of the curve $y = 1 + \frac{2}{3}x^{\frac{3}{2}}$ for $0 \leqslant x \leqslant 3$.

8.3   Mean Values

For a finite sequence of values $\{f_1, f_2, \ldots, f_n\}$ we can compute a **mean** or 'average' value

$$\overline{f} = \frac{1}{n}[f_1 + f_2 + f_3 + \cdots + f_n] = \frac{1}{n}\sum_{k=1}^{n} f_k, \qquad (8.5)$$

which is often an informative measure. The question we now consider is how to extend this definition to a **function** defined on an **interval**.

Given a function f defined on $[a, b]$, we can seek its mean or average value over that interval as follows. We break the interval $[a, b]$ into n **equal** parts, as in the diagram. Choose a representative point x_k in the kth interval, calculate an average of the type in (8.5) and then try to refine it using a limit. We thus define

$$\overline{f} = \lim_{n \to \infty} \frac{1}{n} \sum_{k=1}^{n} f(x_k).$$

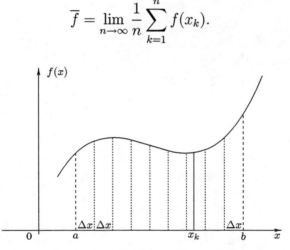

This limit can be evaluated as follows. Since there are n subintervals of equal width Δx, we have $\Delta x = \frac{1}{n}(b - a)$. Then $\frac{1}{n} = \Delta x/(b - a)$ and

$$\overline{f} = \lim_{n \to \infty} \frac{1}{b - a} \sum f(x_k)\,\Delta x$$

$$= \frac{1}{b - a} \lim_{n \to \infty} \sum f(x_k)\,\Delta x.$$

The limit-sum structure here is precisely that described in §8.1. We can immediately move to an integral giving the **mean value**.

Frame 8.3   *Mean value for a function*

$$\overline{f} = \frac{1}{b-a} \int_a^b f(x)\,dx \qquad (8.6)$$

Think about it like this

This formula (8.6), rearranged as $\int_a^b f(x)\,dx = (b-a)\overline{f}$, tells us the area under the graph, given by the integral, equals its width $b - a$, times the average height of the function ($\overline{f}$). This is a natural result: the areas above and below the average height cancel out, as seen in the diagram.

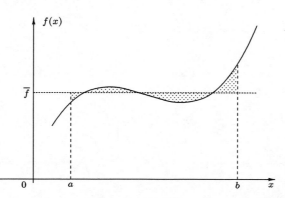

Algebraically, the key difference between (8.5) and (8.6) is that for a sequence we use $\frac{1}{n}\sum$ and for a function we use $\frac{1}{b-a}\int$. These are closely related since n and $b - a$ each give some sort of measure of the number of data values involved, while $\sum$ and $\int$ are corresponding methods for summing them.

Example 8.6   Find the mean values of

(a) x^2 over $[\,1, 4\,]$,   (b) $\sin x$ over $[\,0, 2\pi\,]$.

(a) The mean value is $\overline{f}$, where

$$\overline{f} = \frac{1}{4-1} \int_1^4 x^2\,dx = \tfrac{1}{3}\Big[\tfrac{1}{3}x^3\Big]_1^4 = \tfrac{1}{9}(64 - 1) = 7.$$

Note that this is **not** the same as the average of the end-point values, which is $\tfrac{1}{2}(1^2 + 4^2) = 8.5$.

(b) The mean value is $\overline{f}$, where

$$\overline{f} = \frac{1}{2\pi - 0} \int_0^{2\pi} \sin x\,dx = \tfrac{1}{2\pi}\Big[-\cos x\Big]_0^{2\pi} = \tfrac{1}{2\pi}(-1 + 1) = 0.$$

This function is anti-symmetric about $x = \pi$, so the values in $[\,0, \pi\,]$ precisely cancel out those in $[\,\pi, 2\pi\,]$.

■

Example 8.7   Power in an electric circuit is defined as voltage × current. This may depend on time and hence we define the average power as

$$\overline{P} = \frac{1}{T} \int_0^T v(t) i(t) \, dt.$$

Suppose the voltage is sinusoidal (AC), $V \sin \omega t$, and the current is also sinusoidal, but with amplitude I and phase lead ϕ. We compute the average over a single period $\frac{2\pi}{\omega}$ as

$$
\begin{aligned}
\overline{P} &= \frac{\omega}{2\pi} \int_0^{2\pi/\omega} V \sin \omega t \, I \sin(\omega t + \phi) \, dt \\
&= \frac{\omega V I}{2\pi} \int_0^{2\pi/\omega} \sin \omega t \sin(\omega t + \phi) \, dt \\
&= \frac{\omega V I}{4\pi} \int_0^{2\pi/\omega} [\cos \phi - \cos(2\omega t + \phi)] \, dt && \text{(from (7.6))} \\
&= \frac{\omega V I}{4\pi} \left[t \cos \phi - \frac{1}{2\omega} \sin(2\omega t + \phi) \right]_0^{2\pi/\omega} && \text{(linear composite rule)} \\
&= \frac{\omega V I}{4\pi} \left[\frac{2\pi}{\omega} \cos \phi + 0 \right] && \text{(periodicity of sin)} \\
&= \tfrac{1}{2} V I \cos \phi.
\end{aligned}
$$

Max power occurs when voltage and current are 'in phase': $\phi = 0$ and $\overline{P} = \tfrac{1}{2} V I$. ■

One problem with this definition for the mean is that it may deliver a value for $\overline{f}$ that is uninformative if f takes both positive and negative values, due to cancellation, as in Example 8.6(b). Thus, an AC current specified by a sine function has an average value of zero when measured over a whole number of periods. We could consider using $|f(x)|$ in the definition but the resulting integral is rather time-consuming to evaluate. Instead, it is more common to use the **root mean square (rms)** value. We remove the sign fluctuations by using $[f(x)]^2$. The mean value of this square is then computed and we finally remove the effect of the square by taking a square root.

Frame 8.4   *root mean square value for a function*

$$\text{rms } f(x) = \left[\frac{1}{b-a} \int_a^b [f(x)]^2 \, dx \right]^{1/2} \tag{8.7}$$

In words: *the rms value is the square root of the mean of the square of the function.* Note that the square root is essential if we are to preserve any unit of measurement in the original values of f.

Think about it like this

The rms value is very important. It is universally used for waveforms since it gives a measure immune to cancellation due to the oscillating nature of the wave. The apparently complicated nature of the measure is an illusion: it is often easier to evaluate than alternatives. It is also closely related to physical concepts such as energy and power. Measurements such as mains voltage and amplifier power are usually quoted as "rms", often without stating that.

Example 8.8 Find the rms for the functions specified in Example 8.6.

(a) The calculation is best set out by starting with the square of the rms value:

$$(\text{rms } f)^2 = \frac{1}{4-1}\int_1^4 \left(x^2\right)^2 dx = \tfrac{1}{3}\int_1^4 x^4\,dx$$

$$= \tfrac{1}{3}\left[\tfrac{1}{5}x^5\right]_1^4 = \tfrac{1}{15}(1024-1) = 68.2.$$

Hence rms $f = \sqrt{68.2} \simeq 8.26$.

(b) Again start by finding the square of the value:

$$(\text{rms } f)^2 = \frac{1}{2\pi-0}\int_0^{2\pi} \sin^2 x\,dx$$

$$= \frac{1}{2\pi}\int_0^{2\pi} \tfrac{1}{2}(1-\cos 2x)\,dx$$

$$= \tfrac{1}{4\pi}\left[x - \tfrac{1}{2}\sin 2x\right]_0^{2\pi} = \tfrac{1}{4\pi}(2\pi-0) = \tfrac{1}{2}.$$

Hence rms $f = \sqrt{0.5} \simeq 0.707$.

■

The result of Example 8.8(b) explains the $\sqrt{2}$ in Example 2.11. There are many advantages in quoting such quantities as rms values. The factor $\tfrac{1}{2}VI$ in Example 8.7 can be interpreted as "power = voltage × current", if the rms values $\tfrac{1}{\sqrt{2}}V$ and $\tfrac{1}{\sqrt{2}}I$ are used.

Ex 8.7 Find the mean values of $f(x) = x^2$ and $g(x) = x^3$ over $[-1,1]$.

Ex 8.8 Find the mean values of $f(x) = \cos x$ and $g(x) = \cos^2 x$ over $[0, 2\pi]$

Ex 8.9 Find the *root mean square* (rms) value of $f(x) = \cos(2x+\pi)$ over $[0, 2\pi]$

8.4   Further Applications of Integration

The examples in this section illustrate practical applications and are provided for background reading.

Example 8.9   Find the area of a circle, radius a.

Break the circle into 'ring' elements, with the kth ring at r_k from the centre, with width Δr_k.

The area of the ring is approximately:

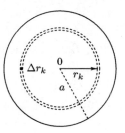

$$\text{length} \times \text{breadth} = 2\pi r_k \times \Delta r_k.$$

The total area is therefore approximately $\sum 2\pi r_k \Delta r_k$. Take the limit, transcribing into an integral:

$$A = \int_0^a 2\pi r \, dr = \left[\pi r^2 \right]_0^a = \pi a^2.$$

■

Example 8.10   A tank of liquid is observed to empty at a rate

$$(1 - 0.002t) \text{ kg s}^{-1}, \qquad (0 \leqslant t \leqslant 500),$$

where t is measured in seconds. Find the mass of fluid that leaves the tank in this period.

Consider the time period from t_k to $t_k + \Delta t_k$. During this period, approximately $(1 - 0.002t_k) \Delta t_k$ of liquid escapes. The total outflow is thus approximately:

$$\sum (1 - 0.002t_k) \Delta t_k \rightarrow \int_0^{500} (1 - 0.002t) \, dt$$
$$= \left[t - 0.001t^2 \right]_0^{500}$$
$$= 500 - 0.001 \times 500^2$$
$$= 250 \text{ kg}.$$

This problem can, in fact, be tackled by a different method. We can set up and solve a **differential equation**. This one is sufficiently simple to be solved without any general theory, and the comparison is informative.

The amount that empties between t_k and $t_k + \Delta t_k$ is

$$\Delta Q_k \simeq (1 - 0.002t_k) \Delta t_k.$$

Drop the k and rearrange:

$$\frac{\Delta Q}{\Delta t} \simeq 1 - 0.002t.$$

Let $\Delta t \to 0$:

$$\frac{dQ}{dt} = 1 - 0.002t.$$

Also, $Q(0) = 0$, since nothing has emptied at the start. Integrate:

$$Q = \int (1 - 0.002t)\, dt = t - 0.001t^2 + C.$$

Since $Q = 0$ at $t = 0$ we find $C = 0$. Then

$$Q(500) = 500 - 0.001 \times 500^2 = 250,$$

as before. ∎

This example indicates why people who model using mathematics find differential equations attractive. The answers are the same, as we would expect, but the differential equation approach has provided a bonus: we have a **formula** that is valid for all t in $[0, 500]$. This allows us to answer questions such as: how long will it take until the tank is half-empty?

In the next two examples the summation argument has been streamlined by omitting the counter k.

Example 8.11 Find the work required to lift a body, mass m, to a height H above the earth's surface.

The gravitational force on the body, at height h, is

$$F(h) = \frac{Cm}{(R+h)^2},$$

where C is a constant and R is the radius of the earth.

To move the body from height h to $h + \Delta h$ requires work

$$F(h)\,\Delta h = \frac{Cm}{(R+h)^2}\,\Delta h.$$

Add these and take the limit as $\Delta h \to 0$:

$$W = \int_0^H \frac{Cm}{(R+h)^2}\, dh = Cm \int_0^H (R+h)^{-2}\, dh$$
$$= Cm\left[-\frac{1}{R+h}\right]_0^H = Cm\left(\frac{1}{r} - \frac{1}{R+h}\right).$$

To move the body to an 'infinite' height, let $H \to \infty$, so $\frac{1}{R+H} \to 0$. The work is $W = \frac{Cm}{R}$. This is the amount of work needed to be able to overcome the earth's gravitation completely, and is the minimum energy that the body must be given if it is to be able to do that.

Suppose, therefore, that the body is given initial velocity v. Its **kinetic energy** must satisfy

$$\frac{1}{2}mv^2 \geqslant \frac{Cm}{R} \quad \Rightarrow \quad v \geqslant \sqrt{\frac{2C}{R}}.$$

When $h = 0$, we know that $F(h) = \frac{Cm}{R^2} = mg$, where g is the *acceleration due to gravity*. Hence $C = gR^2$ and we find

$$v \geqslant \sqrt{2gR} \simeq 1.2 \times 10^4 \, \mathrm{m\,s^{-1}}.$$

This value is the **escape velocity**, the minimum velocity that will allow a body (of any mass) to break free of the earth's gravitational pull. ∎

A further spatial example is the determination of the **centroid** or **centre of gravity** of a body. We shall not pursue this since it is described in detail in many textbooks and because centres of gravity for familiar shapes can often be easily deduced using symmetry.

Instead, consider the calculation of the mass of a body, when the **density** is not constant.

Example 8.12   A rod, positioned between $x = 0$ and $x = L$, has density $\rho(x)$ at position x. The cross-sectional area is A (constant). Find a formula for its mass.

Break the rod into elements and consider a small element of width Δx, positioned at x. Its mass is $(A\,\Delta x)\,\rho(x)$. Insert $\sum$ and take the limit as $\Delta x \to 0$, to obtain the required formula:

$$M = \int_0^L A\rho(x)\,dx = A\int_0^L \rho(x)\,dx.$$

∎

Similar to this is the problem of calculating the **moment of inertia** of a body about a line (or **axis**), often written as I. The moment of inertia plays a role in formulae for rotational motion that is the counterpart of 'mass' in straight line motion.

The moment of inertia of a 'point mass' m situated at distance r from the axis is simply mr^2. For a collection of point masses m_k at distances r_k it is

$$I = \sum_{k=1}^n m_k r_k^2. \tag{8.8}$$

The problem we now address is how to calculate I for a **rigid body** whose constituents are at a **variable** distance from the axis.

The answer is again integration: break the body up into small pieces throughout each of which we are approximately at a constant distance from the axis. Estimate the moment of inertia by adding the contributions from each as in (8.8), then take the limit. This is best seen by example. We shall examine two; in one we approximate the body by a collection of point masses, while in the other we are able to use a rather larger element, whose points are all at the same distance from the axis.

Example 8.13   Find formulae for the moments of inertia, about their centres, of (a) a uniform rod, length L and mass M; (b) a uniform disc, radius R and mass M.

(a) Consider the diagram below.

Break the rod into small pieces and concentrate on one of width Δx_k, at distance x_k from the centre.

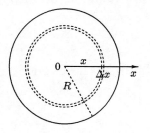

Using proportionality, the small element has mass $M\dfrac{\Delta x_k}{L}$ and hence moment of inertia

$$\frac{M}{L}\Delta x_k\, x_k^2,$$

since the moment of inertia of a point mass is its mass times the square of its distance from the axis.

The total moment of inertia is thus the following integral, which can be evaluated most easily using evenness:

$$I = \int_{-L/2}^{L/2}\frac{M}{L}x^2\,dx = 2\int_0^{L/2}\frac{M}{L}x^2\,dx$$
$$= \frac{2M}{L}\left[\frac{x^3}{3}\right]_0^{L/2} = \frac{2M}{L}\cdot\frac{1}{3}\cdot\frac{L^3}{8} = \frac{1}{12}ML^2.$$

(b) For the second case, we shall drop the subscripts k for ease of reading.

This time we break the disc into small rings where all points are at the same distance from the axis and hence the same moment of inertia. We concentrate on a ring of width Δx at distance x from the centre, as shown in the diagram.

This ring has approximate area given by its circumference times its thickness: $2\pi x\,\Delta x$. By proportionality, its mass is

$$M\frac{2\pi x\,\Delta x}{\pi R^2} = \frac{2M}{R^2}\,x\,\Delta x.$$

Since all points in the ring are distance x from the axis, its moment of inertia is $\dfrac{2M}{R^2}x^3\,\Delta x$. The total moment of inertia is thus

$$I = \int_0^R\frac{2M}{R^2}x^3\,dx = \frac{2M}{R^2}\left[\frac{x^4}{4}\right]_0^R$$
$$= \frac{2M}{R^2}\cdot\frac{R^4}{4} = \frac{1}{2}MR^2.$$

We finish with a further spatial problem, where a simple physical formula cannot be applied directly due to one factor not remaining constant.

Example 8.14   A brick wall of length l, breadth b and height h compresses under its own weight. The compression factor at any point is P/AE, where P is the total load above that point, A is the cross-sectional area of the wall and E is a property of the material of the bricks.

Find a formula for the total compression. This should involve the density of the bricks ρ and the constant g.

The problem here is that the bricks at the bottom are compressed more than those at the top, because of the extra weight above them. This introduces a variability that requires integration.

Choose an axis vertically downwards, with variable z. Consider the cross-section at depth z_k, width Δz_k. The load on this is: volume × density × g, i.e.,

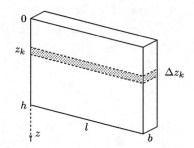

$$P = lbz_k\rho g$$

and hence the compression factor is

$$\frac{lbz_k\rho g}{lbE} = \frac{\rho g}{E}z_k.$$

The compression of this cross-section is calculated as vertical size times compression factor, although only approximately, since the load varies across Δz_k:

$$\frac{\rho g}{E}z_k\,\Delta z_k.$$

Add up all these contributions from $z = 0$ to h, to find the total compression:

$$\sum \frac{\rho g}{E}z_k\,\Delta z_k \rightarrow \int_0^h \frac{\rho g}{E}z\,dz = \frac{\rho g}{E}\left[\tfrac{1}{2}z^2\right]_0^h$$
$$= \frac{\rho h^2 g}{2E}.$$

Note that this is proportional to the **square** of the height of the wall.   ∎

Ex 8.10   Consider a sphere of radius a, with density at distance r from its centre given by the function $\rho(r)$. The sphere can be thought of as a collection of concentric shells at distance r from the centre and with thickness Δr. Use the fact that a sphere of radius r has surface area $4\pi r^2$ to show that the mass is given by

$$M = 4\pi \int_0^a r^2 \rho(r)\,dr.$$

Find the mass when the density is a constant: $\rho(r) \equiv d$.

Find the mass for a sphere with a core of different density from its outer shell, modelled by

$$\rho(r) = \begin{cases} D, & \text{if } 0 \leqslant r < \tfrac{a}{2}; \\ d, & \text{if } \tfrac{a}{2} \leqslant r \leqslant a. \end{cases}$$

Ex 8.11 Consider a dam with a rectangular end face, width L and height H. We wish to determine the total force on the face.

The force on an area A subject to pressure p is Ap, assuming p is constant. The difficulty in this problem is that p is not constant, but varies with depth. For fresh water, $p = 9800x$ (in $\mathrm{N\,m^{-2}}$), where x is the depth below the surface, measured in metres.

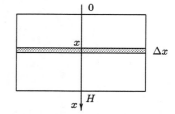

Find the force ΔF on the element of area of thickness Δx, shaded in the diagram. Integrate this to find an expression, as a definite integral, for the total force, for x from 0 to H. Evaluate this integral.

8.5 Revision Exercises

Ex 8.12 Draw superimposed graphs of the functions $y = x^3 - x^2$ and $y = 2x$. Find the (finite) area enclosed between their graphs.

Ex 8.13 Find the volume of the solid of revolution created by rotating the graph of $y = \cos x$ for $-\frac{\pi}{2} \leqslant x \leqslant \frac{\pi}{2}$ about the x-axis, through 2π radians.

Ex 8.14 A body of revolution is formed by rotating the area enclosed by the function $y = 1 - x^2$, the line $x = -1$ and the line $x = +1$, through 360° around the x-axis. Find the volume of this body.

Ex 8.15 Consider the straight line from $(0,0)$ to $(1,a)$. Verify that its equation is $y = ax$. Find $\frac{dy}{dx}$. Use this to show that the length of the line is

$$L = \int_0^1 \sqrt{1 + a^2}\, dx.$$

Evaluate the integral: the integrand is constant in this case.

Verify the answer using geometry.

Ex 8.16 Find the mean value of $f(x) = \sin^2 x$ over $[0, \pi]$.

Ex 8.17 Find the mean value of the function $f(x) = (5x + 3)^2$ over the interval $[0, 2]$.

Ex 8.18 Find the *root mean square* value for $f(x) = \dfrac{1}{\cos x}$, over $[0, \frac{\pi}{4}]$.

Ex 8.19 A bar of metal of density ρ is to be cast and is to have length L. Choose the x-axis to lie along its length. The cross-section at every point has an identical shape, but its area $A(x)$ tapers down *linearly* in x. At one end $A(0) = 1$ (in some unit). At the other end $A(L) = 1 - \alpha$, where we assume $\alpha < 1$. The objective is to find a formula for the mass. Show, first, that $A(x) = 1 - \frac{\alpha}{L}x$.

Now, break the bar into slices, where each slice has two faces that are cross-sections and a thickness of Δx. Explain why, for small Δx, a slice positioned near the point x will have mass approximately $\rho A(x)\Delta x$. Then approximate the mass of the bar by adding those up using a $\sum$.

The precise mass is now found by letting $\Delta x \to 0$ and converting the sum into the integral $\rho \int_0^L A(x)\, dx$. Evaluate this using the expression for $A(x)$ above.

Ex 8.20 A chemical process produces a substance at a rate of Ae^{-kt} gs^{-1}. Calculate how much has accumulated by time T (starting at time 0).

How much would accumulate if the process ran for ever?

ANSWERS TO EXERCISES

Applicable Mathematics

1.1 $-9/2$

1.2 (a) $8xy - 3x^2 + 4y^2$, (b) $x^2 + x - 6$, (c) $(x+3)(x+5)$, $(z-2)/z^2$, $(5x-3)(5x+3)$

1.3 $2x^4 + 3x^3 + 4x^2 + 5x + 6$, 88

1.4 (a) $4 - 3x - x^2$, $x^3 + 3x^2 + 2x$, (b) $\frac{x+y}{y-x}$, $\frac{x+3}{x+4}$

1.5 $(x+2)(x-4)$, $(u - \frac{1}{2})^2$, $x(x-1)(x+1)$, $x(x+4)$

1.6 (a) x^{-1}, $yx^{-2/3}$, y^{-1}, (b) $81x^2$, $3/t$

1.7 y^{15}, t^4, x^3, abc, t, x^4, $4t^2$, $6/x^3$, $1/y^6$, $16/x^4$

1.8 a/b^2, $16k^3$, $q^{9/2}/p^3$ (The first and last should, strictly speaking, have $|\cdots|$ brackets.)

1.9 (a) $x/4$, $(2-x)/x^2$, (b) $\frac{1}{2}(\sqrt{17} + \sqrt{15})$, $\frac{1}{7}(2\sqrt{5} - \sqrt{13})$

1.10 (a) 2, $\frac{1}{6}$, $\frac{3}{4}$, $\frac{113}{90}$, 1, $\frac{9}{16}$, $\frac{3}{16}$, $\frac{3}{2}$, (b) $\frac{2}{x}$, $\frac{2x-1}{(x-1)^2}$, $\frac{abc}{b+c}$, $\frac{2}{(x-2)(x+12)}$, $\frac{1}{2x+1}$

1.11 $x/(x+1)$

1.12 N, Y, Y, N

1.13 $t(m^2 + p^2)/(m^2 - p^2)$

1.14 $x = \sqrt{\pi}r$, $K = 2C/\sqrt{\pi}$

1.15 2

1.16 $y/(y-1)$

1.17 $|\cos\theta|$, $x = \sec\theta$, $1/|\tan\theta|(= |\cot\theta|)$

1.18 1, -4

1.19 (a) $A = 8$, $B = -5$, (b) $A = 1$, $B = 0$, $C = -1$, $D = 0$

1.20 general case: Y, N, N, N; positive case: Y, N, Y, Y

1.21 $x \geqslant 0$

1.22 (a) $[-3, 7]$, (b) $|x+1| < 3$

1.23 (a) $(0, 12)$, $[-4, 3]$, (b) $|x-7| < 4$, $|x-1| \leqslant 3$, $|x-1.5| < 4.5$, $|x + \frac{1}{12}| \leqslant \frac{1}{4}$

1.24 (a) 2.718, 2.7183, 2.71828 18285, (b) 0.005, 0.2%, (c) 0.21

1.25 (a) dp: 3, 0, 10, 0, sf: 6, 4, 3, 3, (b) 0.24%, (c) 84 sec

1.26 (a) $3\sqrt{2} + 4$, (b) 3

1.27 $x^4 - 2x^3 + 3x^2 - 2x + 1$

1.28 $1 - 2x^6 + x^{12}$

1.29 $y = x^2/(1+x^2)$

1.30 $z(z-1)$

1.31 $A = -1$, $B = 1$

1.32 $1 < x < 4$

1.33 $|Q - 17.13| \leqslant 0.29$, 1.7%

1.34 $[3.18, 3.66]$, 7%

2.1 (a) $[a_2, a_3]$, $[x_0, x_1, x_2]$, $[u_4]$, (b) $(-1)^n/(2n+1)$

2.2 $T_n = \frac{1}{2}n(n+1)$, $S_n = n^2$

2.3 0.9524, 1.0244, 0.9880, 1.0061

2.4 0.373 m, $8(0.6)^n$ m

2.5 $x_2 = x_3 = 4.123106$

2.6 $11 - 3n$

2.7 $a_2 = 1$, $a_5 = 10$

2.8 $\frac{1+(n-2)\sqrt{x}}{1-x}$

2.9 $64(0.75)^n$

2.10 10, 20, 40, 80

2.11 (a) 54, (b) 5, 0, -11, 19

2.12 (a) $\sum_{n=1}^{\infty} \frac{x^n}{n(n+1)}$,
(b) $\sum_{n=1}^{\infty} (-1)^{n+1} n x^n$
or $\sum_{n=0}^{\infty} (-1)^{n+1} n x^n$

2.13 1683

2.14 (a) 4950, (b) 328350, (c) 500, (d) 55

2.15 (a) $\frac{10}{9}$, (b) $1 - \left(\frac{1}{2}\right)^{99}$, (c) $3^{10} - 1$

2.16 $12\left[1 - (0.6)^n\right]$, 12

2.17 (a) Y (5), (b) N, (c) N, (d) Y (100/19)

2.18 -6, 34, 154

2.19 $\frac{1}{4}\left(1 - 0.2^{10}\right)$

2.20 $\frac{27}{4}$

2.21 $a_0 = 32$, $r = \frac{1}{2}$, 64, $\frac{128}{3}$

3.1 120, 720, 504, 210, 210

3.2 (a) 40320, (b) 1680

3.3 $9 \times 9 \times 8 \times 7 \times 6 = 27216$

3.4 3, 15, 35, 10, 56, 190, 1140

3.5 5040, 210, 35

3.6 70

3.8 10, 84

3.9 1 6 15 20 15 6 1

3.10 $x^6 + 12x^5 + 60x^4 + 160x^3 + 240x^2 + 192x + 64$

3.11 (a) $x^3 + \frac{3}{2}x^2 + \frac{3}{4}x + \frac{1}{8}$
(b) $32x^5 + 240x^4 + 720x^3 + 1080x^2 + 810x + 243$
(c) $x^5 - \frac{5}{2}x^4 + \frac{5}{2}x^3 - \frac{5}{4}x^2 + \frac{5}{16}x - \frac{1}{32}$
(d) $729 - 2916x + 4860x^2 - 4320x^3 + 2160x^4 - 576x^5 + 64x^6$
(e) $81x^4 + 216x^3 y + 216x^2 y^2 + 96xy^3 + 16y^4$

3.12 16.032

3.13 0.00224, 0.00105, 0.00069

3.14 (a) $17!/(3!14!) = 680$, $680x^{14}$,
(b) $112x^2$

3.15 $^{12}P_4 = 12 \times 11 \times 10 \times 9 = 11880$

3.16 (a) $8! = 40320$, (b) 36, 35, 330

3.17 20, 45, 1365

3.18 $x^8 - 8x^6 + 24x^4 - 32x^2 + 16$

3.19 $32 - 80y + 80y^2 - 40y^3 + 10y^4 - y^5$

3.20 $64x^6 + 192x^5 + 240x^4 + 160x^3 + 60x^2 + 12x + 1$

4.1 $f(x) = -2x + 5$

4.2 1.6919

4.3 1.662, 0.531

4.4 $2x^2 - x - 1$

4.5 $Q(x) = -x^2 + 3x + 7$

4.6 $(x-1)^2 - 16$, roots -3, 5, minimum at $(1, -16)$

4.7 (a) $(x+2)^2 + 1$, no roots, min 1 at $x = -2$
(b) $-2\left(x + \frac{1}{4}\right)^2 + \frac{49}{8}$, $x = -2$ or $\frac{3}{2}$, max $\frac{49}{8}$ at $x = -\frac{1}{4}$
(c) $(3x-2)^2$, $x = \frac{2}{3}$ (twice), min 0 at $x = \frac{2}{3}$
(d) $-\left(x - \frac{3}{2}\right)^2 - \frac{3}{4}$, no roots, max $-\frac{3}{4}$ at $x = \frac{3}{2}$

4.8 (a) $-2 < a < 2$, (b) $a = \pm 2$

4.9 $5\sqrt{3}\,\text{m}$, $\frac{5}{4}\,\text{m}$

4.10 $R = 77.46$, i values are 0.194, 0.387, 0.581, 0.775

4.11 (a) $x^2 + 2x + 5$, no, (b) quotient $x^2 + 3$, remainder 2

4.12 $(x-2)(x+2)(x^2+1)$

4.13 $x = 1$ or -3

4.14 (a) $(x+1)(x-2)(x-3)$
(b) $(x-1)(x+3)(x^2+3)$
(c) $x(x+1)(x+2)(2x-1)$
(d) $(x+1)^2(3x-1)(x-2)$

4.15 (a) quotient 13, remainder 24,
(b) $x + \frac{x-5}{x^2+1}$

4.16 31, 1

4.17 (a) quot. $x+2$, rem. $5x-3$,
(b) quot. x^2-2x+2, rem. $-x-1$

4.18 $y = 1 + \frac{1}{x+1}$, asymptotes
$y = 1$, $x = -1$

4.19 $-x + \frac{1}{x+1}$, asymptotes
$y = -x$, $x = -1$

4.20 (a) $1/(x+1) + 1/(x-1)$
(b) $1/(x+2) + 1/(x-1) - 1/(x-2)$
(c) $2/x - 1/(x-1) + 2/(x-1)^2$

4.21 (a) $3/(x+1) - 1/(2x-1)$
(b) $1/(x-2) - 1/(x+1)$
$\quad - 2/(x+1)^2$
(c) $-1/(x+3) + 2/(x-1)$
$\quad - 1/(x-1)^2$
(d) $1 + 4/(x-3) - 3/(x-4)$

4.22 $\frac{2.5}{x-1} - \frac{1.5}{x+1}$,
asymptotes $y = 0$, $x = 1$, $x = -1$

4.23 $\frac{0.5}{r} - \frac{1}{r+1} + \frac{0.5}{r+2}$

4.24 0.8656

4.25 $4(x-1)^2 - 25$, roots $-\frac{3}{2}$, $\frac{7}{2}$,
min at $x = 1$, value -25

4.26 $(x-1)(x-2)(x^2+x+2)$

4.27 $(x+1)(x-3)(x^2-x+3)$

4.28 $3/(2x-1) - 1/(x+1)$

4.29 $3/(x-2) - 2/(x+5)$

4.30 $3/x - 1/(x-1) + 2/(x+3)$

5.1 v, s, s, v, s, v, s

5.2 0

5.3 $2\sqrt{2}\,\text{N}$, $-135°$ to x-axis (SW)

5.4 $\mathbf{q} - \mathbf{p}$, $\mathbf{p} + \mathbf{q}$, $\mathbf{p} + \mathbf{q} + \mathbf{r}$, D to F

5.5 $7\,\text{N}$, $38.2°$

5.6 $\overrightarrow{AB}$

5.7 (a) $\mathbf{c} - \mathbf{b}$, (b) $\frac{1}{2}\mathbf{c} - \mathbf{b}$, (d) $\frac{3}{4}\mathbf{b} - \frac{1}{4}\mathbf{c}$

5.8 (b) $(8, 2, 9)$, $\sqrt{181}$, (c) $\sqrt{181}$

5.9 (a) $(4, 2, 2)$, (b) $(0, -1, 4)$,
(c) $\left(\frac{3}{2}, \frac{1}{2}, \frac{3}{2}\right)$, (d) $\sqrt{2}$, (e) 3,
(f) $\sqrt{14}$, (g) $\sqrt{5}$, (h) $\left(\frac{2}{3}, \frac{1}{3}, \frac{2}{3}\right)$

5.10 $\alpha = \pm 2$

5.11 $\sqrt{3}$, 1

5.12 (a) $-5\sqrt{2}$, $5\sqrt{2}$,
(b) 13, $-67.38°$ to x-axis,
(c) $7\,\text{N}$, $38.2°$

5.13 (a) $\frac{2}{3}\mathbf{i} + \frac{1}{3}\mathbf{j} - \frac{2}{3}\mathbf{k}$, $\frac{2}{3}$, $\frac{1}{3}$, $-\frac{2}{3}$,
$48.19°$, $70.53°$, $131.81°$,
(b) $(0, 1, -2)$, $(-1, 0, -3)$,
0, $\frac{1}{\sqrt{5}}$, $-\frac{2}{\sqrt{5}}$; $-\frac{1}{\sqrt{10}}$, 0, $-\frac{3}{\sqrt{10}}$,
(c) $60°$ or $120°$

5.14 9, $79°$

5.15 (a) 2, (b) 3, (c) 1, (d) 4, (e) 0,
(f) $\left(-\frac{1}{3}, -\frac{2}{3}, \frac{2}{3}\right)$, (g) $\left(-\frac{1}{3}, -\frac{2}{3}, \frac{2}{3}\right)$,
(h) $\left(\frac{4}{3}, -\frac{1}{3}, \frac{1}{3}\right)$

5.16 $-7\,\text{J}$

5.17 60, 0, -60, total 0; 30, -40, 10,
total 0

5.18 5

5.19 (a) $75.04°$, (b) $90°$, (c) $16.78°$,
(d) $4/3$, (e) 1, 7

5.20 $\overrightarrow{OB} = -\overrightarrow{OA}$, $\overrightarrow{XA} =$
$\overrightarrow{OA} - \overrightarrow{OX}$, $\overrightarrow{XB} = -\overrightarrow{OA} - \overrightarrow{OX}$

5.21 3, 2, 1

5.22 $|(1, 0, -1)| = \sqrt{2}$, $|(3, -3, 3)| = 3\sqrt{3}$; $|\mathbf{0}| = 0$, $|(3, 1, 3)| = \sqrt{19}$

5.23 $\left(\frac{6}{25}, \frac{8}{25}\right)$, $\left|\left(\frac{44}{25}, -\frac{33}{25}\right)\right| = \frac{11}{5}$

5.24 $(2, -1)$, 20% of way from A to B

5.25 $(-1 + 2t, t, 1 - 2t)$, $t = 4/9$, $\sqrt{2}/3$

5.27 (a) $(1, -5, 0)$, (b) 5, (c) $45°$

5.28 (a) $(0, 6, -11)$, (b) 6, (c) $82.34°$, (d) $\left(-\frac{3}{5}, 0, \frac{4}{5}\right)$

5.29 (a) $5\sqrt{5}$, (b) $93.69°$, (c) $\left(\frac{6}{11}, -\frac{6}{11}, \frac{7}{11}\right)$

5.30 $\frac{1}{10}(8, -6)$, $(0.8, -0.6)$, $|(1.2, 1.6)| = 2$

5.31 $\mathbf{b} - \mathbf{a}$, $\frac{1}{2}\mathbf{b} - \mathbf{a}$, $\mathbf{a} \bullet \mathbf{b} = \mathbf{a} \bullet \mathbf{a}$

5.32 $\mathbf{a} - \mathbf{b}$, $\frac{1}{2}\mathbf{a}$, $2\mathbf{b}$, $\frac{1}{2}\mathbf{a} - 2\mathbf{b}$, $\alpha = \frac{1}{3}$, $\beta = \frac{2}{3}$

5.33 $\frac{1}{2}(\mathbf{a}+\mathbf{b})$, $\frac{1}{4}(\mathbf{a}+\mathbf{b})$, $\frac{1}{4}\mathbf{a} - \frac{3}{4}\mathbf{b}$, $\alpha = \frac{4}{3}$, $\beta = \frac{1}{3}$

6.1 $-1 - 5i$, $12i$, $-2i$, $-\frac{1}{2}i$, $\frac{1}{10}(3+i)$

6.2 (a) -25, $-4+i$, $-5-12i$, $\frac{1}{5}(4+7i)$, $2a/(a^2+1)$, $\left[(b^2-1) + 2bi\right]/(b^2+1)$, $-i$
(b) i. $u = -y$, $v = x$;
ii. $u = x^3 - 3xy^2$, $v = 3x^2y - y^3$

6.3 5, -12, $5 + 12i$, 13, $\frac{1}{169}(5+12i)$

6.4 $z_1:$ $\sqrt{13}$, 2, -3, $2+3i$;
$z_2:$ $\sqrt{26}$, 5, 1, $5-i$;
i. $13 - 13i$, ii. $-3 - 4i$,
iii. $\frac{1}{26}(9 + 5i)$, iv. $-1 + 5i$

6.5 $-1 \pm 3i$

6.6 (a) $z = \frac{5}{2} \pm 2i$,
(b) $z^2 - 6z + 10 = 0$, (c) -2, $3 \pm i$

6.7 17

6.8 (b) 1, $1+i$, $2i$, $-2+2i$, -4; then $-4 - 4i$, $-8i$, $8 - 8i$, 16

6.9 (a) line $y = -x$;
circle centre $(0, 1)$, radius 1

6.10 (a) i. circle: centre $(0, -1)$, radius 1, $x^2 + y^2 + 2y = 0$;
ii. line: $x = \frac{1}{2}$;
iii. circle: centre $(2, 0)$, radius $\sqrt{2}$, $x^2 + y^2 - 4x + 2 = 0$;
iv. line: $y = 1$

6.11 (a) $2 + 2\sqrt{3}i$, (b) $\sqrt{3} - i$

6.12 $2\left(\cos\frac{3\pi}{4} + i\sin\frac{3\pi}{4}\right)$

6.13 2, $-\frac{\pi}{6}$, $2\left[\cos\left(-\frac{\pi}{6}\right) + i\sin\left(-\frac{\pi}{6}\right)\right]$;
$2\sqrt{2}$, $-\frac{3\pi}{4}$,
$2\sqrt{2}\left[\cos\left(-\frac{3\pi}{4}\right) + i\sin\left(-\frac{3\pi}{4}\right)\right]$;
2, $-\frac{\pi}{2}$, $2\left[\cos\left(-\frac{\pi}{2}\right) + i\sin\left(-\frac{\pi}{2}\right)\right]$

6.15 (a) $10i$, (b) $\frac{5}{4}(\sqrt{3} + i)$, (c) -64,
(d) $\left(\sqrt{3} - \frac{5}{2}\right) + \left(1 - \frac{5\sqrt{3}}{2}\right)i$

6.16 1, $\frac{1}{2}(-1 \pm \sqrt{3}i)$, ω can be either complex root

6.17 $2\left(\cos\frac{\pi}{3} + i\sin\frac{\pi}{3}\right)$, $\frac{1}{4} - \frac{\sqrt{3}}{4}i$,
$-2 + 2\sqrt{3}i$; $\pm\frac{1}{\sqrt{2}}\left(\sqrt{3} + i\right)$

6.18 $\cos^2\theta - \sin^2\theta$, $2\sin\theta\cos\theta$

6.19 $4\cos^3\theta - 3\cos\theta$, $3\sin\theta - 4\sin^3\theta$

6.20 $\frac{1}{2}(\sqrt{3} + i)$, $\frac{1}{2}(1 + \sqrt{3}i)$

6.21 1, -1, i, $-i$

6.22 (a) $9e^{-\pi i/2}$, $\frac{3}{\sqrt{2}}(1-i)$,
(b) $e^{\pi i}$, $\frac{1}{2}(-\sqrt{3} + i)$
(c) $\sqrt{8}e^{3\pi i/4}$, $1 + i$,
(d) $8e^{3\pi i/4}$, $4i$

6.23 (a) $\frac{3}{2}\left(\sqrt{3} + i\right)$, $\frac{3}{2}\left(-\sqrt{3} + i\right)$, $-3i$,
(b) $\frac{1}{4}(\sqrt{3} + i)$, $\frac{1}{4}(-\sqrt{3} + i)$, $-\frac{1}{2}i$,
(c) $4\sqrt{2}(\pm 1 \pm i)$, (d) ± 8

6.24 $-e^2$, $\frac{1}{2}(e^\pi + e^{-\pi})$

6.25 $\frac{e}{2}(\sqrt{3} - i)$, $\frac{i}{2}\left(e^{\pi/2} - e^{-\pi/2}\right)$,
$-\frac{1}{2}\left(e^\pi + e^{-\pi}\right)$

6.26 (a) $5 + 5i$, (b) $\sqrt{5}$, (c) $\frac{1}{2}(1 - i)$

6.27 (a) $-7 - i$, (b) 5, (c) $\frac{1}{5}(1 + 2i)$,
(d) $8 - 6i$

6.28 13, $12+5i$, $\frac{1}{169}(12+5i)$, $119 - 120i$,
$13\left[\cos(-0.395) + i\sin(-0.395)\right]$

6.29 $z = \frac{3}{2} \pm 2i$

6.30 (a) $-4 \pm 7i$, (b) $2z^2 - 2z + 5$

6.31 $z = 2\left(\cos\frac{2\pi}{3} + i\sin\frac{2\pi}{3}\right)$
$z^2 = 4\left[\cos\left(-\frac{2\pi}{3}\right) + i\sin\left(-\frac{2\pi}{3}\right)\right]$

6.32 64, $\sqrt{2}e^{-\pi i/6}$

6.33 (a) $-2 + 2i$, (b) $\sqrt{2}e^{\pi i/4} = 1 + i$

Mathematical Methods

1.1 b, c, d, f, g are functions

1.2 $x < 1$, $y > 0$

1.3 (a) 2, (b) $y = 2x+3$, (c) $2y+x = 1$

1.4 (a) $(1,1)$, (b) $(2,\frac{1}{2})$, (c) lines are parallel

1.6 $\begin{cases} x^2 + 5x + 3, & \text{if } x \leqslant 0; \\ x^2 + x^4 + 3, & \text{if } 0 < x \leqslant 1; \\ 2x + x^4 + 2, & \text{if } x > 1. \end{cases}$

1.7 $1-4a^2$, $1-z^4$, $1-x$, $2b-b^2$, $x-x^3$, $1 - (1/x)^2$, $x^2 - 1$, $1 - (x+y)^2$

1.10 odd, neither, even

1.11 even, odd, odd, even

1.12 $-\frac{3}{2}$, 2, 0, -1, 1, -1, 0

1.13 -4, -6, $f(x) = (x-5)^2 - 5(x-5)$

1.14 4.1091, $h = 6.583 \times 10^{-34}$, 2.291 eV

1.16 $C = \frac{75}{2T+75}$

1.17 even, even, neither, even, odd, neither, odd, odd

1.18 2, $f(x) = -2\sin x$

1.19 $\frac{1}{2}$, 1, 0, $\frac{1}{2}$

1.20 3, 4

2.1 (a) $3\pi/4$, $11\pi/6$, (b) $120°$, $210°$, (c) $\sqrt{3}/2$, $1/\sqrt{3}$, $\sqrt{3}/2$

2.2 $-s$, s, $-s$

2.4 $-\frac{3}{5}$

2.5 $\sin x = -1/2$, $\cos x = -\sqrt{3}/2$, $\tan x = 1/\sqrt{3}$, $\sec x = -2/\sqrt{3}$, $\cot x = \sqrt{3}$

2.6 $\frac{1}{9}$

2.7 $2\left|\sin\frac{x}{2}\right|$, $\tan^2\frac{x}{2}$

2.8 (a) $\sin 9x + \sin 5x$, (b) $\frac{1}{2}\cos 2x - \frac{1}{2}\cos 8x$

2.9 $\sqrt{29}$, 2

2.10 (a) $\sqrt{2}\sin(t - \frac{\pi}{4})$, (b) $13\sin(2t + 1.9656)$

2.11 $-\sin x$, $-\sin x$, $-\cos x$, $-\cos x$

2.13 $\frac{1}{2}$, $\frac{1}{2}$, 8

2.14 (a) $\cos 2x$, (b) $2\cosec 2x$, (c) $2\left|\cos\frac{x}{2}\right|$

2.15 (a) $\frac{1}{2}\sin 7x - \frac{1}{2}\sin 5x$, (b) $\cos 10x + \cos 4x$

2.16 10, 1

2.17 17, 4π

2.18 $f(t) = 5\sin(\pi t + 0.64)$, 2, $t = n - 0.20$ (2 dp; any integer n)

3.1 e^{2x}, 2^x

3.2 $x = 0$

3.3 $\frac{1}{5}(x - 3)$ (x in $\mathbb{R}$), $\frac{1+x}{1-x}$ ($x \neq 1$)

3.4 (a) 1, 2, 4, 0, (b) $\frac{1}{4}$, $\frac{2}{3}$, $\frac{3}{2}$

3.5 (a) 0.6931, (b) -0.7675, (c) 8.2433, (d) 0.1353, (e) 148.4132

3.6 (a) 5, (b) $\log_5 2 = \ln 2 / \ln 5$

3.7 (a) $\frac{1}{4}$, (b) $2/\sqrt{3}$

3.8 (a) $\frac{8e}{7}$, (b) $a = 2$

3.9 $W = W_T + KT\ln(Q - 1)$

3.10 (a) $y = e^4 e^{-5x} \simeq 54.6 e^{-5x}$, (b) $y = 100 e^{-5x}$

3.11 (c) $m \simeq -2$

3.12 (a) $\log 100$, (b) $\log 4$, (c) $\log 108$, (d) $\log 1.28$, (e) $2\log b$, (f) $2\log a$, (g) $3\log t$, (h) 0

3.13 (a) $\exp\left(\frac{1}{\pi}\ln 10\right) \simeq 2.0812$, (b) $\sqrt{5} \simeq 2.2361$, (c) $\ln 18 / \ln 1.5 \simeq 7.1285$

3.14 $x = e^{-2y}$

3.15 $x = \ln 3$

3.16 $\ln 2, \ln 4$

3.17 $\frac{32}{25}$

3.18 (a) $e^{-1}x^2$, (b) 3

3.19 $x = \frac{1}{2a}\left(1 \pm \sqrt{1-8a}\right)$,
$0 < a \leqslant \frac{1}{8}$

3.20 (a) $25e^{10t}$,
(b) $e^{0.5} \simeq 1.6487$, $4\ln 2 \simeq 2.7726$

4.1 $1, 0.6, 0.4, -4\,\mathrm{m\,s^{-2}}$

4.2 (b) $-0.039\,216$, (c) $-0.039\,920$,
(d) $-0.04 = -\frac{1}{5^2}$

4.3 $3x^2, (1-x)^{-2}$

4.4 $y = -4x + 4$

4.6 (a) $-12x^3$, (b) $22x^{10}$,
(c) $4x^3 + 12x^2 + 12x + 4$,
(d) $10Ax^9 + B$

4.7 (a) $5t^4 + 12t^3 - 2$,
(b) $12x^2 - 3x - \frac{4}{x^2}$,
(c) $-P_0/x^2 + 2/\left(P_0 x^3\right)$

4.8 $4\pi r + 20\pi$

4.9 $y = \sqrt[3]{\frac{Q^2}{gB^2}}$

4.10 $v = -3.75\,\mathrm{ms^{-1}}$, $t = 1$,
$\mathrm{accln} = -6t$

4.11 $k_T = 1/p$

4.12 (b) min, (c) $x = -1$, max

4.13 $\sqrt[3]{2}$, min

4.14 (a) $2x - 3$, (b) 1, (d) $m = 1$,
(e) $y = x - 1$

4.15 $y = 3x - 4$, $y = -\frac{1}{4}$

4.16 (a) $\frac{1}{4}$, (b) $\left(\frac{4}{3}\right)^{3/2} = \frac{8}{3\sqrt{3}}$

4.17 $y = 2x - 3.5$

4.18 1 max, 2 min

5.1 (a) $8x$, (b) $(x^2+1)(4x^3 - 21x^2) + 2x(x^4 - 7x^3 + 5)$,
(c) $(3x^2 + 4/x^2 + 2)(3x^2 + 1/x^2) + (6x - 8/x^3)(x^3 - 1/x)$

5.2 (a) $\frac{4-2x}{(x^2-4x+1)^2}$, (b) $\frac{x^2-4x}{(x-2)^2}$,
(c) $\frac{2x^3+3x^2-4}{(x+1)^2}$

5.3 $\frac{x^2}{x^2+2}, \frac{1-x}{1+x}$

5.4 (a) $\frac{1}{\sqrt{x+1}}$, $x > -1$,
(b) $g(x) = x^2 + x + 1$, $f(x) = 1/x^2$

5.5 $u(x) = x^3 + 1$, $f(x) = \sqrt{x}$;
$u(x) = 1/x$, $f(x) = \tan x$

5.6 (a) $-3x^2/(2\sqrt{1-x^3})$,
(b) $\frac{10x}{3}(5x^2 + 1)^{-2/3}$

5.7 (a) $8x + 24$, (b) $200(2x+6)^{99}$,
(c) $6(5x+1)^2(2x-1)^2 + 10(5x+1)(2x-1)^3$, (d) $\frac{(x-1)(9-x)}{(x+3)^4}$

5.9 (a) $\omega\cos(\omega t - \pi/4)$,
(b) $2\tan x \sec^2 x = 2\sin x/\cos^3 x$

5.10 (a) $-3\sin(3x)$, (b) $\cos^2 x - \sin^2 x$,
(c) $\frac{\sin x}{\cos^2 x}$,
(d) $10\sin(5t+8)\cos(5t+8)$,
(e) $\omega\cos(\omega t + \phi)$

5.12 $-2e^{-2x}$, $2/(2x-1)$, $\ln x$,
$(x - 2x\ln x)/x^4$,
$e^{2x}(2\cos x - \sin x)$, $xe^{x^2/2}$

5.13 (a) $Ae^{-kt}\{\omega\cos(\omega t + \phi) - k\sin(\omega t + \phi)\}$

5.14 $3^n \frac{k!}{(k-n)!}(3x+2)^{k-n}$

5.15 $2e^x\cos x - 2e^x\sin x$

5.16 $v(t) = 2\pi\cos\left(\pi t - \frac{\pi}{4}\right)$,
$a(t) = -2\pi^2\sin\left(\pi t - \frac{\pi}{4}\right)$,
$t = \frac{1}{4} + k$, $t = \frac{3}{4} + k$ (k integer)

5.17 $\tan\theta = \mu$

5.18 $x = \frac{1}{a} - 1$, min ($a < 0$), max ($a > 0$), none ($a = 0$)

5.19 (a) $3x^2$, (b) $(x^2 + x - 2)(6x - 5) + (2x+1)(3x^2 - 5x + 1)$

5.20 $\frac{6-2x^3}{(x^3+x+6)^2}$

5.21 (a) $\frac{1+x^2}{x^2}$, $\frac{1}{x^2+1}$ (b) $\frac{1}{2}\ln x$, $\sqrt{\ln x}$

5.22 $\frac{x}{\sqrt{1+x^2}}$

5.23 $y = x + 1$

5.24 (a) $4(x+1)^3$, (b) $6(2x-1)^2$,
(c) $45(5x+3)^8$, (d) $-6(2-3x)$

5.25 (a) $-8(5x+1)^3(3-2x)^3 +$
$15(5x+1)^2(3-2x)^4$, (b) $-\frac{12}{(3x-2)^5}$,
(c) $6(1-2x)^{-4}$

5.26 (a) $3\cos 3x$, (b) $-\frac{\pi}{2}\sin\frac{\pi x}{2}$,
(c) $2\cos(2x+3)$, (d) $3\sec^2 3x$,
(e) $2\sec 2x \tan 2x$,
(f) $x\cos x + \sin x$,
(g) $2\cos 2x \cos 3x - 3\sin 2x \sin 3x$,
(h) $x^{3/2}\cos x + \frac{3}{2}\sqrt{x}\sin x$
(i) $-\frac{x\sin x + \cos x}{x^2}$, (j) $-\operatorname{cosec}^2 x$,
(k) $4\sin^3 x \cos x$, (l) $\sec x$

5.27 $\frac{1-\cos t}{\sin^2 t}$

5.28 $y = x - \frac{\pi}{6} + \frac{\sqrt{3}}{2}$

5.29 $\ln(2x) = \ln 2 + \ln x$

5.30 $5x + 10x \ln x$

5.31 (a) $3x^2 - 4x + 1$, $6x - 4$, 6,
(b) $10(2x-1)^4$, $80(2x-1)^3$,
$480(2x-1)^2$, $a^m n(n-1)\cdots(n - m + 1)(ax+b)^{n-m}$

5.32 $-4\sin x \cos x$ or $-2\sin(2x)$

6.1 Missing numbers: 400, 0, 150; 150, 550, 700

6.2 $\frac{1}{4}x^4 + C$, $27/2$, $2t^{3/2} + C$, $\frac{1}{2}$

6.3 0, $2/5$, $3/4$, 1

6.4 $a = 0$, $3/2$

6.5 $\frac{1}{3}e^{3x} + C$, $\frac{1}{2}$, $\ln 2 + \frac{3}{8}$, $4\sin\frac{t}{2} + C$

6.6 (a) $\frac{1}{10\pi}$, 0, (b)
$\Delta g = T\left(A + \frac{a}{T} - \frac{a}{T_0} - b\ln\frac{T}{T_0}\right)$

6.7 (a) $2\ln 2 - 7/9$, (b) 9, (c) $1/8$,
(d) $2 - \sqrt{2}$

6.8 (a) 9, (b) $16/3$, (c) 4

6.9 $8/3$, $-5/12$, $37/12$

6.10 0, 0, $\frac{255}{8}$

6.11 $18 = \frac{14}{3} - \frac{1}{6} + \frac{27}{2}$

6.14 (a) $x^7 + C$, (b) $-3x^6 + C$,
(c) $\frac{1}{4}x^4 + x^3 + \frac{3}{2}x^2 + x + C$,
(d) $\frac{1}{11}Ax^{11} + \frac{1}{2}Bx^2 + Cx + D$

6.15 $3562.62\,\text{J}$

6.16 $3/2$

6.17 1

6.18 $\frac{2\pi^3}{3}$

6.19 $2/3$

7.1 $\frac{7}{2}\sin(2x+1) + \frac{3}{5}\cos(5x) + C$,
$\frac{1}{6}\ln|6x-2| + C$, $\frac{1}{3}(x+1)^3 + C$

7.2 $\frac{1}{3}e^{3x+2} + C$, $\frac{1}{2}\ln|2x+4| + C$,
$-\frac{2}{3}(9-u)^{3/2} + C$, $\frac{1}{18}(3t-4)^6 + C$,
$\frac{1}{10}\sin\left(10t - \frac{\pi}{4}\right) + C$

7.3 $\frac{1}{2}x - \frac{1}{12}\sin(6x) + C$,
$-\frac{1}{4}\cos(2x) + C$,
$-\frac{1}{10}\cos(5x) + \frac{1}{2}\cos x + C$,
$\frac{1}{12}\sin(6x) + \frac{1}{8}\sin(4x) + C$,
$\frac{1}{2}\sin x - \frac{1}{14}\sin(7x) + C$,
$\frac{1}{2}x + \frac{1}{2\pi}\sin \pi x + C$

7.4 (a) $\frac{1}{2}\ln\left|\frac{x}{x+2}\right| + C$,
(b) $2\ln|x+5| - \ln|x+3| + C$, (c)
$2\ln|x-3| - \ln|x-1| + 3\ln|x+2| + C$

7.5 $x^2 + x + 2\ln|x+5| - \ln|x+3| + C$

7.6 $\frac{1}{3}\ln 3$

7.7 $\frac{1}{22}(x^2+1)^{11} + C$, (b) $-\frac{1}{2}e^{-x^2} + C$,
(c) $2\sqrt{\sin x} + C$,
(d) $\frac{1}{2}(\sqrt{x}+1)^4 + C$

7.8 $\frac{1}{3}\ln|x^3+1| + C$, $\ln|\sin x| + C$

7.9 $-\frac{1}{3}\left(1-v^2\right)^{3/2} + C$

7.10 12

7.11 $22/3$

7.12 (a) $\frac{1}{4}(x+1)^4 + C$,
(b) $\frac{1}{8}(2x-1)^4 + C$,
(c) $\frac{1}{50}(5x+3)^{10} + C$,
(d) $-\frac{1}{9}(2-3x)^3 + C$

7.13 $2W^{3/2}/(3eE)$

7.14 0

7.15 $\frac{1}{6}\cos 3x - \frac{1}{14}\cos 7x + C$

7.16 $3\ln|x| + 2\ln|x-2| + C$

7.17 $-8\ln|x+3| + 11\ln|x+4| + C$

7.18 $2\sqrt{2 + \sin x} + C$

7.19 $(\ln 3)^2/2$

7.20 $1/(1+\cos x) + C$

7.21 1

7.22 $5/6$

8.1 $32/3$

8.2 32

8.3 $\pi^2/2$

8.4 π

8.5 $\int_0^2 \sqrt{1+e^{-2x}}\, dx$

8.6 $14/3$

8.7 $1/3$, 0

8.8 0, $1/2$

8.9 $1/\sqrt{2}$

8.10 $\frac{4\pi}{3}a^3 d$, $\frac{\pi}{6}a^3(D+7d)$

8.11 $4900LH^2$ (N)

8.12 $37/12$

8.13 $\pi^2/2$

8.14 $16\pi/15$

8.15 $\sqrt{1+a^2}$

8.16 $1/2$

8.17 $217/3$

8.18 $2/\sqrt{\pi}$

8.19 $\rho L \left(1 - \frac{1}{2}\alpha\right)$

8.20 $\frac{A}{k}\left(1 - e^{-kT}\right)$, $\frac{A}{k}$ (g)

Index